SIR WILLIAM PREECE, F.R.S.

Victorian Engineer Extraordinary

Sir William Preece, 1899

Sir William Preece, F.R.S.

Victorian Engineer Extraordinary

E. C. BAKER

HUTCHINSON OF LONDON

Hutchinson & Co (Publishers) Ltd
3 Fitzroy Square, London W1

London Melbourne Sydney Auckland
Wellington Johannesburg and agencies
throughout the world

First published 1976
© E. C. Baker 1976

Set in Monotype Bembo

Designed and produced by
Hutchinson Benham Limited

Printed in Great Britain by The Anchor Press Ltd
and bound by Wm Brendon & Son Ltd
both of Tiptree, Essex

ISBN 0 09 126610 6

CONTENTS

The spelling of Carnarvon (for Caernarvon or Caernarfon) has been adopted because that is how the town's name was spelt during Preece's lifetime.

LIST OF ILLUSTRATIONS

FRONTISPIECE: Sir William Preece, 1899

Plates (between pages 218 and 219)

Figures in the text

AUTHOR'S PREFACE

WE have to picture a very different society to that in which we find ourselves when we try to imagine that electricity has not yet been harnessed to our service, but it was in just such a world that William Henry Preece was born, three years before Queen Victoria's accession to the throne. As Preece grew to manhood so electricity began to be utilized, for signalling and silver-plating. With the discovery of more about the qualities of electricity it was incumbent on physicists to amend their scientific hypotheses; those were found wanting in the light of further practical experiment, to lead yet again to theory revisal – essentially an empirical process, one of trial and error. That process of revising theories was bound up with controversy, a part of the Victorian way of life, which not only captured the attention of the literate public but could be regarded as a form of co-operation by the disputants to reach a reasoned conclusion. On occasion a protagonist might suffer a fit of pique but rarely among the Victorians was there that bitterness of feeling all too often associated with controversy today.

Seemingly during his last year or so Preece had entertained a notion to write an autobiography. He had not kept a journal nor had he any lengthy run of personal correspondence to draw on: the only indication that he made a beginning is to be seen in a few loose pages of faintly pencilled uncompleted anecdotes. After re-writing Preece's textbook of telegraphy, Preece's eldest son, Llewellyn, planned to write, *William Henry Preece and the growth of the applications of electricity*, but the War was upon him before he had scarcely made a start. He was gazetted Lieutenant R.N.V.R. In 1918 he fell victim, at the age of 52, to the influenza epidemic. His own son, who had migrated to Canada before the War, inherited Preece's medals and presentation plate, including the casket designed by silversmiths Mappin and Webb to contain the record of Preece's Freedom of Caernarvon. On one panel of the casket is a view in coloured enamels of the Castle, and its lid is surmounted by a miniature copy of a statue of Science – one of four bronze statues on Holborn Viaduct, opened in November 1869 by Queen Victoria.

The Caernarvon Borough Council and the town's Rotary Club sponsored a bronze memorial tablet to Preece which was affixed to a wall of the local post office building: Amy Preece unveiled it on 23 April 1953. Her sister Mary was present. The Misses Preece were his two surviving children, their brother Arthur having died the year before. They had recently sold Penrhos and were living in a smaller house in the nearby village of Caeathraw.

Arthur had several talks with me after the Second World War about the possibility of a biography of his father: he handed over an accumulation of miscellaneous papers that had been stowed in a cupboard in his firm's offices. I had already drawn upon the recollections of a number of Post Office Engineering Department retired colleagues'(now, of course, no longer with us) who had served under Preece; in particular J. E. Taylor, who was fortunately able to attend the Marconi Company's jubilee dinner in 1950. (We did not refer to the incident in our talks but happily, it seemed credible to me, he had retained no bitter feelings at being inequitably made scapegoat in the House of Commons' 'Marconi scandal' of 1912.)

I am grateful for facilities afforded and assistance given at the:

Bodleian Library; British Library (British Museum reading room, State Paper room, and newspaper library Colindale); Colonial Office Library; Crown Agents records; Caernarvon County Record Office; Caernarvon Harbour Trust records; Greater London Council, Members' Library and Record Office; Holborn Public Library; India Office Library and Records; Institution of Civil Engineers Library; Institution of Electrical Engineers Library and Records; King's College Library; King's College School records; Llanbeblig parish records; Marylebone Public Library; New York Public Library; Paris, Conservatoire National des Arts et Métiers; Patent Office Library; Post Office Records; Registrar General's records; Royal Institution library; Science Museum Library; Swindon Reference Library; Tottenham Borough Council (Bruce Castle); Wiltshire County Library; and Wimbledon Public Library. I must also record my thanks to the present occupiers of houses in which Preece had lived for their courtesy in allowing me access.

Readers of this book will generally not wish to inquire into sources, for statements, not indicated or implicit in the narrative; the appendixes, furthermore, give additional information in chronological order. It has, therefore, been deemed preferable not to splatter the letterpress with numerals and add pages of associated references but to deposit copies, with complete notes of sources included, at the Institution of Electrical Engineers and the American Institute of Electrical Engineers, for the convenience of any scientific, technological, or social historian who may wish to consult them.   E.C.B.

INTRODUCTION

By J. H. H. Merriman, CB, OBE, MSc, MInstP,
FIEE, FKC, DSc (Hon. Strathclyde)

Preece, Engineer Extraordinary, influenced the course of Victorian
telecommunications development in the United Kingdom more
than any other man. It is therefore apt that this record of his life
and times should appear first in the year that marks the centenary of
Alexander Graham Bell's successful invention of the telephone. The
very introduction of Bell's telephone into Britain owes so much to
Preece's own blend of perception, imagination and concern that
public benefit should spring from scientific and engineering invention. It is apt too that this source book of Preece's life should
emerge at a time when Britain's telecommunications stands third
largest in world order, is growing and penetrating into the very
fabric of society in ways that Preece seems to have glimpsed. It is
apt too that that global penetration of telegraphy which he marvelled
at:

. . . The world is now linked by the wonder-working wire. . . . I go to
my office in the morning and there find telegrams from New Zealand,
India and elsewhere . . .

has now been carried forward into telephony to the stage where the
20 million telephones of the UK, the 100 million telephones of the
rest of Europe and the 330 million telephones of the rest of the world
form a single intercommunicating system annihilating distance and
compelling progressive recognition of global unity. The technologies
of space communications, software controlled systems and optical
fibres are replacing the cotton cocooned copper conductor. But
Preece's aim, ' . . . breaking down the obstruction of space . . . ',
remains the same.

Yet at a centenary time of recognition of achievement it is salutary to be reminded of the imaginative yet frustrating toil of beginnings and to share a little of the wonderment of early successes. The first authoritative book on telephone engineering (by William Preece and Julius Maier) published in 1888 starts with a sentence – surely written by Preece:

It is difficult to realise the fact that ten years ago little or nothing was known of the telephone. In July 1877, one of the authors brought the first pair of practical telephones to Europe. There are now 200,000 in daily use.

What delightful satisfaction there must have been in those mid and latter decades of Victoria's reign to have shared in doing so many things for the first time and in having the liberating freedom to achieve so much with slender manageable resources – a few men, a few machine tools, a native wit, a vivid scientific imagination and a strong business-inclined engineering flair. The committees, the organizers, the systems men, the arguments about rights, the intermediaries, the politicians, gathered around soon enough – *ubi cadaver ibi aves*. But in each of the rich succession of disciplines handled by Preece, telegraphy, railway signalling, telephony, lighthouse communication, street lighting, wireless, he played a crucial catalytic part – almost a lone hand – with skill, determination, simplicity and imagination until that discipline became established and institutionalized. Indeed here we have a clue to the character of the man. All that he seems to want is to be allowed to get on with his job – even to the extent of leaving no records of private correspondence, no personal diaries, no daily records, apart from those of three journeys, written clearly for his family, but revealing not a little of his perception, breadth and humanity.

The origins of the man (Welsh, non-conformist, forced to struggle, translated into the fertile society of mid-Victorian London), the web of events that lead to him at the age of 21 falling under the combined influences of Faraday, Latimer Clark, Thomson (Kelvin) and Airy – the convergence of all these forces acted upon him in ways that exposed his innovating capabilities and leadership. Faraday's influence was life-long. Brother-in-law Latimer Clark was there, always, for wise counsel. Yet Preece was a great engineer in that he saw purpose and beauty in his work. He was great also in his ability humbly to observe and to delight in keen observation and the reduction of the abstruse to the simple. To him 'science is organized common sense.'

Yet these comments are but deductions from his own recorded words. For Mr Baker (drawing upon his own formative and distinctive contributions as former Archivist to the Post Office) in collecting, tirelessly, the facts and sources upon which this book is constructed has, wisely, refrained from writing a character or personality study of Preece. He has chosen to collect evidence, to select and arrange it in a coherent pattern to set it in its proper social, technological and administrative contexts and to let that evidence speak for itself. In a sense this is perhaps all that a biographer of Preece should do. It is in the mainstream of Preece's practice and tradition as a professional Engineer. Yet in a sense it is tantalizing and provocative. For the turning of each page generates questions about Preece that cannot be answered explicitly. What drove him to the mastery of his profession? How did he reconcile himself to the potential battles that were fought over his subject areas of telegraphy, telephony and radio? I suspect that Preece's strength came from innate enthusiasm, curiosity and a life-long determination to fill the unforgiving minute. In his formative years these traits were honed and sharpened by the threat of poverty and the need to earn money to support his family. And Preece's professional standing came not only out of brilliant leadership, but from his conviction that at times of dramatic change, engineers and scientists must meet in free and open discussion to enrich knowledge and to inform the public.

In a final and personal sense it is a multiple pleasure to introduce this book. For, as the present inheritor of the former post of Engineer-in-Chief of the Post Office, it falls to me – and my many colleagues – to maintain the traditions of service and innovation in telecommunications engineering that was so surely set by Preece. As a Welshman, a non-conformist, an Old Boy of Preece's school, a Fellow of King's London (as he was), and even living in Wimbledon just round the corner from Gothic Lodge, the multiplicity of parallels are almost too improbable! But perhaps they magnify, justifiably, my belief that this book will be a stimulus, an enduring record and a worthy contribution to the recognition of this year's centenary of the telephone, so signally linked with Sir William Preece – Victorian Engineer Extraordinary.

Post Office, London　　　　　　　　　　　　　　　J.H.H.M.
January 1976

FIRST FREEMAN OF CARNARVON

CARNARVON'S town hall, built on its thirteenth-century town walls, was crowded on the afternoon of Thursday, 21 September 1899 as mace-bearers preceded their mayor and corporation in escorting Sir William Henry Preece into the hall. The mayor opened proceedings by stating that the Council's meeting was a special one to confer the honorary freedom of the borough on Sir William, in accordance with a resolution they had passed in response to a feeling general in the town that Sir William, whose first great act – according to the mayor – was to select Carnarvon as the place of his birth, should be honoured by them for his eminent services to the State. That the first man to be elected to the freedom of the borough should be an electrician, on the centenary of what had been described as the greatest discovery in electricity, the Voltaic pile, was a gratifying fact. In presenting to Sir William a specially designed silver-gilt casket, containing a record of the Council's resolution, the mayor told him that the Carnarvon people had followed his distinguished career with great interest, and now that he had been released from the duties of his official life they hoped he would have greater leisure to participate in public life and to promote the welfare of his native town.

Manifestly this was an opportunity for Preece to reminisce on his childhood in Carnarvon; nor did he, a noted speaker, disappoint his audience. After signing the roll he said:

My signature here is so tremulous that I am sure my banker would not accept a cheque so signed . . . I appreciate this honour more than any other I have ever received . . . it was totally unexpected . . . it is something to be the first freeman of the ancient and historic town of Carnarvon . . . to be the first engineer in the United Kingdom to have been nominated for such a distinction. Sir William Henry White, my colleague and friend, received the freedom of Devonport a week or two ago. That two Government officials, the Chief Constructor of the Navy, and the Chief Engineer of the Post Office, should almost simultaneously receive such a mark of appreciation of their fellow-townsmen speaks much of the esteem held of the public service that the laborious discharge of their duties is not altogether neglected by their masters.

. . . What does this freedom mean? It conveys no right to vote in any Parliamentary or borough election. It exonerates one from no taxation. It confers no pecuniary or political benefit. It is, however, a personal distinction and a great honour much coveted in great cities, but rarely bestowed in boroughs, and now conferred for the first time in Carnarvon. The first mayor of Carnarvon was Mr. J. Morgan . . . the second was Mr. Henry Rumsey Williams, who built the house I now occupy; the third was Mr. Haslam; and the fourth my father, who took the chair in 1843 and in 1844. The mayor has been good enough to enumerate the reasons which have induced the Town Council to be so kind. I cannot help asking myself why does it incite in me such intense satisfaction? We Welsh are an emotional race. We love music, the arts, poetry, and that which is grand and beautiful in nature. 'The wild beast and the whirlwind's roar bind him to his native mountains more.'

No one at that stage was going to ask, 'What wild beast?' and Preece went on to quote the evocative opening lines of the sixth canto of the *Lay of the Last Minstrel* and to ask

what power of homeward attraction exceeds that of the memory of our beautiful hills and vales, or the eyes of those we love. I am a *hogyn o'r dre*.

With that Welsh phrase to emphasize his rapport, as a lad of the town, with his audience, his address was brought to a halt by loud and enthusiastic cheering. When it died down he continued,

My father was a Glamorganshire man, born in the last century. He resided in Carnarvon for . . . 30 years and took a great interest in municipal matters. He was bailiff of the town and twice mayor after the introduction of the Municipal Act. In 1845 he removed to London, where he died nine years afterwards. My mother was born here in the last century and her remains, with four of her little ones, lie buried in Llanbeglig church-yard. These are strong ties to my old native place.

To my mother I attribute all my success in life, habits of industry, love of reading, corporeal and mental energy, the beginning of all wisdom –

the fear of the Lord. I should like to see in this country of ours some branch of education which should teach illiterate mothers how to attend to their children – not alone in cleanliness and healthful, but in mental training.

Someone exclaims in an old play, 'I love everything that is old – old friends, old times, old books, old wines.' He might have added old boots, old schools, and old schoolfellows. Beneath the Ebenezer Chapel, under that upright Christian, John Jackson, I commenced to master the three R's, but owing to his appointment as Harbour Master in 1843, some of us were transferred to Doctor Bransby – in that hall where now another is teaching the young idea how to shoot and training up to eminence some future freeman of the borough.

Preece attended the school in a 'dismal, dark, dreary, dirty school-room' underneath Ebenezer Chapel for two years with a dozen other pupils till he moved to Bransby's school in a chapel at the top of Love Lane. He often remembered what he learnt from Mr Jackson, a 'charming, amiable, delightful man', although 'for the life of him he could not remember what he learnt under Dr Bransby', but was, it seemed, proud of a few prizes he later won at King's College School for he used to show them to his children 'and ask them if they could not try to do the same as their father had done'. He continued:

An old Persian poet has said, 'I came to the place of my birth and cried, "The friends of my youth where are they?" ' That is not my case; I look around this hall and I see familiar faces – the friends of my youth are here, sixty years have not broken the hooks of steel which have grappled us together, and to judge by our appearance those adamantine links are destined to last some little while longer. But there are serious gaps. 'Friend after friend departs. Who hath not lost a friend?' . . .

I have not been idle in this world . . . I have endeavoured to be diligent in my business and to make two blades of grass grow where only one grew before. It must never be forgotten that progress and success in this world depend essentially on self education, commonsense, and an automatic industry. My lot has been very much in the domain of electricity . . . for forty-seven years I have laboured hard in applying it to the comfort, happiness and service of mankind. Here I am now endeavouring to develop its latest achievement by breaking down the obstruction of space – leading to further advance in the system of telegraphy improperly called the wireless system.

The world is now linked by the wonder-working wire into one

B

continuous whole. Time has thus disappeared and distance annihilated. Every morning the newspapers tell us all of interest that occurred yesterday in every quarter of the world. I go to my office in the morning and there I find telegrams from New Zealand, India and elsewhere . . .

We travel on railways by the aid of electricity with comfort and security and I venture to say that the safest place now in the world is a first-class carriage from Carnarvon to Euston.

(His confidence in such safety, and he himself, were severely shaken on a Saturday evening just over a fortnight later when an express to London, on which he was a passenger, ran into two uncoupled coaches (from the Birmingham–Manchester train) at Stafford station: two of the Stoke Football Club team in the detached coaches were knocked out. That accident did not prevent Preece's appearance at the Colchester Oyster Feast at the end of October. The mayor of Colchester, a civil engineer, had included Lord Kelvin, Preece, and Lord Rayleigh among his guests, and they were called upon to speak, as were twenty-one other guests! In such circumstances Preece was commendably brief; after referring to the work of the Institution of Civil Engineers – he was its President – he suggested that the oyster and the engineer made capital after-dinner speakers because they knew when to shut up.)

He continued:

Then by means of electricity our homes are illuminated with pure and innocuous light. The benefits of electricity are a twice-told tale and an enthusiast like myself might become tedious.

Today I am happy. Happiness depends on human sympathy. It is something to have lived in this glorious Victorian Era; it is much to have been invested by Her Majesty herself with the insignia of the Order of the Bath. It is a great deal to know that one has earned the approbation of one's country; it is more to retain through life the sterling friendships of one's early boyhood, but above all is a justifiable pride to have secured the sympathy and appreciation of those who remember my childhood and among whom I hope to end my days.

* * *

Preece reminisced further on his boyhood at a banquet that evening given in his honour at the Sportsman Hotel. Many of the town and county notabilities were present, as was his brother, John R. Preece,

C.M.G. (H.M. Consul at Teheran), and Preece's children, except for Percy, the youngest, a volunteer army officer waiting to be sent to the front in South Africa. After the toasts to the Queen and to the Armed Forces, the mayor proposed the toast of the evening, 'the health of Sir William H. Preece'.

In reply Preece spoke of the overwhelming reception he had been given and of his pride that members of his family were present. He compared Carnarvon of the day with what he remembered as a boy. His first recollection of the town had been associated with the coronation of Queen Victoria, sixty-two years before (28 June 1837: he was then three years and four months old). When in 1897 on the occasion of her diamond jubilee he had stood within a few yards of her on the steps of St Paul's, he thought he could see vividly the scene of the musical ceremony taking place in Castle Square at the time of her coronation. He called to mind standing at one end of a long line of magistrates and members of the old corporation.

Another recollection he had was of parliamentary elections. Those were great events at that time. How many heads were broken and how much money was distributed from hand to hand he did not know, but he did know that he saw the successful candidate raised on a chair and carried above the heads of the mob, among whom he scattered money. Then there were great contests fought between Mr Bulkeley Hughes and Sir Charles Paget, and he remembered the refrain which consigned the former to a 'golden chair' and Sir Charles to a 'hayloft'. Mr Bulkeley Hughes represented the borough in Parliament for forty-two years. He could not forget that for a century and a half Carnarvon was represented by a Wynn, or a Paget, or a Hughes.

In those days the corporation did not own the ferry to Anglesey. The departure of the boat was signified by the ferryman blowing a conch shell, first at the bottom of High Street, and afterwards at other points, and when he had attracted a sufficient number of passengers the boat would leave and land its freight on the other side. Also among his recollections of the town was Ellen Abbott's stall, distinguished because of the large quantity of meat which it displayed. Those nuts perfumed the whole of Palace Street – and even now if he smelt meat anywhere he was reminded of Ellen Abbott. Again, he remembered the days of the flint-and-steel and tinder-box, and the great sensation produced by the introduction of the lucifer match – a much greater wonder of the world at that time than wireless telegraphy is now. Now, what a difference with beautiful electric light. Where was it in Carnarvon? (A rhetorical question which occasioned ironic laughter from many of his audience). That evening they had commenced dinner in a dull, dim, religious light though it had become slightly better as time wore on. Having that beautiful electric light within their reach, why did Carnarvon adhere to dull light? If it was fear of expense, he could say that there was not a single case where a corporation had taken it up and had not made it pay. Being now a freeman he ventured to speak freely on this matter.

Preece commented on the development of railway travelling and on the uses of electricity. A cabby once asked him whether 'this new electricity was anything like beer', which he thought was as near the mark as that of many who had attempted to explain what is electricity. . . . In the application of electricity to the driving and drawing of trains . . . one saw the greatest changes. Those of them who lived in London would appreciate the introduction of electricity on the underground railways. Then there would be the absence of heat, there would be no sulphurous smoke and the breath would not be affected by that fearful atmosphere to which all passengers were subject in the present day.

Referring to the electric telegraph he pointed out that it had revolutionized the press; it had actually made the provincial press, which had become a great power in the country. The London press had lost its hold of the provinces, and all this was owing to the admirable manner in which the Post Office transmitted news at a ridiculously low rate. Now there was not a single town of any size which had not its daily newspapers. Another feature of the effect which electricity had had on the press was that it had destroyed the leader-writers. Leading articles in newspapers were not read. They were not wanted. The man who wrote leading articles in the present day might be compared to the leader-writer of the *Killahoe Observer* – which had an immense circulation in Ireland and was presided over by an Irish editor. Before the Crimean War commenced a leader in that paper opened with the words, 'We warn the Emperor of Russia, our eyes are upon him.' But the war was not stopped. The leader-writers of some of the London papers now wrote their articles as if the editor were the ruler and the regulator of the universe, but public opinion was not now formed by anonymous writers: it was rather formed by men of light and learning, whose opinions were distributed throughout the country. Engineering had run side by side with electricity. He claimed engineering as the great civilizer of the day . . . the engineer accompanied the soldier to all uncivilized parts of the globe.

He concluded his speech by thanking his fellow townsmen for the very kind reception they had accorded him . . . an occasion which brought man and man together. It established patriotism in the country and *esprit de corps* in a community . . . to enable men to work in harmony together: to feel that they received the appreciation of their confreres was the source of the greatest happiness.

And while we listen to harp playing and Welsh pennillion singing which completes the evening we look at the principal guest who, on attaining his sixty-fifth birthday on 15 February that year, had retired from the position of Engineer-in-Chief and Electrician to the Post Office. His was what is called a well-set figure, five feet nine inches tall, squarely built, with a head slightly out of proportion in its massiveness, brown hair with a few strands going grey, and a full beard: we note his broad forehead though the twinkling alertness of his large brown eyes are partly hidden by the gold-framed small-lens spectacles he is wearing. His Welsh listeners, used to a high standard of public speaking, are fully appreciative of his magnetic influence over his audience.

2

IN THE DAYS OF MY YOUTH

A SERIES of articles by public figures, consisting of recollections of their juvenile years, had been published weekly for over two years in a now long-forgotten magazine when Preece's contribution appeared on its pages in 1900. (Deletions he made when checking printers' galleys are in brackets.)

If I am allowed to consider my career as a successful one, I am justified in answering the question: To what cause am I to attribute that success? I answer unhesitatingly *industry*, and this habit of industry I acquired from my mother, not by enforcement, precept, or dictation, but by example, I do not believe in dictation. (There is in a child a species of original sin, a kind of cussedness which prompts him unwittingly to do that which he ought not to do, and to do that which he is told not to do by his pastor and master, and especially by his father. Why this is thus passeth human understanding, but that it is so will, I think, be admitted by the majority of sons.) A boy's habits are acquired from his mother – mine were – and they were the result of early inseparability, maternal sympathy, and that mental telegraphic association that accompanies filial love. The effect is permanent when the mother is clever, well read, deeply observant, always doing something, philosophically inclined, and gifted with a grand memory. These were the attributes of my beloved mother. I must not decry my father. I was walking with him along the banks of the river Seiont, that debouches into the Menai Straits at Carnarvon, my native place. I was then eight years old. We heard the sounds of a blast in the slate quarries in the mountains near Llanberis. (I fear I must have been a terrible foolish question-asker but I never remember being bullied or checked for practising such a habit.) I asked, 'How is it we hear those sounds from such a distance?' – the distance was eight miles. 'Look here, my boy,' said my father, chucking a stone into a placid pool of the river, 'see how the water is disturbed. See how I have excited waves in it, and how those waves progress in circles with definite velocity, and' – putting his hand in the water – 'I feel those waves breaking against the back of my hand. The air, although you cannot see it, is as material as the water. You feel it in every puff of wind, and see it in every bending bough. The explosion of gunpowder in the quarry has disturbed this medium as the stone disturbed the water. Waves of air have been excited, they have speeded from Llanberis here, they have broken inside the ear, and they have given you that sensation which we call sound.'

This was my first scientific lesson. It gave me food for thought: it spurred my observant faculty. I grasped the conception of invisible media, and very early in life, thanks to Faraday, realised the presence of the ether in space, whose undulations convey to the eye the twinkle of every little star, and impart to the brain the impression of light as the air through the ear impresses on the consciousness the sensation of music and noise. Science is organized common sense. Scientific thought is putting two and two together, tracing effects to their causes, determining the *this* by observation and the *thus* by deduction. Castles in the air become real palaces of delight when they are built upon the solid facts of Nature. The book of Nature is ever open, and its facts are apparent to every observant eye. Reading is generally taught too early, and doing is rarely taught at all. Children should be encouraged to acquire their own facts by observation alone, and not from the pages of the variable and often untruthful text book.

(It was many years e'er I saw a text book.) My earliest recollection is of the festivities and ceremonies that celebrated the coronation of the Queen. (What delight we feel in the scenes of our childhood when the memories are of pleasure and happiness.)

The house in which I was born was built on ground associated with the name of Helen, the mother of the great Emperor Constantine, and called Bryn Helen. Close behind us was a fine, well-preserved specimen of the wall which surrounded the Roman fortress Segontium. In front of us was the magnificent Norman castle of Carnarvon, built by Edward I, in which the first Prince of Wales was born, in 1284. The presence of the Roman and Norman is evident everywhere about the beautiful country between the Snowdonian range and the sea. Dinases – the intrenched kopjes of the Roman – and the round stone tower of the Norman, still exist – imperishable evidence of the determined opposition to oppression and the love of freedom of the ancient Briton. I love to show my American friends these markings in the rocks of time. 'Why!' said one, inside the old castle, 'think this was this built and inhabited by courtly lords and ladies before America was discovered!'

I remember as though it were yesterday every mountain in sight proclaiming by its bonfire the joy of Wales at the presentation to it of a Prince. [Edward the Seventh was born 9 November 1841.]

In those days the tool of every housewife was the tinder box with its flint and steel, and I often and often watched the generation of heat and the kitchen fire lighted by the sulphur-tipped match of thin dry wood, then in use, kindled by sparks from flint. The phosphor-headed lucifer match, lighted by mere friction, created a great sensation on its introduction in the early forties, and many a box I wasted in idle experiment. The wax vesta and the patent safety are quite modern improvements.

I have seen the rushlight, and I have in my possession a rushlight holder that was in use in those days of my youth. The common source of illumination was the tallow candle, but on high days the expensive and luxurious wax light was allowed. The farthing 'dip' had a rush for its wick, and it was generally home-made in the farms around and about, but those who were in or near the town were able to indulge in the more expensive cotton wick. The snuffers were the necessary article of furniture in every room, and the periodical operation of snuffing is invariably recalled to my memory by certain smells, even now – sixty years after; smells are wonderful exciters of memory. The snuffers were allocated to the museum by the introduction of the composite candle, which rendered snuffing unnecessary.

The first non-snuffing wick that I remember was a cotton string wound around with a very fine wire. The moulded spermaceti non-snuffing candle also came in in the early forties. Paraffin was extracted from mineral oil as early as 1847, by Young, but ozokerit [a wax-like fossil resin used to make candles] and all Field's great improvements are quite recent.

I do not remember oil being used for domestic purposes in Wales, but when we moved to London in 1845, camphine [distilled from oil of turpentine] gave a brilliant light, but frequently became unmanageable, and I have seen many a white tablecloth blackened by the unruly flame.

Gas was but little used and the streets of Carnarvon, as far as I can remember, were not lighted at all in the days of my youth. They are badly lighted even now, but electricity is looming in the minds of our Town Councillors.

I can just remember the flint-lock sporting gun. The percussion cap appeared amongst us about 1840. It was called the copper cap. The first form was made of smooth copper. Boys used to amuse themselves by producing loud detonating reports by planting them on stones and striking them smartly with another heavy stone. The copper, on explosion, used to fly about. That was about 1842. My upper lip was cut and bears the scar still, but a schoolfellow, on the same day, lost one of his eyes. This defect of the cap was quite cured by corrugating the copper.

Breechloaders were introduced in 1853, and now the hammerless gun, with its choked bore, ejecting apparatus, safety catches and smokeless powder, have completely supplanted the old muzzle-loader.

I have always been very fond of cricket. I captained my King's College School eleven in 1848-49 and my College eleven in 1851. I remember the All England eleven playing at Lords in top hats. Lillywhite, who introduced round-arm bowling, wearing a black hat and Clarke, the champion underhand slow bowler, wearing a white one. A century in the forties was a phenomenon. Now it seems to be the accompaniment of every first-class match, and to indicate rather the weather than the game. Indeed centuries are now so common that only a double century is regarded as the prize. It looks as if we ought to add a fourth stump, for the bat has mastered the ball. I have a sketch of Rowlandson's showing that in the early days of this century only two stumps were used. The change has, therefore, a precedent.

The changes in transportation have been startling. When I left North Wales in 1845 not one mile of railway had been constructed there. My father, who frequently went to London, went by coach through Shrewsbury. In those days of my youth the journey cost about £8.00; it can now be done for less than £1.00. The journey by road took forty-eight hours; yesterday I did it by rail in six hours and a third!

I remember on one occasion the coach in which my father sat collided on Shrewsbury Bridge with a dray. The wheels of the two vehicles were locked, but the occupants of the outside seats of the coach, including my father, were suspended over the river. He often referred to the coachman's argument in favour of a coach: 'When you are on a coach and an accident happens, why, there you are; but when you are in a railway train and an accident happens, where are you?'

My first journey to London was a drive to Menai Bridge, a slow steamer – the *Erin-go-Bragh* – to Liverpool, a night's rest in the Adelphi Hotel, then the train to London *via* Birmingham, with an hour there for dinner, and a ten hours' railway journey – a journey now done in half the time, with a comfortable and well-cooked dinner on board the train.

The express train in 1845 consisted of mail-coach bodies on wheels. They were cribbed, cabinned, and confined. The modern coach, thanks to our American friends, and especially to Pullman, is a roomy, luxurious, comfortable lounge warmed in winter with steam or hot water and lighted by gas or electricity. I have just dined sumptuously in the Euston Hotel, and at 11.50 p.m. I start for Glasgow in a comfortable sleeping-car. If all is well, I shall sleep the sleep of the just, and when I awake, find myself in Glasgow at 7.50 a.m., and after a bath as fit as a fiddle for breakfast and business. I may not be so lucky, for returning last year from Ireland I was smashed up in a sleeping-car near Stafford and knocked at death's door. However, I score off my father, for he often had to spend two nights on the outside of the mailcoach when travelling from London to Carnarvon. Our Scots friends suffered martyrdom in winter; now they gain two days and do not lose a night's rest.

I was taught in my early schooldays in Wales that there were seven wonders of the World. 1. The Pyramids of Egypt. 2. The mausoleum at Halicarnassus. 3. The temple of Diana at Ephesus. 4. The walls and hanging gardens of Babylon. 5. The colossus of Rhodes. 6. The ivory and gold statue of Jupiter Olympus. 7. The Pharos of Ptolemy at Alexandria. But now there is an eighth, Telford's suspension bridge over the Menai Straits, opened in 1825. Stephenson's bridge, the Britannia Tube, completed in 1850, excelled Telford's structure and was made the eighth wonder; but many other wonders have arisen since then, and we must be content to confine the seven wonders to the ancient world.

I was a frequent visitor to Wales during the construction of the tubes, and watched with great earnestness the grand engineering operations going on – cold iron sheared like paper with the scissors, holes punched in thick iron plates with greater ease than saddlers punch holes in leather straps, great plates riveted together with deafening blows but with red hot iron as plastic as cheese, the great tubes floated down with the tide to their positions and lifted to their eyrie positions above the 'stately ships sailing by' by hydraulic power.

The engineer in charge of the iron work under Stephenson was Edwin Clark, and it was my good fortune to enter his office, and through him and his brother Latimer to enter the new world governed and controlled by electricity.

Before that I had frequent opportunities of examining the London and Croydon atmospheric railway and the London and Blackwall wire rope railway – experimental lines that had a short life and succumbed to their mightier rival, steam.

Hungerford Bridge, a suspension bridge which crossed the Thames where now Charing Cross Bridge carries the South-Eastern Railway, was opened in 1845, but it was removed to Clifton in 1862; and the Thames Tunnel, which was opened in 1843, were the engineering novelties in London. Penny steamboats ran up and down the river, and I remember one terrible boiler explosion on board one of them – the *Cricket* – which resulted in sad loss of life.

I was privileged as a student of King's College to be taken by Professor Cowper – a splendid teacher – to see the construction of the Palace of Crystal in Hyde Park, then being erected for the Great Exhibition of 1851 – the parent of all international exhibitions. Said Prince Albert, President of the Society of Arts in 1849: 'Now is the time to prepare for a great exhibition – an exhibition worthy of the greatness of this country, not merely national in its scope and benefits, but comprehensive of the whole world; and I offer myself to the public as their leader if they are willing to assist in the undertaking.' Nobly did the public respond, nobly the Prince led, and great and lasting were the benefits derived by the Country from that great exhibition.

In the forties a certain Captain Warner had a secret process by which he could destroy shipping. He blew up a ship off Brighton, which caused great sensation. His secret died with him very shortly after, but it was probably something of the nature of a torpedo.

The growth of the size of ships has been remarkable. The first wonder was the *Great Western*, launched in 1838, length 236 feet; then the *Great Britain*, in 1845, 322 feet, and finally the *Great Eastern*, in 1847, 692 feet long. The vast changes in warships followed the Crimean War and were posterior to the days of my youth.

I mentioned that the early coaches were mere mail coach bodies. These were first class. I often travelled third class to Portsmouth and Brighton in open trucks, but seated, and I remember seeing fourth class carriages on a Scots railway, where passengers had to stand with no greater comfort than cattle are allowed now.

Intercommunication has been similarly revolutionized. I remember the introduction of the penny post and Mulready's envelopes well. One coach then carried all the mails to Scotland, now several trains are required.

My connection with telegraphy commenced in 1852, and not in the days of my youth. It was, however, brought into great prominence in 1845 by the capture at Paddington of a great murderer – Tawell – a Quaker, who had poisoned his paramour at Slough. Tawell nearly escaped, for the instrument could not give the letter Q. Tawell was described as a 'Kwaker' which the receiving clerk had great difficulty in deciphering.

I was very early introduced to the realms of science in the lecture theatre of the Royal Institution. Faraday was then in his prime. His lectures on a 'Candle' contained more of romance to me than all the operas, plays, and books that I was allowed to see and read. Faraday became my ideal hero. The summit of my ambition was to become his assistant, and this was realized in 1853.

(Science was quite fashionable then. The Adelaide Gallery, where Wheatstone showed his telegraph, flourished where the Lowther Arcade is now; the Polytechnic in Regent Street displayed the atmospheric railway and the diving bell, the Coliseum in the Regent's Park, the Panopticon in Leicester Square (now the Alhambra) showed all that was new in light, sound and electricity. Few places have done more good in their day than the Polytechnic. The names of Pepper and King remain pleasantly in the memory of many a grey-haired man, who was an eager listener to their clear expounding in the late forties.

Lord Rosse created great sensation by making and erecting a gigantic telescope in Parsonstown, County Clare, Ireland. Immense sensation was created in 1846 by the simultaneous discovery of the planet Neptune by Adams in Cambridge, and Le Verrier, in Paris.)

Chloroform, the first of those anaesthetics that have proved such a boon and a blessing to man, appeard about 1847, and photography made its appearance a little earlier. I have an excellent daguerrotype of my father, taken in 1844 in the Adelaide Gallery. The sewing machine was invented in 1846, but all the great advances that science has made in its practical applications have been the events of the seventies and eighties.

The steel pen supplanted the quill in this period. The original makers, Gillett, Perry and Mitchell, are still to the front. I very early acquired the art of making a quill pen. My father was an adept at it and a beautiful penman. I wish I had inherited his gift.

(Sanitary science had made great strides in this country of ours during the Victorian era. It has not driven out influenza from our shores, but cholera and plague are things of the past. In 1848–9 we had a severe attack of cholera; this was its last visit. Its chief source was to be found in impure water supply. The discovery of its cause was followed by its cure, and the legislature has facilitated in every way the establishment of remedial measures by local authorities. Pure air, pure water, pure food, pure soil and cleanliness are the secrets of health, and strength, and wealth. The nation is all the richer and stronger through that beneficial legislation which has characterized the period through which I have passed.

My father was a politician. He was a great bilingual speaker on religious and political subjects. Indeed, the fame of his Welsh oratory exists in Carnarvonshire to the present day, though fifty-five years have elapsed since his departure from his native land. His great ambition was to enter Parliament, but he did not amass sufficient wealth to enable him to do so. He died in 1854. Fortunately, for me, he lost in the panics of 1848 and

1851 all he had made. I was forced to work for myself. I entered the engineering profession, in which for forty-two years I have been an earnest and industrious worker.

He was fond of discussing politics and current events with me. He was a great admirer of Cobden and Bright – of the sterling earnestness of the one and of the magnificent oratory on the other. He impressed me with the iniquity of the Corn Laws and with the principles of Free Trade, but he thought that these principles should be confined to raw produce and to food, but not to manufactured goods, for Free Trade would drive many trades out of the country.)

How well I remember the conversion of Peel, his fall from his horse on Constitutional Hill, and his consequent death. The figure of Wellington was a familiar object and I remember well his military dispositions for the defence of London against the Chartists in 1848. I passed through the Chelsea Hospital at his lying-in-state [10–17 Nov. 1852], and saw the grand funeral procession march through Pall Mall. The riderless charger, with its trappings and dead hero's boots, was an impressive object. A child who saw this is said to have asked her mother, 'When we die, mother, shall we end in boots?'

How the events of those days of old pass through my mind: the mad pranks of the wild Marquis of Waterford; the disaster at Cabul; the recovery and wounding of Lady Sale; the avenging army under Pollock and Nott; the capture of Scinde by Sir Charles Napier in 1843; the Sikh wars of 1845–48 and those in Caffraria and China; the revolutions on the Continent in 1848; the flight of Louis Phillippe to England; Louis Napoleon and his romantic return to France.

I have often heard it stated that Napier, determining to rival Caesar in the brevity of despatches, sent home simply 'Peccavi' (I have sinned). But I now find that this story is apocryphal, and is to be found in the columns of *Punch*.

The agitation that led eventually to the abolition of toll gates was commenced in South Wales, in 1843 by 'Rebecca and her daughters' – a set of well-led men dressed in female attire, who appeared irregularly in unexpected places to destroy and remove toll gates and toll houses, which they did effectually. [Gen. 24: 60. Rebekah . . . let thy seed possess the gate of those which hate them.] I am not sure that their identity was ever discovered. They created great excitement in North Wales, and the numerous gates there made me wish for their meteoric appearance.

In music I recall Jullien, his cheap concerts, his podgy figure, his waving locks, and his antics with his *baton;* the split in the operatic world when Mario, Grisi, and Alboni appeared at Covent Garden and Jenny Lind entranced the town in the Haymarket; Balfe and Wallace, with the ever favourite *Bohemian Girl* and *Maritana*. In painting, Turner and Landseer graced the walls of the Academy; and in architecture, Barry fashioned that noble palace of Westminster. In books, Moore, Wordsworth, Tennyson wrote poetry; Macaulay and Prescott wrote history; Dickens, Thackeray, Bulwer Lytton, Disraeli, Marryat, Fenimore Cooper, G. P. R. James, Harrison Ainsworth wrote novels. *Punch* appeared in 1841 as the wise, facetious, stern censor of the age, never overstepping the bounds of morality, and rarely, if ever, descending to those regions of vulgarity and coarseness so characteristic of foreign facetious papers. The *Illustrated London News* came out at the same time, and started that illustrated press that has had such an immense influence in assisting the education of the young.

The ballet was in its prime. I never saw the famous *pas de quatre* danced by Taglioni, Duvernay, Cerito, and Ellsler, but I well remember Carlotta Grisi, Cerrito, and Lucille Grahn doing the *pas de trois*. Lola Montes passed from the stage to the palace. On the stage Macready, Phelps, and Charles Kean expounded Shakespeare; Charles Matthews, Leigh Murray, Alfred Wigan adorned drama; Buckstone, Harley, Paul Bedford, Wright, Robson were the funny men; the inimitable Keeleys were everywhere; Planche showed that extravaganza could be graceful and witty without being grotesque and repulsive, and Madame Celeste managed the Adelphi, and Madame Vestris showed how scenery could be made artistic and beautiful without being glaring and pretentious. Astley's with its horses on the stage, was open in the forties, and I often saw *The Battle of Waterloo*.

Duels had not quite died out. Lord Cardigan and his black bottle controversy, that led to the death of Captain Tuckett was not forgotten when we moved to London, and shortly after our arrival there, Lieutenant Hawkey killed his own brother-in-law, Mr. Seton. This was the last duel fought in England. That foolish and senseless practice exists still on the Continent. Ridicule will perhaps drive it out eventually. It was never a test of courage nor did it maintain a code of honour. It was simply a test of skill and the weapon of the bully.

The Prize Fight has also disappeared, but in the forties it was in its zenith – one member of the Ring had become a Member of Parliament – it had its own language in the columns of *Bell's Life in London*. Ben Caunt and Bendigo held receptions in their different taverns and many of our noted bruisers were seen on the seats of the mighty.

(Modes of advertising have always taken prominent and often offensive forms. In the days I speak of one method became so obstructive in the streets that it had to be put down by legislation. Great vans paraded the town placarded all over with specific remedies for disease, tooth-powder, hair oil or grease, new clothings.

A very objectionable form of taxation was exacted in 1695, and lasted until 1851, when it was repealed. This was the window tax. I remember well the taxing agent surveying our house, and recording the number of windows, upon which something had to be paid annually. My present house in Wales has several blank windows blocked up to evade tax.)

Another familiar institution of my youth was the use of the dog as a beast of burden. I remember well hawkers, knife-grinders, milk distributors, etc., with their light carts drawn by willing dogs. I am not sure that this practice does not still exist in Belgium. I saw it quite recently in Brussels. It was not only cruel but it fomented rabies. It was abolished in England only in 1854.

(Giants and dwarfs have always been more or less objects of attraction and fleeting fancies of fashion, but rarely has the town been so effectually captured as it was by General Tom Thumb in 1846. His well-formed diminutive figure, his graceful performances, his marriage, and his return from America with his still smaller companion, Commodore Nutt, are fresh in my memory.)

Why is it that certain crimes and murders attract so much public attention? The hanging of Parnell, Rush, the Mannings man and wife, and Palmer and Rugeley, which happened in the forties, are not forgotten now. Yet 20,000 accidental deaths occur in this country every year without a record in the press!

Spirit rapping and table turning was all the rage in 1851 and the murmur of something akin to it is occasionally heard even now.

How my pen has run away with me in thinking over the days of my youth:

> Sweet childish days that were as long
> As twenty days are now

I fear that none but my contemporaries will follow my memories for my reminiscences are scarcely footprints on the sands of time, but only fleeting visions of days that were happy and times that have passed.

*   *   *

Preece's memory was at fault when he referred to Faraday's lectures on the Chemical History of a Candle; they were not given till 1860–61. He was first taken to the Royal Institution to hear Faraday's annual lectures to children in January 1846 by the doctor who was attending his father, and he seems to have persuaded the doctor to take him to subsequent Friday evening and juvenile lectures by Faraday though when, in 1898, he told a journalist who was writing a biographical page for one of the penny weekly magazines then making their appearance that he had 'heard all those famous lectures', that statement can be treated with the mild reservation usually accorded childhood recollections. But Preece seems to have retained unusually clear memories of physical sensations. He gave in January 1880 two juvenile lectures – on light and sound – at the (Royal) Society of Arts, having sought advice from Silvanus P. Thompson on the presentation of experiments. (Thompson had inaugurated, with marked success, juvenile Christmas lectures on physics three years before at Bristol.)

In reviewing the history of domestic lighting Preece told his young audience of

the time when I used to be taken to bed with a farthing dip, or something very like one, with a piece of wire-work around it, which was allowed to burn down, and the final smoulder of which gave off an odour of almost unbearable nastiness, which scarcely left my nostrils by next morning's rising time.

Doubtless he intended a later comment to be taken literally:

When I was a boy at school, we often used to be left in the dark.

3

FOURTH MAYOR OF CARNARVON

DURING the latter half of the eighteenth century coastwise trade increased through the Menai Straits: in 1793, the year of an outbreak of war with France, Carnarvon had 250 boats engaged in the slate trade alone, some of them crossing the Atlantic. Two thousand coasting vessels and half that number of foreign ships cleared at the port of Carnarvon during 1801. A larger harbour with safer approaches became an urgent need and under an Act of 1817 a Harbour Trust was constituted to make essential improvements; to meet the cost the Trust was authorized to levy a port tax on coal and tea. Its first undertakings were to blast dangerous rocks at The Swillies and to construct a new quay. The Trustees, elected from influential townsfolk, held their meetings in the town hall. Today they meet in the boardroom of their office building on the Slate Quay. In that room hang a number of large, framed, photographs of past chairmen, spanning the years 1839–1958. The first, and most impressive, is of 'Richard Mathias Preece: Chairman of the Carnarvon Harbour Trust 1839–1843'. The photograph of his massive head and shoulders shows him clean-shaven, except for side-whiskers, with dark wavy hair; his open coat discloses his plain dark waistcoat; the two points of his white collar protrude above a wide dark stock. Unmistakable is a resemblance to William Henry, his eldest son.

Richard, a Wesleyan Methodist true to the traditional interest of that movement in literacy – for it was held to be a cause for shame not to be able to read the Bible – was a schoolteacher in Cowbridge, Glamorgan, where he had been born in 1797.

He came to Carnarvon before he was twenty and started a school in the town. He married Jane Hughes, the nineteen-year-old daughter of John Hughes, a local shipbuilder, in 1818. Their first child, Jane

C

Elizabeth, was born the following year. During the next twenty-four years they had eleven more children, of whom four died in infancy. William Henry, born 15 February 1834, was their eldest surviving son.

Richard was elected and sworn in as a Burgess of the Borough at a meeting of the Court of View and Frankpledge and Court of the Borough, on 23 September 1823 at the town hall, being described in the register as a 'gentleman'. Eloquent in Welsh and English alike, he had become a welcome preacher throughout the county's increasing gatherings of Wesleyans: he devoted some of his time to raise funds to build a Wesleyan Chapel in Carnarvon; the inscription on the foundation stone of the Ebenezer Chapel, in Chapel Street, reads: 'Laid 1st March 1825 by W. Davies, Minister, and R. M. Preece': thereafter he served as one of the chapel's two trustees. The same year he secured a post in the 'Bank', the Carnarvon branch – opened in 1812 – of the Chester and North Wales Bank, which had been founded by Owen Williams, son of the Anglesey 'copper king', and two colleagues with interests in copper mines, smelting works, and slate quarries. Three years after obtaining that post he had been elected one of the town's two bailiffs. So seriously did he take his duties as bailiff that he incurred some unpopularity as he strove to tidy obscure corners of the walled city's streets, with their insanitary and derelict buildings, and ramshackle structures propped against the castle walls. In the first census, 1801, the town's population had been recorded as 3600 and already it had nearly doubled: it seemed, too, that the town council was not empowered to levy rates so he promoted a Bill 'for paving, lighting, and improving the town' but was able to raise, by voluntary subscriptions, only £234 towards the much greater cost of its promotion. The Recorder drafted the Bill, to examine which a local committee was elected. One member of that committee was John Jones, a liquor merchant. The Bill was revised and settled. Some of the townsfolk organized themselves to oppose it and John Jones became their chairman. The Bill, after its first reading in the Commons, was defeated at its committee stage. A manuscript and tracing of June 1827 by Robert Williams, a Carnarvon solicitor, records Richard's advent in the town and describes him as a respectable young man and notes his moves to get the Bill approved. After its defeat, writes Robert Williams, Richard was ridiculed by Jones and the other oppositionists and 'had every sort of disrespect manifested towards him'. Jones commissioned a local artist to make a watercolour drawing, on a card, of a shield quartered with bootmaker's tools and with a boot as a crest. Sketches fill the card's four corners: first a cobbler sits at his last with a 'balloon' from his mouth, 'The wisdom contained in my head ought certainly to be devoted to another purpose.' Then he sits in a tail-coat observing, 'Thank God I am now becoming a gentleman.' Next he is in a pulpit haranguing a congregation standing below, 'O, miserable sinners you will never enter Heaven without you pay your ministers well and let them live like gentlemen.' The remaining corner contains a drawing of a brick-built, slate-roofed bank. Additional legends are: 'If I succeed in passing the Corporation Bill my happiness will then be complete: I certainly have wonderful talent', and 'Oh! the unhappy hour the Bill is lost. I must go to Liverpool till all is blown over. My talents, thank God, will yet support me.' It has also a couplet in Welsh to which, for the benefit, presumably, of Robert Vaughan Richards of the Temple (to whom the manuscript is addressed), a translation is appended, 'Though Dick had only milk and water at home, he became without much effort a judge of wine.' Richard's fellow bailiff, Robert Humphreys, in common with other customers at Jones's shop, was shown the card for his amusement, and on a pretext of wishing to show it to his wife took it along to Richard, whose solicitor goes on to make the points that his client was never a shoemaker and that while it is true he occasionally preaches at the Ebenezer Wesleyan Chapel he is not paid to do so, and although he went to Liverpool at the time news of the Bill's defeat was heard in the town he did so only to bring back a nephew of his to Carnarvon. Since the brief remained in the family's possession, Counsel's implied advice endorsed on it – little short of downright discouragement – must have persuaded Richard that the possibility of getting £50 damages from the liquor merchant was not worth an admission that he took the matter seriously, when we may agree that Counsel's fee of one guinea made his advice a very good bargain.

In his *History of Caernarvonshire* (1968) A. H. Dodd gives most credit for inciting opposition to the Bill (which involved departures from the terms of the borough charter granted by Edward I, in 1284, to the English community he settled in the walled town associated with his castle) to a doctor O. O. Roberts, who had come to the town in 1823, 'a man of violent Protestant and anti-clerical sentiments and an inveterate exposer of every kind of "abuse"'. (Roberts had been particularly active before that in stirring up feeling against 'Romanism' – which in Carnarvon tended to be associated with the despised Irish immigrants and the Catholic Emancipation Bill.) He attended the House of Commons as a hostile witness for the town improvements Bill, claiming that it would make Carnarvon a 'closed corporation'. On his return after the Bill had been defeated his supporters gave him a public dinner, grateful that they would not be called upon to pay local rates.

The corporation, meanwhile, continued to raise money from private donations, public subscriptions, letting property (which brought in £800 a year) and borrowing from local tradesmen: it sank still further into debt. None the less it carried out some needed improvements, and brought, in 1829, the first water supply to the town, from Llyn Cwellyn, improved the town drains and, during the next decade, built markets and installed gas lighting, though the corporation later leased the gasworks to a private contractor.

By 1831 the corporation's debt totalled £14000: three years later the Court of Chancery appointed an official receiver. Within twelve months the Municipal Reform Act had dissolved the old corporation and all 'male ratepayers of three years' residence' were empowered to hold an election and choose their own corporation and mayor. (Hitherto the Constable of the Castle had been mayor, although he had usually left the management of town affairs to his two bailiffs.) Carnarvon was also granted a Commission of the Peace. The new corporation inherited its predecessor's debts together with an associated law suit.

Several years passed before a clear picture of the financial situation could be seen and in the meantime the corporation kept expenditure to a minimum.

*　　*　　*

A weekly newspaper, the *Carnarvon Herald*, the first Liberal newspaper in North Wales, began publication at the beginning of 1831. During its first few months it recorded the election campaign on the proposed Parliamentary Reform Bill with local candidates Sir

Charles Paget, as an advocate of Reform, against William Ormsby Gore, who had been returned unopposed at the previous election largely as the result of Dr Roberts whipping up local feeling against the sitting member, Sir Charles Paget, who had supported Peel and Wellington when, in 1829, they forced the Catholic Emancipation Bill through Parliament. But in May 1831, despite Dr Roberts's opposition, Paget won a close contest.

Two months later the *Herald* carried an advertisement that 'R. M. Preece and Co.' had become its proprietors and would also be opening a printing, book-selling, and stationery business. John Pindar Wright, the original editor, was retained: he was drowned at Beaumaris Bay regatta in August 1833, but by then fifteen months had elapsed since the publishing company had 'by mutual consent' dissolved partnership 'as far as relates to Mr Preece and in future will be under the firm of William Potter and Company'.

The Harbour Trustees, at a meeting on 1 February 1831, 'ordered that Mr Preece be elected a trustee in the room of Sir Robert Williams, deceased', and the minutes of the next meeting, 1 March, included his signature among the twenty-seven appended. At their October meeting they approved a plan to extend the new pier out to the Deadman, and accepted the Carnarvon Bank's offer to lend the necessary money.

Generally less than ten members attended meetings and occasionally a quorum was not present, as when Richard found himself with only three other trustees at a meeting in July 1836 – his first attendance since December 1831. Not till the latter half of 1838 did he begin to attend regularly, when he was almost invariably elected to the chair for the meeting; a regular chairman being appointed only after December 1844, the meeting which saw his last attendance.

The Carnarvon Bible Society held its twentieth annual meeting in October 1834, in the New Market, Palace Street. The rector of the parish (Llanbeblig), the Rev. J. W. Trevor, was in the chair and Richard reported, as one of the two secretaries, that a record had been achieved during the past twelve months with subscriptions of £240 (remitted to the parent body) and sales at Carnarvon local depot of 435 Bibles and 247 Testaments in Welsh, and 85 and 84 respectively in English. The Town Council gave Trevor a public dinner, at the Uxbridge Arms, with the deputy mayor, W. Roberts, in the chair. The *Herald* reported that Trevor, in proposing the formal toast of 'Bishops and clergy', had concluded,

let Churchmen and protestant dissenters give the hand of fellowship to each other, and make a stand against Popery and infidelity.

Richard begged permission from the Chair to say a few words before that toast was drunk; he belonged to a religious body (legally) dissenters. (Under the Toleration Act chapels had to be licensed as 'places of worship for Protestant Dissenters' from the closing decades of the eighteenth century. Methodists were disinclined to brand themselves as Dissenters but without doing so were liable to prosecution.)

The Church of England was not capable of the whole of the spiritual necessities of the inhabitants . . . places of worship were not numerous enough to contain them . . . auxillary means were necessary. When he saw Roman Catholics, Infidels, Socinians and the rank Dissenters of the country combining together . . . for the destruction of the Church he thought it was full time that we should forget our minor differences. . . . This, he was happy to say, was the conduct of Wesleyans generally . . . all that was noble [was] identified with the Church . . . if Church or Dissent was to fall, in God's name, let Dissent perish.

Amidst great cheering Trevor heartily thanked Richard for expressing sentiments which,

if more common, might lead the way to the regaining of those who had separated from the Church . . . he admitted an insufficiency of churches for the increasing population and concluded with a toast, 'The health and happiness of our dissenting brethren who coincide with the sentiments of Mr. Preece and are prepared to act upon them.'

Following another outburst of cheering, Richard, 'being generally called upon', told the meeting that

his parents were Wesleyan and an attachment to Wesleyan Methodism had grown with his growth . . . it had not clashed with his high esteem of the Church of England – he was not what is generally understood as a *Dissenter* – there [in the Church] he had baptized all his children.

Power, he was aware, was much sought after by mankind . . . Wesley's last letter to his brother, he reminded them, contained the phrase, 'They who are enemies of the Church are enemies of me'. . . . He trusted she [the Church] would continue as long as the sun and moon endure, to improve this land of our birth and our affection. (*Great cheering*)

John Morgan proposed the health of the Bible Society's local committee, for whom Richard responded, paying a tribute to 'lady helpers of influence' as he did so. Trevor proposed 'the *Herald*', his respondent being James Rees who, as acting proprietor, had been connected with the paper since its start with his arrival, as a printer, in Carnarvon in 1830.

The *Herald*'s next issue carried two letters criticizing Richard's speech:

inconsistency glaringly manifest . . . last election but one he [Preece] denounced . . . Church of England . . . bishops especially . . . as a Wesleyan speaker he had given great offence: not two years since he said in public that if he lost everything in the world he should go to his grave gratified if he lived to see Paget returned. His great object appears . . . to throw contempt upon dissenters.

But the following week a correspondent assured readers that

the general report of Mr. Preece's speech has given unmixed pleasure to a great many christians of different denominations.

Another recorded that

clergy were seen voting for Paget . . . the bishop had told them to act according to their own wishes.

Richard who had, in addition to his work at the bank, evidently been operating as a stockbroker on his own account, had occasion to seek further means to augment his income, for in July 1833 he advertised to let, furnished, the villa Bryn Helen, giving a good description of the house in which he was living and where William Henry Preece was to be born the next February:

Within ten minutes walk of the town . . . the house consists of a neat entrance hall, drawing room, dining room, and study, five good bedrooms and attics, convenient offices, coach house, harness room and a two stalled stable. Attached to it is a well-stocked garden in about an acre and a half of ground, neatly laid out in shrubberies and parterres. Within the premises of the celebrated St. Helen's Well, which yields an abundant supply of the most excellent water. The house stands on an exceedingly beautiful and salubrious mount, immediately above the river Seiont, and commands, in addition to a wide range of mountain scenery, the splendid ruins of Carnarvon Castle and the picturesque domain of Coedhelen.

It may be that an appreciation of romantic scenery, which for fifty years had been growing in England, was not yet particularly noticeable in North Wales because Bryn Helen, despite its scenic attractions (which it still possesses; in a truncated form, alas, for riverside road and railway have taken much of the garden and at its rear an ugly terrace of brick-and-slate houses masks the distant mountains), remained unlet, as can be seen from an advertisement in the *Herald* of 2 November.

Bryn Helen to be let for winter months at very moderate rent, or may be let for the year or term of years; also to let a neat and well-furnished house in the town. Application to be made at Bryn Helen; or, if by letter (postpaid) to Mr. Preece, Bank, Carnarvon.

Carnarvon's new corporation took some time to get organized and not till December 1835 was a list of candidates for the town council published; it included Richard and his colleague at the bank, John Morgan, who was also nominated as mayor. That the prospective mayor and Richard were among those anxious to effect economies was emphasized for, clearly, prospective ratepayers were not going to invite more than the barest essential expenditure.

With the appointment of William's first teacher, John Jackson, to the Harbour Trust, Richard sent William to the Rev. H. H. Bransby, who had advertised in the first issue of the *Herald*:

School for the education of a limited number of young gentlemen. Boarders 32 guineas, Day boarders 4 guineas and scholars 2 guineas per annum: English, Latin, Greek, Elocution, composition, writing, arithmetic, ancient and modern Geography, History, Use of the Globes and natural and moral Philosophy.

Richard, elected mayor in November 1842, determined that during the two years he would be in office he would strive his utmost to leave his mark on the town. At the end of his service the editor of the *North Wales Chronicle*, a conservative newspaper (founded in 1828, published in Bangor), was moved to write a leader on the report his paper bore of the inauguration in Carnarvon of a new mayor:

. . . the right judging inhabitants of Carnarvon perpetuate on 'tablets of silver' the serviceable mayoralty of their first magistrate. That Mr. Preece's merits as a public officer should be thus appreciated is honourable to the individual and creditable to the community. The active and businesslike ability of the man, with the befriending help of the munificent Mr. Assheton Smith wrought an almost magical change in the method and fortune of the county town, which he hands over to his successor in good order and condition – a state of things certainly in marked contrast to that which presented themselves to his vigorous mind two years ago when he took office. To cleanse the Augean stables was a tough job and dirty enough to deter ordinary men. Mr. Preece, however, applied his herculean shoulders to the task and how well he has succeeded is seen in the gratitude of his compeers.

The new mayor, in returning thanks for his election, had referred to the services of the late mayor, Alderman Preece, as 'beyond all praise'. He had proposed that the council should show their sense of those services by something more substantial than a vote of thanks and proposed opening a subscription list. Richard said he was taken by surprise:

he had attempted to do his duty faithfully and fearlessly . . . they were now in circumstances very different from those in which they were when they did him the honour to elect him mayor . . . he had succeeded in obtaining an Act of Parliament by which they were constituted a legal body and were therefore in a position to effect all the purposes of local government . . . their ancient and beautiful maces were literally in pawn . . . the town was in a wretched state; there were no police; its streets were inadequately lighted; property was seriously deteriorated, and the place was a bye-word for filth, misrule and every description of irregularity. The munificence of Mr. Assheton Smith having enabled them to put an end to their legal difficulties and to preserve the corporation from literally insolvency, and legislative relief having been obtained, and the council legally protected, the evils to which he had referred were in part, if not altogether, removed . . . the incoming mayor was also architect of his own fortune. . . . He asked them all to forget party distinction and private feeling and unite together to make Carnarvon . . . a town in which it would be a comfort and happiness to reside. (*Great applause*)

The *Herald* editor, in his next issue, rancorously commented:

That Mr. Preece the worthy ex-mayor of the Borough has succeeded in causing the removal of the nuisances around the Castle walls so disgraceful to the town and so derogatory to the Castle itself is a fact that not even the fulsome garnish of our contemporary can disfigure and degrade but the writer must have strange notions of mankind if he imagines his present eulogies can erase the memory of past abuse or that Mr. Preece will mistake his venal rhapsody for the voice of fame.

*   *   *

Disenchanted by local factiousness Richard had concluded that he had reached the peak of his endeavours in Carnarvon; in the meantime he had built a good connection with the brothers Peppercorne, stockbrokers, of Broad Street, London; the future of his five daughters would be more promising in a less restricted society; he had three sons to educate; and there would be new worlds to conquer – for he had yet to experience the effect of the strains to which he had subjected himself during his years in Carnarvon. He decided, therefore, to move to London where, from his frequent visits, he knew his way about. The Welsh settlement in Wisconsin, which had begun about ten years before and had attracted many from the district – particularly miners and slate-quarrymen – made no comparable appeal to him.

About £200 was collected to pay for 'the tablets of silver', which consisted of 'a candelabrum and a salver both of massive silver and both beautifully chased and ornamented'. Each bore an inscription,

'Presented to Richard Mathias Preece Esq. by the Town Council of Carnarvon and the other Friends connected with the Borough, not only as a memorial of their gratitude for his judicious, active and most important services, during the two years of his mayoralty, but also as an offering, however inadequate, of sincere personal esteem. Carnarvon March 1st 1845.'

Richard made his last public appearance in Carnarvon on the same date as that engraved on the plate; he sat as one of the magistrates on the bench with the mayor when they had issued a certificate to Martha Winstanley, to prevent her being arrested for begging, to confirm that she and her four small children were the widow and orphans of William Winstanley, who had been lost when the *Amity* foundered on a voyage to Sydney, Australia. The silversmiths were unable to complete work on the presentation plate before the end of the month.

On 2nd April the mayor wrote to Richard at New Hummuns, Covent Garden (an hotel on the site now occupied by Russell Chambers):

Your friends regret that you are not likely to be in Carnarvon for some weeks and that they are denied the satisfaction of delivering to you personally and in public the Articles of Plate which are intended as a memorial both to your strenuous and successful exertions in promoting the interest of the Borough, and of their gratitude and kind wishes. The Committee has therefore requested me to place them in your hands. I have no doubt that you will esteem it one of the highest honours of your life to receive them; and I am also sure, that wherever Providence may cast your lot, they will never be looked upon, either by you or your family, without feelings of pride and exultation. Thomas Henry Evans.

Richard replied:

No words can express what I feel at being put in possession of the splendid Articles of Plate which accompanied your letter . . . I regret exceedingly that it was altogether out of my power to go to Carnarvon and to receive those valuable and gratifying memorials of their approbation. I should then have had an opportunity of assuring them, in person, that I am sensible, most deeply sensible, of their kindness, and that to be thus distinguished by them, I, indeed, 'esteem as one of the highest honours of my life'. I must beg that you . . . will have the goodness to convey to them my sincere and cordial acknowledgements. Though I have ceased to reside at Carnarvon, it is impossible that I can ever be indifferent to the prosperity of a town in which I spent so many of my best and happiest years. The encouragement which it has there so long been my privilege to enjoy, has left an impression upon my heart which no change of outward circumstances, and no time, can efface. While I fondly cherish the remembrance, it will serve to stimulate me in all my endeavours to discharge the duties of a more extended sphere, and to merit the good opinions of a larger community.

4

DOLCE FAR NIENTE

RICHARD rented 24 Park Square East, Regent's Park, and brought his family to London. He entered William Henry at King's College School in time for the autumn term, 1845, obtaining a nomination from an original shareholder ('Proprietor') in the College which enabled him to board his son with Dr J. R. Major (at 40 Bloomsbury Square) at a reduced fee of £22 for two terms. (Masters had groups of pupils lodging with them during term.) After attending school and college William Henry, he planned, would apply for a commission in the army – anticipating the Duke of Wellington's requirement of four years later that no one should receive a commission unless he was of good average ability and had received the education of a gentleman. King's was strictly Church of England denominational, financed by churchmen's contributions, and requiring its tutors to satisfy a religious test. It was the Church's answer to the 'godless' University opened in Gower Street in 1827. This sectarian emphasis would, as we have seen, pose no difficulties for his father.

The Treasury withheld its annual grant of £1700 in 1894 till religious tests were withdrawn from tutors. The Dean of St Paul's moved at the College's council meeting,

That considering the support which the College is now receiving from churchmen it is not expedient to entertain a proposal for such an alteration to its constitution as the Government requires.

Eight of the twenty-five council members voted against him; subsequently five of them, including William Henry, resigned from council. Next year the Treasury, with no reference to its previous tests stipulation, restored the grant.

Although William Henry was to be elected a Fellow of the

College in 1885 and be named approvingly by F. J. C. Hearnshaw, the College's centenary historian, in 1928, he did not distinguish himself as a scholar, but he was popular with his contemporaries and good at games.

The College opened a Military Department at Easter, 1848,

for the benefit of the numerous class of Gentlemen who may be expecting Commissions in the Army or direct appointments to the Honorable East India Company's service.

Altogether, thirty-five students had been admitted when the 1850–51 intake, which included Preece, was added and he was also listed in the Department's nineteen students for the next twelve months. Its syllabus comprised: religious instruction; Latin and ancient history; mathematics; English literature; modern history; geography; natural philosophy including mechanics, hydrostatics, and practical astronomy; machinery; French; German; fortifications and military tactics; military drawing and fencing.

Organized games were yet to be included in the curriculum of school or college, nor did King's own playing fields: that did not deter schoolboys and students from selecting teams and arranging matches. Cricket, at which William proved adept, had become immensely popular, and in 1851 – ten years before an English team first toured Australia – there were representative matches between Americans and English immigrants in New York City. An American reporter wrote:

A knowledge of cricket is considered by Englishmen essential to a complete education, and their love thereof being early implanted, it may be considered a national custom. It lends to muscular development and is one of the healthiest pastimes known.

Richard M. Preece soon left his Regent's Park address and rented a smaller house, No. 2 Southampton Street, Fitzroy Square. (It leads from the north-west corner of the square to Warren Street. Rebuilt, it was renamed Conway Street. The square retains its central lawn, now overshadowed from the south by the Post Office Tower.) On 30 March 1852 one of the daughters, Mary Catherine, four years older than William, married Alfred Wilks Drayson of Gosport.

Richard's business was not prospering and later in the year he had to determine what further retrenchments in his outgoings were possible. To withdraw William from college he deemed unavoidable; he could not now afford to buy his son a commission and pay for his maintenance in the army. William was supposed to be studying at home during the remainder of the year. He certainly attended a Friday evening lecture at the Royal Institution when, on 11th June, Michael Faraday spoke

On lines of magnetic force; their definite character; and their distribution within a magnet and through space.

That experience could scarcely fail to capture his interest and fire his imagination.

With the Britannia Tube Bridge completed, Edwin Clark – assistant to Robert Stephenson – had been appointed, in August 1850, chief engineer of the Electric Telegraph Company and his brother Josiah Latimer as assistant. Latimer, a widower, who lived in York Terrace, Regent's Park, a short walk from the Preeces, became a frequent visitor, marrying Margaret Helen in the summer of 1854, Frederick Charles Webb having married her sister Eliza Anne in February of that year. His brother Francis Hugh subsequently married another of the Preece daughters, to leave only the eldest, Jane Elizabeth, fifteen years William's senior, a spinster.

William visited the Electric Telegraph Company's office in the Strand during the autumn and was impressed by a time-ball in its window, operated by an electric telegraph signal from Greenwich Observatory each afternoon at precisely one o'clock. He was stimulated to write his first description of electrical phenomena and equipment, that of the standard battery then in use:

'I have here as you see' my guide explained, 'a gutta percha trough, 18 inches long by 14½ inches broad; this trough is divided into twelve partitions each distinctly and perfectly independent of its next door neighbour; in each partition is placed a plate of zinc and a plate of copper four inches square. Each zinc plate is joined by a small copper strap to the copper plate of its next-door neighbour. So that we have at one end of the trough a copper plate free and at the other end a zinc plate free, each intermediate plate being joined two by two. Each partition we then fill with sand, which is well moistened with sulphuric acid diluted with water. This, what we call a *battery*, is now complete. I will fasten a wire to the free copper which we call the copper or positive pole of the battery, and the same to the zinc or negative pole of the battery. If you place the wires upon your tongue you will perceive what we call a current of electricity.' I did so but the moment my tongue touched the wires I experienced a sharp stinging sensation through the tongue to its very roots. It seemed as if a flash of lightning passed before my eyes. Such a curious shock pervaded my whole body which though very peculiar and for the moment painful was anything but unpleasant. 'That,' said I to C. – who seemed to enjoy my experience of the current as a very good joke and laughed uproariously – 'you call a current but how does that drop the ball?' C. then gave a description of how the ball was released by an electrical current transmitted from Greenwich which operated an electro-magnet, and mentioned that there was another time ball over the Head Office at Lothbury, and others had recently been installed at Manchester and Liverpool; in a few weeks the balls at Greenwich, Lothbury, Strand, Manchester and Liverpool will be dropping at the same instant by that wonderful agency whose powers have called forth the beautiful remark, 'Is it not a feat sublime, intellect has conquered Time.'

★   ★   ★

William has filled the space for each day in a Letts' pocket diary for 1853 to mid-February when, as with so many young men who have included 'keep a diary' in their New Year resolutions, entries become less frequent: the last he made was for 16th March. Cryptic though they are, these entries enable us to visualize him as he nears his seventeenth birthday, and give us a glimpse of the tragedy developing for his family. He has filled in the blank pages at the beginning of the booklet with comments on the weather:

The eventful year 1852 has closed quietly and comfortably with shocking bad weather. I have never seen such a continuance of wet weather and trust I never shall again. God knows when it is going to stop.

Since a regular activity of his was to go for walks he was particularly likely to rail at wet weather as on Sunday, 2nd January, 'Miserably wet. Went to church, wretched sermon.' The Church was Holy Trinity in the Marylebone Road, on the southern edge of Regent's Park and five minutes' walk from Fitzroy Square. Consecrated in 1828 it was one of the 'Waterloo churches' for which, seven years earlier, Parliament had voted a million pounds in thanksgiving that the country had escaped invasion by Napoleon. Sir John Soane, the Bank of England's architect, had designed it for the new parish of Holy Trinity, with a seating of more than a thousand, at an expenditure of £20 000. The church had been called for as a greatly increased population had found St Marylebone parish church unable to provide sufficient accommodation. (A century after William's diary entry most of the resident population had receded to the suburbs, their houses and studios replaced by blocks of offices, and Holy Trinity Church taken over by the Society for Promoting Christian Knowledge as its administrative headquarters.)

12th Jan: Still rain! Everlasting rain! I do not think we have had twelve hours fine for four months.

The weather improved but the first day of February was marred by

heavy dismal fog. People carrying torches in their hands. It had a very curious effect. Picturesque.

2nd: The fog this morning was worse than yesterday. Cleared up in the afternoon and turned out beautiful.

12th: Snowing fast.

In mid-February he records that frost has at last set in and

we may expect some skating. 17th: Caught a cold somehow or other in my eye for I awoke this morning and found it very much inflamed. Very inconvenient at present for the frost setting in it will spoil my skating. 18th: My eye still bunged up. Better though. Can't read. Can't do nothing. Very awkward. 21st: Out at last. Had a skate in the Botanical gardens [Regent's Park]. Got on capitally though it was only the second time I ever had skates on. Glorious weather. 22nd: Had a glorious skate in the morning. The weather changed however about one o'clock and we were obliged to return home. A regular thaw.

From the weather William moved to a personal assessment:

1852 has by me passed most unprofitably. Idle and lazy the whole year.

He commented on the Duke of Wellington's death in November, on Louis Napoleon re-establishing the French Empire, and then returned to family affairs:

Our Christmas passed off rather dull. The Governor's attack put a damp upon our fun but despite all that I made a good dinner and, what's more, enjoyed it.

I commenced the present year with an empty purse, may I finish with a full one. I am in debt. May they all be paid. I am well, may I continue so, and please God I have a clear conscience (though wicked thoughts come into my head now and then) may I remain so.

That his debts amounted to more than a pound or two is unlikely. He made a note of his daily spending for most of January. Much the largest sums are: 3s. 4d. (cigars 1s. 4d., return train ticket Waterloo–Wandsworth 1s., buses 6d. and 4d., beer 2d.); 2s. 9d. (cigars, cab fare, and tipping a servant); and 2s. 8d. (cigars 11d., cab 1s. 6d., beer 3d.).

His father, whom he usually refers to as the 'Gov', is ill indoors throughout the period of the diary. His cough is mentioned on one occasion and he is often described as 'in bed' or 'very low'. William's entry for 10th January reads, 'Gov. still bad and very squiffy with me', from which we may suppose that his father thought his eldest son should be doing something more useful than going, as we shall see, to New Year and Twelfth Night parties. His rebuke had a slight effect upon William for he records that next morning he spent an hour and a half

studying dynamics. Gov. a little better. Spent the rest of the day at Wandsworth. After dinner played billiards with Mr. Jones. Won two and the fifth I was 47 to his 42.

At that stage they must have noticed the hour was late for he concludes with 'had a good run for the last train' to Waterloo. On February 12th he records that he went to Wandsworth with his brother-in-law Drayson and played billiards all day,

he gave me 20 out of 50 and licked me. Mr. Jones not at home.

Mr Jones seemingly kept open house for Welsh compatriots and their friends.

Earlier, 29th January, William had noted,

Went to the Welsh School with Gov's polling paper. Spent the rest of the day at Wandsworth. Had two games of billiards with Mr. Jones. He rather savage. Had a long talk with me about my debts etc.

We can guess that Mr Jones lost those two games and that he had

D

lent William a little money at some time, but probably he had been worrying about the future of the Preece family and urging William to get a job.

Brother-in-law Drayson was a member of White's Club in St James's Street, to which he took William on 11th February: 'D. played pool and won a good lot.' That Friday evening William went to the Royal Institution: 'heard a capital lecture by Tyndall (a new man) on magnetism; a fluent, graceful, and excellent lecture'. Five days later he was again at White's with Drayson, where he played billiards and pyramids. The day before had been his birthday and he records that 'Frank' (Francis) Webb had dined with the family and they were joined by another friend in the evening; 'we had a merry party'. He goes on to note wryly, 'The first birthday ever spent without receiving a present', a sign of the Preeces' straitened circumstances.

On 2nd February they had been informed that Mary had suffered a miscarriage during the night. As William walked with their informant back to Mary's house she told him, to his 'great regret', that he was the cause of his sister's mishap in that he had frightened her by passing a lighted piece of paper rapidly before her eyes.

Mem. Beware of playing practical jokes on young married women whilst in a certain state.

He noted next day that she was getting on very well and was better the following day:

Lucky my foolhardiness has not caused more mischief. D. very amusing Pol [Mary] asked him if she thought she had better get up. He answered that when he was in the same state he stayed in bed six or seven days.

William had welcomed in the New Year at home with three of his friends. A few days later he had spent an afternoon with another smoking a cigar. Opportunities for smoking had to be created, he would not be allowed to smoke in the company of ladies (even of his mother and sisters), in public, or at the theatre. At White's Club a ban on smoking had been maintained until 1845, when it became permissible to smoke cigars in a room assigned for that purpose. Other friends came to his home, 'We had a capital racing game. Won 3d.!' (that was an evening when his father was 'squiffy' with him).

Another evening with friends he 'supped at Evans' – Supper Rooms in Covent Garden – London's first music hall above ground, where he

heard one or two good comic songs from Edwards and Sloman and some excellent glees. Came home half past two.

Four days later one of those friends, after dining with the Preeces, took William off to the Haymarket Theatre.

Saw *Masks and Faces*, an excellent comedy. Mrs. Sterling as Peg Wolfenden very fine. The Christmas piece, *Leo the Terrible*, very poor, slow, drawling and tiresome. The farce, *Box and Cox, Married and Settled*, very droll and excessively amusing . . . forgot my latchkey . . . compelled to remain half an hour outside the door.

Theatres at that time were providing a five- to six-hour programme, starting at half past six or seven o'clock and comprising a farce, a three-hour drama, and an extravaganza or pantomime. On another occasion, after a visit to White's, Drayson took him to the Lyceum Theatre to see *Good Women in the Woods*,

the best extravaganza they have there. The scenery is gorgeous, particularly the last and the dialogue full but drawling; the actors, however, made up for it. *Little Toddlekins* an excellent and amusing farce.

He records having a Welsh rabbit with a friend at the Cock Tavern, which was then on the north side of Fleet Street. His comments on his friends and acquaintances are usually complimentary: 'a very nice fellow' (of several), 'an excessively good fellow but inclined to be very talkative and conceited', 'an amusing fellow, would show me all his accounts', 'an affable kind-hearted creature' (of an older man), 'the cleverest fellow in Addiscombe and a very nice chap too' (of a cadet named Champain at the East India Company's military college). At the end of January he visited King's College where he met 'lots of friends' but described one with whom he went for a walk as 'a conceited ass, fancies himself a dab in literature and poetry'. On another occasion he had gone for a long walk with a friend whom he characterized as 'a rum young fish! Not disagreeable but particularly fond of swearing.' His comments on local parties to which he had been invited are also interesting. One was, rather contradictorily, 'slow, dull and no pretty girls. Good fun though.' He returned home

at half past eleven on Twelfth Night, having spent the day with
Francis Webb who was sick, 'just in time to cut the Twelfth cake.
Capital fun.'

On the morrow he went to a party at

the Maudes. It was a juvenile affair and I was there about nine o'clock.
Found about thirty there. Danced the first dance with M. Maude and
subsequently with the two Misses Harries, two very pretty girls particularly the youngest (Helen). Miss Spottiswoode another very pretty girl
and a beautiful dancer, danced with her several times and took her down
to supper. The little Fishers looked very nice little ladies, like wax dolls.

– they, presumably, were part of the juvenile element – 'Altogether
enjoyed myself uncommonly.' Next morning he observed that he
was 'not at all seedy after last evening for a wonder'. Just over a week
later he met the 'delightful Misses Harries' when walking with a
friend down Regent Street, a street which at that time had been
described as a great trunk road in Vanity Fair, an avenue of super-
fluities, a fashionable promenade with smartly dressed men and
women strolling along the wide clean pavements and looking at the
shop window displays of fancy watches, jewels, French gloves, per-
fumery, point lace, shawls, hosiery, haberdashery, millinery, fancy
stationery, music and confectionery. Carriages draw up at the kerb
from which ladies descend and, each accompanied by a liveried foot-
man, pass by itinerant sellers of puppies, pen-knives, cheap jewellery
and the like, to enter one of the luxury shops. The sound of horses
clop-clopping on the wood surface of the road, as they trot along
drawing elegant carriages, drowns an Italian's piano-organ music.
Nash's cast-iron columns which formed an arch along the Quadrant
(where the street turns through a quarter circle) had been removed in
1848 to allow more light to reach the shop windows.

Next day William was at another party where he danced chiefly
with the four young ladies he had named; 'enjoyed myself immensely, never more. Helen a delightful and charming girl.' He
awoke, however, 'uncommonly seedy'. On another of his walks he
met Helen and her sister, 'but like a fool never joined them, only
bowed'.

Although the only record he made of study, other than that
already noted, was a single morning on statics, he managed to do a

certain amount of reading. He took an occasional opportunity to look at a magazine in a coffee house when in the City visiting a bank for his father (once had 'balanced banking account etc.' while there). He described an editorial review on Tom Moore in *Fraser's Magazine*, together with an article on Thackeray's idiosyncracies reprinted from the *Boston Recorder*, as 'pompous'. He enjoyed *Bentley's Miscellany* January number and noted with approval an article which argued that English ladies who were demonstrating their sympathy with slaves in the United States should first turn their attention to conditions worse than slavery taking their toll at home 'where all charity should begin'. Another day he found 'nothing particular' in *Tait's Magazine*, which

speaks of the likelihood of Disraeli one day forming a ministry. Instead of the deluge coming after it will come before this time I expect.

(here he would appear to be echoing his father for he was never really interested in party politics).

All the talk at present is about Louis Napoleon's marriage with the Spanish beauty Countess de Tiba. Poor girl, what will her end be?

'An excellent thing in *Punch*,' he wrote another day, 'Book-keeping taught in one lesson: don't lend them.'

One day he called at Mudie's circulating library; on another he

read the Life of Lord Bacon and also of my celebrated countryman Williams in Campbell's *Lives of the Lord Chancellors*.

Later he read those of Clarendon, Notting, and Shaftesbury, and was horrified by that of Jeffreys: he made a number of notes on that of Lord Thurlow.

He once said to George the Third, after he had been reading some Bills for his approval, 'It is all damned nonsense trying to make you understand so you had better consent to them at once.' When the colonel of the muster once said to him, 'Mr. Thurlow I never look out of the window but I see you passing under it', he replied, 'And I never pass under the window but I see you looking out of it.'

He was not likely to recognize inaccuracies, for which the book is notorious in the legal profession where it is held to have added a fresh sting to death.

In February he was reading Lord Brougham's *Statesmen of the reign of George the Third*:

Do not like the style of it, pompous, tedious. Very fond of using uncommon words. . . . From what I can observe it presents his conclusions impartially, carefully, and thoroughly sincerely.

        *   *   *

During the course of these relaxations William was also looking for a job. He had visited Latimer Clark in January 1853 and discussed the possibility of being given a post with the Electric Telegraph Company. Latimer introduced him to his brother Edwin on whom he made a favourable impression. Nor would Edwin Clark be likely to regard an interest in cricket unfavourably, for he had spent a good deal of time at Marlow, 1828–32, in rowing and playing cricket before he decided to adopt engineering as a profession. In February Edwin gave him a letter of introduction to the Company's secretary, who interviewed him; 'Made a fool of myself, asked for £150 a year.' On hearing no more from the Company he contemplated the advisability of going to Latimer and offering to work in his office without pay in order to learn the business. Before he had made up his mind to act on that idea the brothers Clark summoned him and arranged for him to start as a clerk at the Company's office at 448 West Strand on 16th March at thirty shillings a week. He found four young male clerks in the office and wrote in his diary that evening, 'Bad commencement – obliged to find out everything for myself.' Their unco-operative behaviour had surprised him by its contrast to the response his friendly exuberance had hitherto evoked. Its effect was to stiffen him in his resolve to make a success of his job.

5

THE ELECTRIC TELEGRAPH
COMPANY

To understand the contribution Preece made to electric telegraphy we must review, briefly, events leading to its first practical use when he was but three years old and its development thereafter till, fifteen years later, he joined the Electric Telegraph Company.

In Heidelberg, in March 1836, Professor Muncke, during a lecture on electricity, demonstrated a method devised by Baron Schilling of indicating the movement of a needle suspended at its centre on a fibre and in a surrounding coil of wire. In such a 'galvanometer' the needle moved through 180 degrees when the direction of current in the wire was reversed. On the side of the fibre he stuck a disc, marked on one side with a cross, the better to demonstrate the needle's movement.

Among his audience was William F. Cooke, who had been awarded a commission in the East India Company's army eight years before, at the age of nineteen, but had left to study anatomical modelling in wax, for which opportunities were provided at Heidelberg's anatomical museum. Such modelling had been given an emphasis in India where a plan to train native surgeons had been obstructed by religious prejudices against dissection. The Company, in an attempt to solve that problem, commissioned the surgeon of Middlesex Hospital, in 1829, to make full-scale anatomical figures in coloured papier mâché.

Cooke knew nothing of electricity but as he watched the movements from 'cross' to 'blank' of Muncke's indicator he suddenly saw that it might be adapted to send messages long distances. Signalling from a distance by electricity was not a new idea: it had occurred to a number of experimenters in Europe and America though few had developed their ideas, for the majority were too absorbed in discovering more electrical phenomena to take time off for utilitarian ends.

Something of static electricity – in addition to lightning – had been known for many centuries, as had the properties of magnetic iron oxide, and a widespread interest in it flourished from time to time, as in 1782 when a German visitor to England wrote,

Electricity is the plaything of the English. Anyone who can air views about it is sure to make a stir.

Galvani of Bologna described nine years later how he had by accident touched the hind legs of a frog he had skinned and dissected when the legs moved convulsively as they would have done if they had received a discharge from a static electrical machine. He thought that indicated a natural source of electricity in the frog's legs: his countryman Volta of Como thought it due to contact between dissimilar metals and, after many experiments, produced a pile of silver (or copper) and zinc discs assembled alternately but separated by pieces of cardboard (or cloth) soaked in a dilute saline solution: when a wire was attached to the copper disc at one end and to the zinc disc at the other an electric current 'flowed' through it. Such a sustained supply was quite different from the instantaneous discharge from static accumulators and enabled those working in laboratories to make many more experiments.

Sir Humphry Davy of the Royal Institution, popularly famous for his miner's safety lamp, discovered in 1802 that after placing two pieces of carbon in a circuit with a battery of Voltaic cells he could by drawing the carbons slightly apart, generate a most brilliant light between them. Professor Oersted, of Copenhagen, discovered in 1820 that a wire carrying an electric current, on being placed parallel with and close to a magnetized needle free to rotate about its centre, deflected that needle, the direction of deflection being consistent with the direction of the current and its extent dependent on the strength of the current. Coiling the wire multiplied the current's effect on a needle suspended in the coil. Ampère, a French scientist, recognized that the current was deflecting the needle against the power exerted by the earth's magnetism. He neutralized that power by mounting two needles parallel but with the north pole of one adjacent to the south pole of the other and by winding a coil around each needle in an opposite direction allowed the current to deflect both needles in the same direction: thus constructing a recording instrument which he named a 'galvanometer'.

William Sturgeon, of Kirkby Lonsdale, discovered at the same time that a core of soft iron became a strong magnet when placed within a coil of wire carrying an electric current, reverting to its original state when the current ceased. Joseph Henry, of Albany, New York, made many improvements during 1828–31 in Sturgeon's electro-magnet. The Russian, Baron Schilling, had, as we have seen, devised about 1825 a system of signalling with galvanometers. He spent ten years travelling around demonstrating his apparatus and had given a duplicate to Muncke in 1835. Two years later the Russian government instructed Schilling to carry out his proposal to connect St Petersburg electrically with Kronstadt by a cable across the Gulf of Finland: unfortunately, within two months of receiving that instruction, Schilling died.

A few days after listening to Muncke, Cooke wrote to his mother to inform her that he was working on

an instrument should I succeed in bringing it to practical perfection [will] merit a visit to London. The mechanism requires a more delicate hand than mine to execute or rather instruments which I do not possess. These I can readily have made for me in London. . . . As I do not wish my motives for returning to London to be generally known . . . ascribe them to modelling. . . .

In London, he arranged to have a telegraph made but was not satisfied with the apparatus when, after a number of delays, it was completed; nor did he know the limiting distance over which an electro-magnet that he had incorporated in his telegraph could be operated. He therefore asked Michael Faraday, Davy's successor at the Royal Institution, to inspect his apparatus. Faraday confirmed that it was constructed on sound principles but had no information on the distant operation of electro-magnets.

Cooke, who saw how useful his telegraph could be to control railway traffic, asked the directors of the Liverpool and Manchester Railway to allow him to demonstrate it at a tunnel near Liverpool.

He received no encouragement. Still doubtful about his apparatus being able to work over long distances, he got in touch with Professor Charles Wheatstone. He learnt that Wheatstone had also gone some way towards developing a practical electric telegraph. They tested Cooke's apparatus over four and a half miles of wire in Wheatstone's laboratory to find that the resistance of the circuit reduced the current to an amount insufficient to actuate his electromagnet. Cooke thereupon reverted to his earlier idea of using a galvanometer, only to discover that it was on such a system Wheatstone had been working. They decided to join forces and applied for a patent to cover needles actuated by galvanometers. Their patent was granted on 10 June 1837.

Robert Stephenson, Engineer to the London and Birmingham Railway, became interested in their telegraph. Not only did he get permission for it to be demonstrated but he also managed to get a grant to cover the cost of the demonstration. They tried the telegraph on 25th July between Euston and Camden stations to control traffic on an endless cable whereby trains were pulled up the incline to Camden (hitherto signals had been given by forcing air through a long pipe to operate a whistle). The instrument used was one of Wheatstone's, more cumbersome than Cooke's variant, it had the advantage of indicating signals which could be read on sight with no special training. Five conducting wires were suspended along the track side, the earth being used as a common return. Any two of five needles, pivoted on a bar across the centre of a diamond-shaped dial, could be selected to swing either towards the dial's upper or lower apex to point to a letter of the alphabet arranged in two triangular 'hatchments' of ten letters (G, J, Q, U, X and Z being omitted).

Cooke laid a permanent line by imbedding the conductors in an impregnated strip of wood. Stephenson recommended that his directors extend the telegraph to Birmingham, but they allowed the Euston–Camden Town lines to go out of use after six months. Meanwhile, Isambard K. Brunel, then constructing the Great Western Railway, arranged for Cooke to instal a telegraph from Paddington to West Drayton, which Cooke completed in 1839. He ran cotton-covered copper wires in iron pipes alongside the railway track: their insulation proving unsatisfactory, Cooke strung the wires on earthenware insulators on the cross-arms of poles, taking out a patent for his overhead line in 1842. At his own expense he extended the telegraph to Slough, by which time he was using iron wires, thus reducing capital costs.

*   *   *

Preece learnt what happened after that many years later when, in February 1887, Thomas Home of Brill, Buckinghamshire, wrote to him to ask for the address of Cooke's widow, and continued:

I may tell you that when Sir W. F. Cooke erected the Telegraph on the G.W.R. Paddington to Slough (by kind permission of the Directors of that line) as an experiment, I at that time was assistant to Mr. Cooke and directly its extension to Slough was completed . . . I made an offer to Mr. Cooke which resulted in my becoming 'Licensee' of the said Telegraph. . . . My License was about £170 a year. I continued Licensee for about 4½ years or until the formation of the Telegraph Company to whom Messrs. Cooke and Professor Wheatstone sold their respective patents in Telegraphy.

As you may naturally wish to know how I recouped the said License fee, I must tell you that I opened the offices (Telegraph) at Paddington and Slough to the public and charged an admittance fee of 1/- per person. I also sent telegrams at one uniform charge of 1/- each, *irrespective of length or number of words* – porterage being added according to distance. I therefore claim the honour of having sent the first paid telegram by electricity.

I had in each office . . . the various instruments then perfected by Messrs. Cooke and Wheatstone – Cooke's double and single needle; Wheatstone's printing telegraph, and his Electro-magnetic Telegraph: in this latter a disc, having all the letters of the alphabet on it revolved and letters required were brought to an aperture. Wheatstone's instruments I *seldom or never* used, as they could not be relied on. The needle instrument *invariably* worked well.

I very extensively advertised the Telegraph in all the London daily and weekly papers, and had men (*sandwich* men) distributing hand bills to notify that the Telegraph at the two offices named was on view. . . . Great numbers called to see it, including many of the Crowned Heads of Europe; but when I resigned I had absolutely nothing over and above my expenses.

The Telegraph, I must tell you, was never used by the Great Western Railway Company unless on extraordinary occasions and then no charge was made by me in return for the privilege given to Mr. Cooke to erect it as an experimental line. . . . I it was who received the telegram to detain John Tawell who poisoned Sarah Hart at Salt Hill, Slough. He was hanged at Aylesbury. I name this as Tawell was the first murderer detected through the instrumentality of the Telegraph. . . .

The Tawell incident was in January 1845; John Tawell had been recognized, although he was disguised as a Quaker, boarding the train at Slough and a description was sent to the London Police via Paddington. This incident stimulated popular imagination to an immensely greater extent than an earlier report, in *The Times*, 15 April 1844:

The first intelligence of the arrival of His Royal Highness Prince Albert in this country from Germany on Tuesday last was communicated to Her Majesty at Windsor Castle by means of the Telegraph on the Line of the Great Western Railway. Within one minute of the arrival of His Royal Highness at the Paddington terminus the information had reached Slough: at which station a special messenger mounted on one of the fleetest horses of the Royal Stables was stationed by command of the Queen, who proceeded with the gratifying intelligence to the Castle, where he arrived in eight and a half minutes from the time of leaving Slough.

(The kind of incident most stimulating to the public imagination did not appear to alter after seventy-five years, for a similar interest was aroused in wireless telegraphy when the populace learnt of its use in the capture of Doctor Crippen.)

Robert Stephenson had constructed the London and Blackwall Railway from the Minories to Brunswick Pier, Blackwall, in 1840, when he arranged for Cooke to equip it with an electric signalling system to control traffic: next year the cable railway was extended to Fenchurch Street.

The Lords of the Admiralty had operated a visual telegraph between London and Portsmouth for just over half a century when, in 1844, they agreed to pay Cooke £1500 a year for twenty years and £1000 a year for the following twenty years to set up an electric telegraph to Portsmouth. Cooke persuaded the South Western Railway to help finance him and to allow him to run his line along its route.

In 1821 Sir Francis Ronalds had proposed to the Admiralty that electric telegraphs should be established but had received a reply that they were unnecessary: that reply was later severely criticized although Ronalds's telegraph, the operation of which depended on static electricity, was not practicable in the field. When Cooke's practical telegraph came to their notice my Lords had certainly risen to the occasion and thus had given invaluable and early encouragement to the development of electric telegraphs.

The *Morning Chronicle*, on 25 January 1845, reported:

The first trial of the electric telegraph on this line constructed by Messrs. Cooke and Wheatstone, the patentees, for the joint use of the Admiralty and the South Western Railway Company between Nine Elms and Gosport, a distance of eighty-eight miles, took place on Friday last; several of the directors of the company and scientific gentlemen were present on the occasion. On hearing that the suspension of the conducting wire was completed, Mr. Cooke left London by the three o'clock train and stopped at Bishopstoke, 72 miles, he then proceeded by the next train and the hour was occupied in carrying the wires into the office at Gosport on the branch line, so that it was only a little before ten o'clock that all things being ready he despatched the first signal to London; four or five minutes of anxiety elapsed before any reply was obtained, when his London assistant excused his inattention, on the ground of having fallen asleep before the fire, the signal passed with the utmost precision and a long conversation with his London correspondent over the intervening distance of eighty-eight miles. Confidence in this system of insulation was thus proved, the experiment never having been tried until seventy-two miles were completed when the apparatus was applied at Bishopstoke about a fortnight back. Directions for his London assistant to start for Gosport by the first morning train closed the correspondence for the night.

Professor Wheatstone joined by appointment at Nine Elms about twelve next morning and some thousand signals took their flight between London and Gosport. In Mr. Wheatstone's experiments no perceptible time was occupied in transmission. Among many others, the following inquiries and answers preceded by the ringing of the alarum occupying about four minutes were made at the request of one of the company's officers: 'Q. Have you any mackerel for tonight's goods train? A. No, we cannot catch them now. Q. Why not? A. Because the nights are moonlight and the fish see the net. Other communications respecting the shipping took place, subsequently the professor's new magneto-electric telegraph was brought into a long circuit of wire and worked to perfection through 288 miles. The apparatus dispenses with the batteries altogether, a steel magnet being the source of power. The Admiralty are to have a pair of these machines, and a pair of Wheatstone printing telegraphs for their distinct use. For railway purposes Mr. Cooke prefers his 'two needle telegraph' and in this opinion Professor Wheatstone agrees, as its rapid colloquial questions and answers character is perfectly adapted for railway exigencies. There is a good deal of painting to be done on the line which will require fine weather and some days to complete, as soon as this is done the apparatus will again be worked and two wires placed at the command of the Lords of the Admiralty; the other with the branch line to Southampton will remain in the company's hands for their own railway purposes and the use of the public. The result of Friday night's experiment was considered rather unsatisfactory as the state of the weather was most unfavourable to insulation, the posts thoroughly wet, and the wires strung with myriads of water spark like gems. The following day was fine and though the points of connection were all wet, nevertheless, the insulation was excellent with the last experiment. Mr. Cooke is prepared to accept a challenge to lay down a telegraph from London to Falmouth, Liverpool, or Edinburgh, without any intermediate stages, the last practical difficulty is overcome by the present system of insulating, and Mr. Wheatstone need only add a letter folding and sealing apparatus to his printing machine to prepare the communication for the post office. This is the result of Messrs. Cooke and Wheatstone's invention after eight years' perseverance, and it would be idle to suppose that the commercial world will long neglect the power this invention is capable of conferring on the commercial capitals of Great Britain, by laying their closer contiguity, as regards their commercial intelligence and transactions; seeing that by it may be known on 'Change at Liverpool, or in London, every fluctuation of price, and every variation in stock or shares, within two minutes of the transaction being closed in either place. The entire cost of the telegraph between London and Portsmouth is £24,000 to be paid in equal proportions by the Admiralty and the company. Negotiations are being entered into with Government for laying down sections of it on the Chester and Holyhead line, now in course of construction.

Last evening, at the annual conversatione of the Society of Arts, the apparatus was exhibited, worked by Mr. Cooke and Mr. Rowland, his assistant. In the course of conversation Mr. Cooke stated that the invention, by a slight modification of the symbols, might be adapted to an almost endless variety of uses; that by means of the galvanic process conversation might be sustained uninterruptedly between Liverpool and

London; that musical compositions might be transmitted with exactitude from one place to another; and that even games of chess might be conducted between the players in two distant districts. Last evening, the words 'Liverpool' and 'Adelphi' were described by the manipulator on the dial, and telegraphed by means of the wires to an assistant operator at the other end of the room, who immediately announced the import of the communication. In cases where express accounts of public events are required, the instrument promises to be available, since it is calculated by the patentee that were a telegraph to be laid down between Liverpool and London, accurate reports of speeches might be transmitted from either place, and be put in type and circulated long before any express train could possibly make its arrival.

When Cooke, later in the year, obtained a contract with the South Eastern Railway for a system between London and Dover he decided it was time to form a public company: it was registered in September as the Electric Telegraph Company, with J. Lewis Richardo, M.P., as chairman, and four other directors, including Cooke himself. The Company's head office was in Founder's Court, Great Bell Alley (later renamed Telegraph Street), Lothbury, in the City of London.

Alexander Bain, a Scotsman, had patented an apparatus in which a moving perforated slip of paper transmitted signals by a spring connected with a battery whenever a perforation passed under the spring, the period of current flow being determined by the length of the perforation. He arranged his receiving apparatus so that the incoming current marked, via a 'pen', a moving slip of paper electrolytically, as the paper tape had been impregnated with prussiate of potash and sulphuric acid the flow of current produced a dark blue line. Bain devised a code of long and short marks – dots and dashes – to indicate letters of the alphabet. The perforated sender and the impregnated receiver tapes were moved by clockwork released, when a message was sent, by a detent actuated by an electro-magnet. The Electric Telegraph Company purchased his patent for £7000 and used his instrument during the next few years.

The Company had 1500 miles of wire, running to Edinburgh, Glasgow, Yarmouth, and Southampton, but by 1848 was not yet a success. Cost to the public of a message of twenty words to Scotland was 17s. 6d., to Yarmouth 8s. 6d. and to Southampton 3s. The directors had overrated the immediate demand for a telegraph service, had spent all their capital, and that expenditure had greatly exceeded receipts. To reduce expenses they discharged four-fifths of their clerks on 27 March 1848. The Company was rescued by Mr Richardo, who advanced money to clear debts of £3000 and took upon himself the burden of other shareholders who had lost confidence in the Company which, at that time, was receiving only £100 a week for messages. Edwin Clark replaced W. H. Hatcher as Engineer and in the next two years he increased wire mileage from just over 2000 to 11000 – of which 300 was put underground in London and large towns – and the Company's gross revenue rose to £50000 for 1851, the year of the Great Exhibition.

6

WORKING WITH FARADAY

PREECE did not stay longer than a few weeks in the Strand office of the Electric Telegraph Company. He was appointed, on 14th May, an assistant on the Engineer's staff: Edwin Clark was the Engineer and his brother Latimer his chief assistant. Preece spent the next few months studying telegraph practice, which included batteries of primary cells: he learnt much from John Fuller who had modified Daniell's cell to replace Cooke's sand batteries. Fuller later invented a bichromate cell: his modified Daniell cell was used in telegraphy for over forty years.

Latimer Clark and Preece then undertook experiments with G. B. Airy, the Astronomer Royal, to whom the rapidity of transmission of a telegraphic signal seemed to promise a means of determining terrestrial longitude to a hitherto unattainable degree of accuracy. Such a signal could be used to alert observers in, say, Greenwich and Paris to make simultaneous observations for later comparison. The E.T.C. was only too ready to co-operate. Latimer wrote to Airy, 13 October 1853, to inform him that E.T.C. engineers had observed an appreciable and variable retardation of signals when long lengths of underground or submarine wire had formed part of a circuit and, since the submarine telegraph cable to France must form part of the circuit to the Continent a retardation of signals by currents thereby induced would defeat Airy's purpose. Airy approached Michael Faraday, who was pleased to learn of the induced delay for it confirmed what he had foretold when carrying out experiments at the Royal Institution to demonstrate that the phenomenon of induction preceded conduction when electricity flowed in a conductor. Faraday described at the Royal Institution, in January 1854, experiments which followed. They – Latimer, Preece, Airy and Faraday –

E

went to the Gutta Percha Works in Wharf Road, Stratford, for whom Faraday had examined gutta percha, a vegetable gum from Malaya, in 1848, to pronounce it an excellent material for insulating electric wires, whereupon the Works, hitherto concerned with making speaking tubes, ear-trumpets, dolls and the like, expanded rapidly to meet a new, larger, use and were insulating half-mile lengths of copper wire. Faraday, after acknowledging his debt to Latimer for bringing to his attention the retardation phenomena noticed 'in the course of the extraordinary expansion of the Electric Telegraph Company', went on to recount how they had submerged 200 coils of half-mile lengths of conductor, joined in series, from the sides of barges floating in a canal at the Works, and had used a battery to prove that current took an appreciable time to reach the far end of the cable and in the process stored a quantity of electricity which, when the circuit was broken, began to dissipate despite a high standard of insulation, although sufficient remained to be detectable twenty to thirty minutes after the cable had been separated from the battery. When the experiment was repeated with the cable in dry air no such effect was produced. Faraday deduced that the cable, when submerged, had acted as a giant condenser with a charge on the copper wire inducing an opposite charge on the surface of the water touching the outer coating of the gutta percha. He calculated the surface of copper to be 8300 square feet and the outer coating of water to be four times as much, which made the quantity of electricity stored enormous, although its intensity could only equal that at the battery poles. For such an effect to be absent when the cable was surrounded by air constituted, said Faraday, a beautiful experimental proof that static and dynamic electricity were identical:

I understand that a hundred miles of wire stretched in a line through the air so as to have its whole extent opposed to earth shows no such effect, then it must be the distance between the wire and earth and the much lower specific inductive capacity of the air as compared with gutta percha which causes the negative effect.

Faraday went on to describe experiments made over E.T.C. cables from Lothbury in October, when eight wires to Manchester were connected in series to give a continuous conductor of 1500 miles. Because of the delay caused by the underground portions of the circuit it took two seconds for a signal to traverse the total distance, but, since the insulation was not as good as that of the cable at the Works, the charged condition fell more rapidly. Latimer arranged, on Alexander Bain's chemical telegraph, to use three 'pens' a tenth of an inch apart, under which an impregnated paper tape was pulled at a regular rate by clockwork, thus the pens would produce by electrolysis regular lines of Prussian blue when a current flowed through the pens. Pen *a* was connected to a short overhead circuit, *b* with a long overhead circuit, and the third pen, *c*, with a long underground circuit. A telegraph key was arranged to send signals simultaneously over the three circuits: *a* and *b* signals produced equally thick lines, starting and ending almost in parallel across the tape, *b* starting a shade later than *a*, but *c* did not start till some time later and continued after *a* had ceased; further, its mark was faint at first, grew to a maximum intensity, and when the battery was cut off continued to record, gradually diminishing to nothing. Thus a series of short impulses, while being indicated by short separate marks on *a*, became a continuous line on *c*. Faraday, Latimer Clark and Preece carried out many variations of that experiment but always with similar results.

Faraday described further experiments in which four underground wires, gutta percha insulated, were laid between London and Manchester and connected to give a 768-mile circuit: measured velocity of current transmission along it was 1000 miles a second with a battery of 31 Daniell cells, and that velocity was unaltered when the battery was enlarged to 500 cells. These were a few of their experiments – some of which Preece carried out on his own.

To work closely with Faraday was an experience invaluable to young Preece, who could not fail to benefit from watching Faraday's imaginative yet logical approach to problems, his dexterity, lucid expression, and open-mindedness in the face of conflicting theories, illustrated by his comment on electro-magnetism:

The hypotheses as yet put forward give no satisfaction to my mind. It is better to be aware, or even to suspect, we are wrong rather than be unconsciously or readily led to accept an error as right.

Preece wrote, years later,

I was thrown very much in contact with Sir George Airy . . . he was much occupied with transmitting Greenwich Mean Time over the

United Kingdom by means of the electric telegraph. He was great on terrestrial magnetism . . . earth magnetic currents were disturbing our wires. On his direction we put up two circuits at right angles in Greenwich Park . . . daily recording the variations of those (earth) currents, which were found to be permanent but occasionally subject to great disturbances from solar influences. . . . In experiments on static induction that we were then carrying out with Airy and Faraday as consultants it was important to know how rapidly our relays responded to current.

To determine the 'constant' of the relays they arranged these in series to be actuated by each other in succession and added to the series until exactly one second elapsed between making the circuit and actuating the last relay: thirteen were needed.

This was our introduction to retardation of signals by electro-magnets. Faraday was delighted, for it confirmed his recent discoveries.

*   *   *

Preece also saw something of William Thomson (later Lord Kelvin) who visited Faraday at the Royal Institution whenever he could find the time. Thomson was ten years older than Preece, who was present one day when Thomson was glancing through printers' galleys of a book on mathematics. He handed some to Preece saying, 'This is the only proper language of engineers.' Preece confessed to replying, off-handedly and with all the assurance of youth, 'I cannot worry myself, when I can get it done for thirty shillings a week': he wished to imply that the ordinary work of an engineer's office was routine with a mechanical use of simple formulae. Whereupon Thomson took him to task and demonstrated that such enterprises as building a large bridge or laying an inter-continental submarine cable could not with reasonable confidence be undertaken in the absence of a preliminary mathematical analysis of the problem. Preece was suitably chastened: he later claimed that primarily because of Thomson's exposition he 'conceived a lasting reverence for the work of mathematicians'. Preece was never an advanced mathematician any more than, for that matter, was Michael Faraday.

Thomson was as interested as Preece in everyday usages of science. Lecturing in 1883, he was most emphatic in his statement,

There cannot be a greater mistake than that of looking superciliously upon practical applications of science. The life and soul of science is its practical application, and just as great advances in mathematics have been made through the desire of discovering the solution of problems which were of a highly practical kind in the mathematical science, so in the physical science many of the greatest advances that have been made from the beginning of the world to the present time have been made in the earnest desire to turn the knowledge of the properties of matter to some useful purpose to mankind.

Professor W. E. Ayrton confessed his surprise when, on beginning to study electricity, he found that it was not book knowledge but something thoroughly practical and alive.

Up to that time of my boyish life I had imagined that it was only by the application of mathematics that science ought to be advanced, and that experimenting was a degraded form of trying to grope for information not resorted to by those who understood mathematics.

He once said of a critic of one of Preece's lectures:

Sometimes inquirers bring higher mathematics to bear on a subject and do not apply the simple reasoning of commonsense.

Vestiges of that mental attitude are still to be seen in the implications of such terminology as 'pure' and 'applied' mathematics, which arose from centuries of university education largely restricted to the classics, which perpetuated

the Platonic conception of activities that did or did not become a gentleman

whereas from the outset anyone adumbrating a theory at one of the scientific societies was expected to be able to produce an illustrative mechanical model.

7

THE USES OF ADVERTISEMENT

THE Electric Telegraph Company was not held in any great esteem by the general public and, in the light of a growing realization of that fact, Preece sorted out his ideas on what are now known as 'public relations'; he set them down, on 23 April 1855, in a memorandum:

The course of policy pursued by our Directors with respect to the admission of strangers and 'Saxons' to view our apparatus and modes of working the telegraph is, I consider, very detrimental to the interests and progress of the welfare of the Company. Secrecy is a bad policy because it gives the idea of under-handedness, and once this feeling pervades the public confidence is overthrown. Hence our Company is looked upon as composed of knaves and swindlers, since you hear it abroad on every side and hence whenever an opposition Company springs up we are deserted by our previous supporters. When permission is demanded to show a stranger over their establishment they refuse because they cannot perceive that it will do us any *good*, at the same time acknowledging that it will do us no harm. Granting that it will do us no direct good, that is, not to increase our business, is it not absurd to follow that policy which tends to create ill feeling, for where a favour is demanded and refused, ill feeling must follow however politely that refusal may be worded. But I maintain that it does produce good. It produces confidence, which is essential to a large public undertaking, in the public mind, and confidence leads to business. As long as people imagine that their messages receive some juggling, and they are kept in the dark as to the means whereby their messages are transmitted, depend upon it they would rather fly to the post or any other conveyance with which they are acquainted and can depend upon, than make use of the Telegraph, of which they know nothing.

I do not for a moment recommend that the public should be indiscriminately admitted into our establishments. I only think that those who feed the public mind, namely Authors, Editors and scientific men should be introduced. Why should Americans be so far ahead of us in these matters? Because there the public know what they are about. They understand what operations their messages undergo and they have confidence in the result, but in England the public are ignorant, the mode by which their messages are transmitted is a secret and hence they doubt the powers of the telegraph and do not make use of it.

I believe if this Company had adopted an open hearted policy, had courted public favour, had taken every step to make the telegraph known, that we not only should have met with such active competition, but that we should have commanded a business far superior to what we now possess.

Everyone acknowledges that we are no favourite with the public and it is absurd to attribute this to the fact that we were once a monopoly, because it is in those very places where we are not a monopoly, London, Liverpool, Manchester and Glasgow where we are most in disfavour, where our policy is brought into direct comparison with that of other Companies, which is characterized by direct opposition to our own. To command success and accession of business we must command confidence and that is not obtained by secrecy. But what advantage do we gain by this secret policy? Does it attract business? No. It repels it, for the reasons I have shewn. Does it prevent competition? No. It invites it, because the public are dissatisfied. Does it avoid the piracy of our principles and our practices? No. Experience has shewn the contrary. Does it canvas improvements? No, because it circumscribes experience to the few, declining the observation of the many. Then what does it do? It produces distrust and ill will and surely these are evils which ought to be rectified. This is a course of policy which ought not to be pursued. Court the public and the public will court you.

The rhetoric of that last paragraph suggests Preece had learnt, or lately read, Falstaff's catechism in *1 Henry IV*. There is no evidence that his memorandum reached the Board. Latimer would have dissuaded him by promising to speak to Edwin Clark, for he would have known that their directors would be unlikely to welcome such a criticism from a twenty-one-year-old employee, nor would his Welshman's reference to 'Saxons' strike a sympathetic chord. The memorandum, nevertheless, is particularly interesting for, on the principles Preece there postulated, he acted when opportunity came his way and by going to considerable trouble to keep the public in the picture he made a notable contribution to the rapid development in its use of electricity.

Next year he drafted a memorandum on advertising, which was in more acceptable terms, and illustrates further his valuation of publicity:

In advertising the business it is necessary to discover the sort of people who use the telegraph to the greatest extent and then take the best means of acquainting them of the fact of the existence of a Telegraph Office and the rates of charges. Business men of all classes freely use the telegraph. In their case the presentation of handbills with personal interviews to explain the system is an excellent plan. Travellers commercial and ordinary also frequently adopt the wires. Bills and maps hung up in the coffee and commercial rooms of Hotels are excellent means of attracting their attention. If one bill in one hotel attracts the attention of one person and tempts him to send one message it is sufficient to pay the cost of the advertisement. Travellers are very fond of examining the bills and placards in their room. Placards and notices should be freely placed about a station where there is an office. The best means of attracting people's attention to the telegraph is probably the delivery of lectures. A good lecture while it amuses and instructs cannot fail to call the attention of the audience to the advantages of the telegraph. There are few classes of person who do not benefit by the use of the telegraph, but business men such as shipping agents, captains of ships, lawyers, corn, coal and other merchants, stock and share brokers, hanker to use it to the greatest extent.

To find out the best customers it will be my next plan to get a return from my clerks-in-charge showing the names and addresses and businesses of those who use the telegraph to the greatest extent. This will guide me in opening a new station, in calling upon and forwarding handbills to those most likely to support us. The advantage of personal interviews is that it enables you to explain the process of transmitting a message, about which a great amount of ignorance exists. A good fact to become acquainted with is the number of messages transmitted weekly and the number of complaints made. This will enable me to point out the chances against an error occurring in a message. People rarely hear the good but evil is sure to come to their knowledge. I should always be supplied with a form both sent and forwarded properly filled up, to show the proper mode of filling them up.

The extension of new business should never be neglected but this might be made dependent on the number of private messages of the same description. All exchanges and newspaper proprietors should be visited and the probability of obtaining subscribers discovered. Notices should be placed in exchanges and indeed in all public resorts.

When Preece wrote that memorandum he had lately been appointed to the post of Superintendent.

In 1854 the E.T.C. staff began to publish a journal, *Our Magazine*, with the circulation confined to the Company. The magazine was printed in York with Edward Graves as editor, he also contributed articles on literature and history. It had but a brief existence, Preece being responsible for the few technical articles which appeared in it: one, in the autumn 1855 issue, was

On Deflexions caused by electric storms and lightning discharges to galvanometer needles of telegraph receivers.

In compensation for his lack of years he used the pen-name 'Senex'.

8

SUPERINTENDENT AT
SOUTHAMPTON

before 1925!

PREECE's father died, after a long illness, early in 1854. To find less urban surroundings for his mother he rented a house next year in a newly built terrace in a cul-de-sac, Bernard Street (renamed Chamberlain Street about (1938) off Regent's Park Road. Brother-in-law Frederick Webb moved into a house in the opposite terrace. The builder had made concessions to the prevailing taste for classical architecture (which was even reflected in the casings of needle-telegraph instruments; Preece described them as, 'massive Greek Temples fashioned in wood') by ornamenting his brick façades with Portland stone. Pilasters flanked each front door, windows were given stone surrounds, and a stone coping hid small attic windows from the street level. Opposite each door, at the pavement's inner edge, two pillars supported a small flat roof to form a porch, with a flight of stone steps rising to the front door. That door opened on to a passage with doors to front and back rooms along one side. On the two higher storeys front rooms were the width of the house. The rear downstairs room had an exterior flight of steps from a french window to give access to a small, walled, garden. Iron railings protected the semi-basement, to which there was no access from the street. The facing terraces were comprised of six and eight houses respectively and Preece occupied No. 7 of the larger group. Stone pediments on each end house gave an effect of a terrace being a single unit. On Preece's side the rear outlook at that time was entirely over wooded parkland.

From Bernard Street Preece took out his first patent (No. 2608: 1855) for duplex telegraph systems – to double the carrying capacity of circuits – on which he had been experimenting. The heaviest capital cost of a system was the line itself; that existing lines should be enabled to carry more traffic was an obvious economy. The principle of duplex wiring is to render a receiving instrument insensitive to signals transmitted from the same station while simultaneously recording signals from a distant transmitter.

Preece's invention was not brought into use by his Company, although he had occasion to operate it for short periods from time to time, because traffic was rarely overloading existing circuits. The growth of press messages would by 1864 have justified such a system but by then the Company had brought into service Wheatstone's high-speed automatic telegraph, admirable for such traffic.

The Company appointed Preece to be Superintendent of its Southern District: manifestly his three years' work as an assistant engineer had impressed its directors. That promotion meant that he would have to live in Southampton and he took up his duties there on 15 March 1856. Next year the directors commended him for the arrangements he made for a special telegraph circuit to Epsom racecourse grandstand when, for the first time, the result of the Derby was telegraphed direct from the course to London and provincial towns.

The Channel Island Telegraph Company formed in 1858 had laid a cable that August from Portland to Alderney, Guernsey, and Jersey ($93\frac{1}{4}$ miles in all). The E.T.C. directors came to an agreement with that Company on handling inland telegrams from Portland and Preece found himself with an additional appointment, Engineer to the cable company. Messrs Newall had manufactured the cable and had determined its route: service to Jersey opened on 7th September. 1858

Preece had to travel many times between the mainland and the islands during the next three years, for the cable was too light to withstand tidal movement over the rocky bottom which, for much of its length, it had been laid. It broke fourteen times and when next it parted, 16 June 1861, repair attempts were unavailing and the Company abandoned it, when the only telegraph communication to the islands was then via France, the cost of which would preclude all but most urgent messages.

Preece's experiences of that cable convinced him that it was essential to make a careful survey of the sea bed along a proposed route before laying a cable. He communicated his findings at a meeting of the Institution of Civil Engineers – which he had joined as an Asso-

ciate in 1859 – in November 1860, with a paper 'On the maintenance
and durability of submarine cables in shallow waters'. His recommendations became standard practice and the Institution awarded
him its Telford Gold Medal. The medal has Telford's head on its
obverse and, particularly pleasing to its recipient on that occasion,
on its reverse a representation of Telford's graceful Menai Straits
suspension bridge.

In a discussion on submarine cables thirty-seven years later Preece
referred to that paper, when he had urged the necessity to survey the
bottom accurately before cable-laying:

you would scarcely credit it, but my proposition was received with
laughter and was treated with that ridicule that ignorance always treats
words of wisdom that come from experience.

Someone must have had second thoughts thereafter for Preece, an
Associate member at the time, to have been given a premier award,
but that he had not exaggerated is borne out by Charles Bright
junior:

at an I.C.E. meeting Preece said we ought to know as much about the
bottom of the sea as we do about the crust of the earth, for which he was
severely taxed by the eminent engineer presiding on that occasion.

The Council of the Institution had not awarded a medal to Preece
because of any element of novelty in the subject generally, for the
Institution's weekly meetings from 16th February to 23rd March had
been devoted to discussions of submarine cables. The first of the
papers, 'On submerging submarine cables', referred to a generally
accepted statement three years before at the British Association's
Dublin meeting that

it was mathematically impossible, unless the speed of the vessel, from
which the cable was payed out, could be almost infinitely increased, to
lay a cable, in deep waters, say two miles or more, in such a way as not to
require a length much greater than the actual distance as from the inclined
direction of the yet sinking cable, the successive portions payed out must,
when they reach the bottom, arrange themselves in wavy folds, since the
actual length is greater than the entire horizontal distance.

Next week Frederick C. Webb (five years older than Preece, he
too had joined the E.T.C. in 1853) read a paper 'On the practical

operations connected with the paying-out and repairing submarine telegraph cables' and, after explaining that,

through the hesitation of those who had charge of the works in publishing facts, which might affect the commercial value of such enterprises, he was unable to supply complete details of the operations performed in submerging those cables on which he had not been practically employed,

he described his experience when laying cables to Holland. The task of summarizing and preparing for publication those papers and the discussions on them was delegated to Preece.

9

ATLANTIC CABLES

As soon as a telegraph cable had been successfully brought into service across the English Channel, in 1851, there was talk on both sides of the Atlantic of a possibility of one day connecting Europe with America by cable; which led, mainly because of the enthusiasm of a New York financier, Cyrus W. Field, to the formation of the Atlantic Telegraph Company in October 1856 with Professor William Thomson on its board and Edward Orange Wildman Whitehouse as its Electrician; later Charles T. Bright was brought in as its Engineer. Thomson had presented a paper at a Royal Society meeting, in 1854, in which he had argued the practicability of such a cable; as, indeed – though in a more prophetic vein – Samuel Morse had done eleven years before.

Anticipating by a few weeks its first attempt to lay an Atlantic cable, the Company published, in July 1857, *A history of the preliminary experimental proceedings and a descriptive account of the present state and prospects of the undertaking*. Preece bought a copy of the book, which described experiments, equipment, and a plan of campaign in conjunction with the interested Americans, interspersed with a few purple passages, such as:

Valentia has been chosen for the eastern terminus of the cable, not only because it is the point in which the British Isles make their nearest approach to the shores of Newfoundland, but also because it is remarkably fitted for the distinction which has been marked out for it. It seems indeed as if the hand of the Old World, which is here stretched out towards the extended hand of its western neighbour, the New World, actually had its finger raised in invitation of the desired communication.

Preece made a number of comments in the margin of his copy,

particularly on descriptions of experiments which tended to make up for clarity by prolixity and 'blind with science' potential investors. To 'successive charges of electrical influence . . . each following the other, as the successive undulations of the tidal wave chase each other along the River of the Amazons' he added 'or the Fleet Ditch'. His dissatisfaction with the described experiments attributed to White-house must have hardened into prejudices against that gentleman when later he learnt that Whitehouse was the book's author, for he implied in correspondence published in technical journals that Whitehouse should have stayed in Brighton at his practice as a surgeon.

The first Atlantic expedition centred on U.S.N.S. *Niagara* and H.M.S. *Agamemnon* and started from Ireland in August, but the cable parted and was lost. Next June those two ships, loaded with cable, met in mid-Atlantic, spliced the cable, and separated, the American vessel setting course for Newfoundland and the British for Ireland. Their laying was completed on 5th August and congratu-latory messages via the cable were exchanged between Queen Victoria and President James Buchanan. Said *The Times*:

since the discovery of Columbus, nothing has been done in any degree comparable to the vast enlargement which has thus been given to the sphere of human activity.

The Queen knighted Charles T. Bright, who had designed the special laying equipment, the youngest of her subjects – he was twenty-six – to be thus distinguished for many years and the first associated with the electrical profession.

Thomson devised a mirror galvanometer which enabled signals to be received at three words a minute, to double the speed hitherto reached. Although Whitehouse in his book had quoted Michael Faraday as saying that an increased amount of power would not increase velocity through the cable, he nevertheless proceeded to step up the voltage having got it into his head that he could thereby increase speed of transmission. He increased the voltage from about seventy to over two thousand, whereupon somewhere in the depths of the Atlantic, at a point where the gutta percha might have been imperfect, it was ruptured and, after only twenty days of working, the cable made useless.

Eight years passed before a second, and unsuccessful, attempt was made to lay a cable and C. F. Varley had replaced Whitehouse as Electrician, but that second cable was recovered from the ocean bed, repaired and completed, after a third cable had, in 1866, been successfully laid.

Meanwhile there had been a great deal of comment and conjecture in the technical press. The *Philosophical Magazine* published a paper J. N. Hearder had read to members of the Plymouth Institution on 16 December 1858, in which he discussed electrical inventions and the Atlantic cable breakdown. Preece was stimulated to send a letter to that journal; in it he referred to Hearder's paper and consequent correspondence. He stated very clearly the points on which he differed and concluded:

I think his paper most admirable and I only wish some of our more practical electricians would follow his example and lay before the public the result of their thoughts and experimental research.

*   *   *

The Red Sea and India Telegraph Company was formed in 1858 and the British Government became financially involved in this project to lay a cable between Suez, Aden and Karachi, but the cable never worked as a continuous circuit and soon became so damaged as to be unworkable. Because of its failure and that of the 1858 Atlantic cable, with joint losses of more than a million pounds, the Government next year appointed a Committee of Inquiry on the Construction of Submarine Telegraph Cables and the best methods of laying and maintaining them. Four of its members were nominated by the Board of Trade, including Captain Douglas Dalton as chairman, and four by the Atlantic Company. The committee produced a most valuable report which served for many years as the standard reference work.

Preece was called as a witness before the committee on 20 December 1859, when they asked him how long he had been connected with telegraphy, to which he replied, 'About nine years, the last four years as superintendent of the Electric and International Telegraph Company's South Western District, with 3000 miles of telegraphs.' He added that he was also Engineer to the Channel Island Telegraph

Company: the only cable he had been engaged in submerging, except after repairs, was an Irish Cable (in 1854) from Holyhead to Dublin (Howth). He showed specimens of the Channel Island cable where it had been fractured by abrasion on rocks and spoke of four such breaks in fourteen months. He described his experiments in London with Latimer Clark and Faraday. Asked about the relative merits of rubber and gutta percha as an insulating material he said he would be guided more by their relative prices.

He was invited to comment on earth currents, of possible importance when the earth was used as a return circuit: he had observed that they could be positive or negative and could reverse direction during a day. They were not as strong as a single Daniell cell. Wires in an east–west direction rarely picked them up; south–east–north–west seemed to pick up the strongest currents, particularly when the aurora borealis was visible. Rarely had he an opportunity to make detailed observations, for his telegraph wires had to be used for traffic, but he had sent the Astronomer Royal a record of all such readings as he had obtained over the past three years. He had noticed that earth currents coincided with electric storms.

Preece remained interested in terrestrial magnetism and we find on 15 May 1869 the first of a number of his letters (the last was in April 1894) to *The Times* on the effects of the aurora borealis and thunderstorms on telegraph circuits. He wrote:

It may interest your readers . . . from 3 to 5 p.m. yesterday . . . very strong intermittent earth currents on telegraph circuits in the south of England. . . . Barometer at 9 p.m. 30·47 inches, aurora borealis visible. Some three weeks ago exactly similar phenomena occurred and in 24 hours, with a change of wind direction, warm weather set in . . . interesting to watch if the same happens now. The sunset last night was most remarkable (for Southampton).

10

LONDON AND SOUTH WESTERN
RAILWAY

In the light of the increasing use the railway was making of the Electric Telegraph Company's telegraphs along its routes the London and South Western Railway directors decided, in 1860, to have circuits of their own. With such an end in view, they appointed Preece as Superintendent, to establish and organize a system for them, thereby beginning an association which proved rewarding to all concerned with efficient control of railway traffic and safety of passengers. Nor were the E.T.C. directors other than pleased for Preece to undertake a dual function: the future success of the E.T.C. depended on a continuance of good relations with railway companies.

The E.T.C. Secretary wrote to Preece in June that year to tell him the Board would raise his salary to £200 a year from 1st July: with the Company's financial position continuing to improve, that figure was increased to £250 in September 1862.

Preece managed to find some time for social activities, during which he met Agnes, daughter of George Pocock, a Southampton solicitor, and fell in love with her. They married at the end of 1863, an occasion which provided Preece's colleagues with an opportunity to show their regard for him: they presented him with a gold watch and an illuminated address with their signatures, about 150, appended. In his letter of thanks he wrote:

I can never contemplate this splendid watch nor read this eloquent address without feeling that however much I may have failed in doing my duty, I have at least gained your regard and esteem . . . I hope I shall continue to merit your goodwill. I will at least endeavour to deserve it.

He later pencilled a note on his draft of that letter:

The watch was stolen at South Kensington Station in 1887 – a pickpocket rushed me.

Preece and his bride went to Paris for their honeymoon, to stay in the Boulevard des Capucines at the Hotel Grand, which had recently been built. Preece noticed that instead of wire-pull bells for signalling it was using electric bells, a new invention of Antoine Breguet. Preece, on his return to Southampton, wrote a number of newspaper articles on electricity and its practical applications, including an enthusiastic description of Bréguet's electric bell: one of these attracted the attention of Sir James Truscott, who asked Preece to fit such bells in a house Truscott had just purchased in Park Crescent, Regent's Park. No English firm could undertake their manufacture so Preece bought them from Paris, and two of his telegraph linesmen, under direction by a man of Bréguet's, fitted them.

This led to the first of Preece's publications, on 20 May 1864 from 15 Park Terrace – where he had set up his home in Southampton – *The application of electricity for domestic purposes*. In it he commented,

nothing surprised me, in a recent journey to Paris, so much as the extensive use which our neighbours make of this new application of that wonderful science . . . electric bells . . . everywhere – in private houses, public institutions, in merchants' offices, etc.

He described, and illustrated, a zinc-and-copper battery, wiring, a press button, bell, and indicator tablet: but his description was of Prud'homme's system rather than Bréguet's, whose bell rang continuously till a signal was acknowledged at the indicator tablet, whereas Prud'homme's, in which a bell rang only as long as a button was pressed, was the cheaper.

Preece was entrusted with negotiating a continuance of the E.T.C.'s agreement with the South Western Railway: he was so successful that the telegraph company's General Committee resolved, 16 January 1866,

That the thanks of the Committee be given to Mr. Preece for his exertions and integrity in negotiating the agreement with the South Western Railway Company: and that Mr. Preece's salary be increased from £250 to £300 per annum to date from 1st January 1865.

He negotiated later in the year an agreement with a new railway company (which on 2nd October opened a line between Alton and Winchester Junction) for running a telegraph along their route and the E.T.C. increased his salary for 1866 to £350 and awarded him,

a gratuity of £50 in consideration of his services in the matter of the Mid-Hants Railway Telegraph.

* * *

A member of Preece's staff, writing thirty years later, gave a picture of the Southampton office (which formed a corner of the railway yard adjoining the station) about 1869 and the life of telegraph clerks. A spiral staircase in the middle of the messengers' lobby and learners' room led to the instrument room above. The messengers sat on a bench under a window at right angles to the wall which had a door to the public counter, their cupboards ranged along the wall opposite their bench: the door in the fourth wall led to Preece's office. Messengers could practise on two old drop-handle double-needle instruments while they waited. (The double-needle worked to a code made up of combinations of left and right swings by each needle: the sender grasped the handles below the two dials with needles to swing those handles exactly as he intended the distant pivoted needles to move. In later versions horizontally mounted keys replaced those pendant handles. The double-needle was largely replaced by a single-needle telegraph, which halved the line wires needed.)

In the fullness of time the messengers were either bounced or appointed clerks, as Providence and their conduct directed.

The writer, Preston, as the only 'learner', was the most favoured messenger at that time and was able to hire a skiff from the boat-yards for three months at a cost of half a crown, with which he rowed out to yachts and ships to be paid by them seven shillings and sixpence for each telegram thus delivered: but the counter clerk exacted a commission from each payment.

Salaries were very, very small [about £1 a week for qualified telegraph clerks], and on the principle that 'from him that hath not shall be taken away, even that which he hath', most of the punishments took the form of fines; and when a clerk had been unusually indiscreet, the stopping of two days' pay seriously inconvenienced him at the end of the week. Perhaps this induced reflection and reform, perhaps it did not; for taken as a body, a more jovial, reckless, happy-go-lucky, devil-may-care set of men than the Company's servants in any large town could scarcely be found, only equalled perhaps by a man-of-war's crew on liberty leave ashore.

In a country town like Southampton, when a man was on day duty (8 a.m. to 5 p.m.), after leaving, having tea and the customary 'wash-and-brush-up', he would go for a walk or promenade the High Street, and before the evening was out would usually turn up at the messengers' lobby, which became quite a club, and would climb up to the instrument room to see 'how they were getting on' and send a message or two if luck favoured him with an opportunity.

One side of the instrument room was occupied by an old Morse embosser-printer and a Morse inker which worked to the E.T.C. head office in Great Bell Alley, Lothbury. The embosser had a sharp metallic point which came in contact with a paper tape under the control of signal currents, but the embossed tape was not very legible. The instrument was improved by substituting for its stylus an inked disc to give clear black markings.

The old embosser . . . looked for all the world like a clock with the case off . . . it really was a clockwork contrivance, which wanted constant winding up, and the reading of which from the tape was very trying for the eyes, though the best Telegraphists generally read as now [1905] by the sound of the Armature . . . [the] Inker writer was much better, though in both cases there were chronic troubles of adjustment.

The opposite side of the instrument room contained needle instruments, double and single, and those not only carried E.T.C. commercial work but did all the railway service work as well, including train signal messages. Train signals, known as 'T.A.s', were of paramount importance; everything had to give way to them.

In the middle of a message to Woking you would be suddenly interrupted with a 'TA', and until Basingstoke had sent his train signal to Micheldever you had to stand clear.

There was a rule, honoured in the breach by Preece, that clerks off duty were not allowed on working premises. Preece's assistant, W. E. Langdon, was regarded as a strict disciplinarian and one night when the 'club' was more nearly full than usual – one member had brought in a set of boxing gloves and a couple were having a lively mill – a messenger dashed in to warn them that Langdon was on the railway platform. They bundled everything into cupboards and rushed out, mostly in their shirtsleeves, into the yard to clamber into an empty goods truck, opposite Preece's windows, where they shivered in the frosty night as they watched Langdon leisurely write a few letters while a big Newfoundland dog, which apparently belonged sometimes to Langdon, sometimes to Preece, and at other times to the office (for he divided his time among the three according to circumstances), stood at the outer door, 'growling like a little thunderstorm' each time anyone stirred in an attempt to warm himself.

As we did the Railway work, we had the privilege of a pass on the line during holidays and on other occasions, one of which was the annual dinner. Our district (Mr. Preece's) comprised offices as far as Exeter, and Brighton to the South coast and extended northwards to Waterloo Station . . . two men, being in disgrace, were refused passes for their holidays. . . . They paid their single fares to the Metropolis, and on the last day of their leave calmly walked into the Waterloo office and announced by wire they were unable to get back, as they were without funds . . . their passes arrived by the next train.

Racing work was our privilege and our pleasure. Southampton and Brighton made up the staff for all the southern race meetings, such as Epsom, Ascot, Goodwood. . . . Four Morse inkers, two up and two down sufficed . . . in those days and the racing staff were allowed three shillings per diem expenses. The work was hard, but we got through it; the living and lodgings precarious and rough, but we enjoyed it; and when after a hard day at Ascot we got back to Reading at night for dinner, and our Superintendent, Mr. Tubb, reared his six feet five (more or less) inches over the table and said grace, it would have been difficult to have found a happier party in Huntley and Palmers' town.

SAFETY ON RAILWAYS

SYDNEY SMITH, in the summer of 1842, wrote some of the last of his famous letters: they were on railway safety. He pointed out that there were

two sorts of danger which hang over railways. The one retail dangers where individuals only are concerned; the other wholesale dangers, where the whole train, or a considerable part of it, is put in jeopardy. For the first danger there is a remedy in the prudence of individuals; for the second there is none. Railways travelling is a delightful improvement of human life . . . sixty miles in two hours. . . . Everything is near, everything is immediate – time, distance, and delay are abolished. But, though charming and fascinating as all this is, we must not shut our eyes to the price we shall pay for it. . . . There will be every now and then a great combustion of human bodies, as there has been in Paris.

(On 8th May forty-two people had been killed in an accident between Versailles and Paris.) Many of those whom Smith was able to alarm were reassured next month when Queen Victoria took her first railway journey, from Windsor to Paddington, 'in half an hour free from dust and crowd and heat': she pronounced that she had been 'quite charmed with it'.

At that time the British Isles had 2000 miles of railway routes, which were quadrupled during the next twenty years. Mechanical defects had caused less than a tenth of accidents; well over half of them were the result of collisions. To prevent a train running into the rear of another, time intervals between trains were enforced, which was scarcely satisfactory if the leading train lost speed from any cause. Block working was therefore introduced, whereby a line was divided into lengths, or 'blocks', on which only one train at a time was allowed. The unacceptable alternative was to lengthen the time interval by reducing the number of trains running over a line.

A satisfactory space-interval system was made possible with the electric telegraph: otherwise signalmen would have to be within sight of each other, as indeed they were in the earliest days of railway working. Cooke had proposed block working in 1842: a use of the electric telegraph which Edwin Clark, with Preece as his assistant, put into practice eleven years later on the London & North Western Railway, adapting a double-needle telegraph to work with one needle for the up line and the other for the down. He used three signals: 'on line' (caution), 'line blocked' and 'line cleared'.

Brunel had testified before the Parliamentary Select Committee on Railways, 1841, that most signalmen could neither read nor write. Nor had that appreciable handicap been entirely overcome when Preece was sent to Southampton. He saw the advantage of making block signalling as simple as possible and, to that end, devised apparatus which included a miniature semaphore to duplicate the position of the semaphore outside the distant signal box and included a 'check' by electric bell whereby a signalman would know that his colleague at the distant box had received, and acted upon, the signal sent. Preece's immediately comprehensible system was, in due course, widely adopted, for it was the only system which recorded at the operator's post the position of the block signal at the distant signal box. Three wires were needed to work it, but Preece also devised a one-wire version, where the switch did not directly operate the miniature semaphore arm, an unavoidable difference which entailed the use of a signalling key to operate the miniature. Preece designed an associated bell that was markedly successful in meeting the requirements that it had to be loud enough for any signal box and capable of rendering beats with rapidity and clearness – necessary for block working, in which, as it was developed, up to thirty sound signals were used: for example, one beat called attention, two signalled that a train was entering a section, a series of nine to the signal box ahead and four with a pause before five more to the rear signal box indicated that a train had passed without a rear light. (The last instance is from Spagnoletti's code, which not all railways were using.)

Preece's miniature semaphores were particularly welcome in India

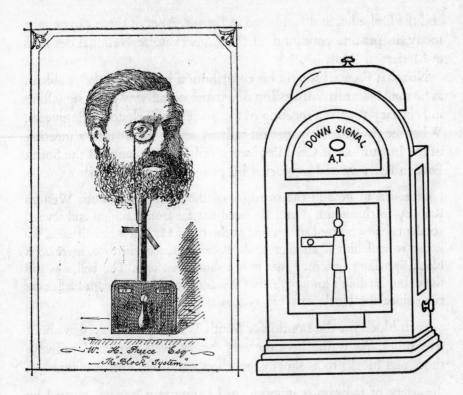

W: H. Preece Esq:
—The "Block System"—

From F. Preston, *Electro Plates*, 1875

To warn distant signal, bell-key is
operated; on 'line clear' being
confirmed the semaphore arm falls
through 45° to 'all clear'
position, being restored to
'danger' when the distant
signalman accepts the train on to
the block

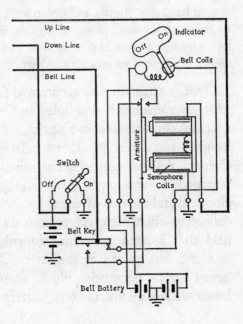

and the Colonies, and were used in France. A set of them can be seen today, in pristine condition, at the Conservatoire National des Arts et Métiers in Paris.

Not that Preece thought his contribution had solved the problem, as he made clear in a discussion of a paper on railway gong signalling in February 1882 at a meeting of the Society of Telegraph Engineers. When he presented a paper on railway safety in 1863, at a meeting of the Institution of Civil Engineers, only the manager of the South Eastern Railway had supported his proposals. He recalled:

I succeeded in getting the manager of the London & South Western Railway to change his mind. He lived not far from London and several accidents had occurred on his line at the time. He had a bell fitted at his house to call him if another took place. I induced him to agree to a block signalling system. I met him a short time ago. The bell was still there, but he didn't know whether it was in working order. It had never rung since the block working system was established.

Each block on the London & South Western Railway was about five miles. As traffic became very heavy well-protected railways shortened blocks to as short a length as one mile. Preece continued,

the safety of railways is supposed to be improved but not secured by electrical apparatus . . . the only possible safe way of working a railway was to have one engine and one train. . . . I strove very hard at one time to bring about uniformity of signals, but every railway company likes its own ideas to run in one groove. . . . Had a proper block system been used the recent Canonbury accident . . . would not have happened.

Preece's criticism was accurate as far as it went: on 10 December 1881 several trains had collided in Canonbury tunnel, which was in a section controlled from a signal box at the junction with the North London and Great Northern railways. Board of Trade Inspector, Colonel Yelland, conducted an official inquiry into the accident. He regarded as unacceptable any suggestions that interlocking the electrical and the out-of-door signals would have prevented the three collisions – in which five persons died and many were injured. He held that a rigid adherence to rules would have prevented the accident, but went on, somewhat illogically, to recommend that 'seven beats – permissive block' should be struck out of the North London Railway instructions. Clearly the signalmen had been handicapped with two different codes of signals to operate. At least that accident led to a more uniform system of signalling being brought into use during the last quarter of 1884 – twenty years after Preece had first pressed for such an improvement.

Continuing his review, Preece asserted,

No telegraph system is more simple than the single-needle and less liable to get out of order ... we English telegraphists look upon it as our first and early love and it has a special function in its application to railway working.

The lecturer, Von Trevenfeld, commented that in countries like Germany, Russia and France a recording telegraph was preferred, for such countries were

very much inclined to discipline and if anything goes wrong they want to find out who has done it.

Safety measures were not invariably adopted with celerity by British railways: usually the Board of Trade had to put pressure on directors and it needed an Act of Parliament, 1889, to ensure block working throughout the country. Several directors had argued for years that the good effects of improvements in signalling and other safety measures would be more than lost by a resultant carelessness and inattention on the part of train drivers and signalmen.

Between 1864 and 1874 Preece took out five patents for improving railway safety, including communication between passengers and guard. His Institution of Civil Engineers paper in January 1863, 'On the application of electricity to the signalling and working of trains', provoked discussions which occupied the next four weekly meetings. The traffic manager of the London, Brighton & South Coast Railway averred that his company was not opposed to train signalling by telegraph but he held that it should be used as an auxiliary for it would tend to lessen caution incumbent upon an engine driver and that would increase rather than diminish danger. He condemned block working as impracticable, for such a large number of signalmen and signals as would be needed would increase liability to mistake and so render the alleged additional safety very questionable.

Advances are not easily won and it was a long time before some of Preece's proposals were adopted. W. E. Langdon, when Telegraph Superintendent of the Midland Railway, wrote in 1896, electrical intercommunication on trains in motion has made practically no progress; it is in use on the South Eastern, the London, Brighton & South Coast, and the Hull & Barnsley railways; on the other lines 'cord' communication [a cord was threaded through holes in the handles of off-side carriage doors throughout the length of the train – a system so inconvenient that, in 1869, the cord was run under the eaves of carriages] complies with the Board of Trade requirements, the primary object being the prevention of outrage.

Nor had electric lighting on trains made much progress. The Lancashire & Yorks and the Great Eastern railways had made a few unsuccessful experiments. A Pullman car on the Victoria–Brighton run had been fitted in 1881 with accumulators charged from a stationary engine and dynamo at Victoria. Forty such coaches were in use in 1896, otherwise electric lighting was to be found only on the Great Northern and the Dublin–Belfast lines (from a dynamo driven by belting or gears off a wheel axle to charge accumulators in the guard's van), which trains were all run *en bloc*, that is, not broken up during a journey.

*   *   *

Preece felt that he was not blameless for the delay in the introduction of electrical intercommunication.

I remember well [he said, over thirty years later] having brought the thing to a very fair state of working order, when my vision of fortune and success was dashed to the ground by two very silly and foolish blunders . . . in those days any application of electricity attracted an immense amount of attention . . . the room was crammed with general managers, chairmen and directors and all the swells of the railway world. . . . I had actual models . . . some worked very well . . . there was a mode by which the breaking away of the train was communicated to the guards and to the driver. The coupling was fixed to a hook . . . worked by a very strong spring. When the carriage broke away the hook was forced by the spring in contact with a stud, which communicated with the second wire or the earth and set all bells ringing. With a great flourish of trumpets I explained all this to the audience. I said, 'Now gentlemen, when I pull the coupling you will see the alarm will at once be raised.' The alarm was not raised, and the sceptical general managers who did not then believe in electricity as much as they do now, laughed me to scorn. I was taken aback. I was not accustomed to addressing audiences in this hall [he was speaking in the lecture hall of the Institution of Civil Engineers] as much then as I am now, and I passed it away with a very silly excuse – that 'perhaps some dirt had got on to the stud'. Mr. Allport who was then the great general manager [of the Midland Railway] the leader of the railway world, said, 'Well, if some dust in the Institution of Civil Engineers causes this system to fail, what will it do on the railway line where dust is in the ascendant?'

Of course I felt very chagrined. But, however, the London & South Western Railway were so pleased with themselves that it did not deter them. . . .

One of my assistants . . . found that the audience, before the lecture commenced, was very anxious to try those different things, and they would go and make this alarm go off. To prevent this he took a small bit of paper, wetted it with his saliva, put it on the stud, and never told me a word about it. . . .

On another occasion on the London & South Western Railway, two or three trains were fitted up; but there was one special train which travelled with all the railway people . . . who were invited to a great lunch somewhere . . . the carriages were full, and just as we passed Clapham Junction the alarm sounded, the train stopped, and we all wanted to know what was the matter. No one could stop them ringing. I was confused and everybody was confused. . . . Again I was laughed at. However, we did after a while find out what the fault was, and we went on, and the day passed pleasantly. But prejudice against the system was established . . . railway managers fought shy of electricity. . . . In each guard's van [which were the first and the last coaches making up the train] I had placed a lineman to see that everything was in working order; and in the front van the lineman – one of the smartest fellows we had – thought that the bell did not ring well enough, so, having a spare battery, he put the second battery on to get all the power he could . . . the whole essence of the system was the balancing of the electromotive forces on the circuit . . . in each of these cross circuits . . . say ten or twelve volts . . . you must maintain the voltage exactly the same . . . the balance disturbed, currents flow and bells ring.

That I.C.E. lecture hall incident must have occurred on 17 December 1864, on which day the *Southampton Times* reported that Alderman Coles and a group of local notorieties, on 16th December, inspected at the railway terminus a first-class carriage which had been fitted with an 'improved method of ensuring safety on railways', designed by Mr W. H. Preece, c.e., of Southampton. That was the first time it had been exhibited and it would be submitted to the authorities in London on the morrow. The system enabled passengers to communicate with the guard and it met the requirements that means of operation was easily accessible to every passenger, it indicated the particular carriage from which the signal had been operated – which could not be replaced by a passenger – it sounded an alarm easily heard by the guard who had the power of attracting the driver's attention from any portion of the train. Tattersall's mechanical system already had a limited success on the South Western Railway. Two hundred intercommunication proposals had been sent to British railways but they did not meet all requirements: Preece's electro-mechanical system 'should be accepted'. He had fitted tasselled bell-ropes between seats and net racks, to operate a semaphore carrying a disc (replaced by a red light at night) at either end of the carriage (depending on the train's direction): two wires, supplying electricity to these and to the guard's alarm bell, were fitted underneath the train. The batteries would last for twelve months unattended.

Five years later the private telegraph companies were taken over by the State and it became incumbent on Preece as a civil servant to relinquish his post with the railway, an unwelcome step which he was allowed to delay till October 1879. He was gratified when, a few days later, he heard from the Company's secretary that the railway directors

appreciate very highly the services you have, for so many years, rendered to this Company, and view with great satisfaction the eminently successful results of your skill and inventive knowledge, as well as practical experience, which have been attendant upon the adoption of your Electrical Signalling arrangements; – as well as upon the whole extent of the electrical system upon this Railway, and which experience has proved second to none in this Kingdom. The Directors – equally with yourself – have no desire to sever your long connection with this Railway Company – but have quite the contrary feeling, and they would highly appreciate your permitting yourself to be still on the Company's staff List as the Honorary Consulting Telegraph Engineer.

Five years later the Company's secretary minuted:

'It was agreed that Mr. W. H. Preece be appointed Consulting Electrician to the Company at a fee of fifty guineas per annum during the pleasure of the Board', from 1st April, 1884.

That fee was doubled fifteen years later. Sir Charles Owen, general manager of the railway, met Preece on Waterloo Station in November 1904 to let him know that under current economies Preece's post would disappear. Preece was distressed by that information and wrote to Owen to say so.

It is not the loss of £100 a year that affects me – that is a mere bagatelle – but it is that a personal connection of 48 years should cease so abruptly ... there is no part of my service that I appreciate more than that on your railway.

And he went on to outline his contribution to the system, including

appliances ... experimentally developed at my own expense and the Railway Company has never been asked for any compensation.

His plaint soon produced a reply from the secretary that his directors were willing to retain Preece in the new year on an honorary basis and he would continue to be entitled to his annual first-class pass over the railroad: an enlightened decision which left everyone happy.

W. E. Langdon was elected President of the Institution of Electrical Engineers in November 1900 and, in the first year of the new century, addressed his crowded audience in a euphoric spirit. He recalled that

with the advent of railways there sprang into existence a new life ... the past stands before us hallowed by the magnificence of the work accomplished. To us it is the gift of a century to improve; still to advance.... How to facilitate our movements; how to economize time ... three subjects present themselves for urgent consideration; the overcrowding of our cities; the advantage of electric traction; the distribution of electrical energy ... the electric tramcar – those moving palaces of light – has come to stay....

Preece moved the customary vote of thanks during which he commented on the attendance and told the audience that at the start of their society their council was thankful to have two rows of members present and that he had often lectured to one row in that hall (the Institution of Civil Engineers' lecture hall). Langdon and he had worked industriously together for nearly twenty years to improve railway services as far as they could. He assured them,

I have always looked on my railway career as the best time of my life.

12

PREECE'S LAMBS

An electric telegraph system promised to be of immense value in the administration of the great sub-continent of India so an Indian Telegraph Department was formed as early as 1850 and after five years its offices were opened to the public for the transmission of private messages. (The telegraph's importance was emphasized when, two years later, sepoys of the East India Company's army mutinied.) Sir William O'Shaughnessy, head of the department, decided to introduce the Morse system in place of the needle system then in use. He came to England in 1857 where he ordered eighty instruments from Siemens and recruited forty young men whom he arranged to be trained in Morse-operating at Gresham House, London. His recruits were chiefly orphan sons of Indian Army officers and some were as young as fourteen and fifteen. Despite their having been told that in India they must expect years of hard work and small pay, there was no shortage of applicants for the post of Morse Assistant. O'Shaughnessy reported: 'I specially cautioned some three or four young gentlemen who I knew were indulging in visionary notions of "the East".' The number of recruits was increased to seventy-four. After six months' instruction the first detachments were sent to Bombay, Madras and Calcutta and at once began to teach local probationers. The department expanded rapidly and their position improved accordingly.

Lieut.-Col. D. G. Robinson, in charge of the department in 1866, began to reorganize it: since advertised open competitions had failed to provide sufficient or suitable recruits he came to England to arrange a different system of recruitment. The outcome was that prospective officers, between the ages of eighteen and twenty-four, 'who had decided claims on the State for public service

G

rendered by their parents or near relations', were asked to sit an examination in English, history, geography, elementary mathematics and physics, classics and a modern language and to obtain at least fifty per cent marks in each subject. Successful candidates were granted £100 each to cover expenses during a course of training, on the satisfactory completion of which they would be nominated for appointment as Assistant Superintendents with pay £240 × 30 × 500, and given a passage to India. For the first six months they were to attend a course of lectures under Professor Tyndall, in mathematics, chemistry, physics and electricity at University College (then the School of Mines) London. Anyone who obtained a certificate of 'high efficiency' was awarded a bonus of £50 and three months' extra training, in 'delicate electrical measurements and tests', in Glasgow under Sir William Thomson.

Those who had met Professor Tyndall's requirements were to be sent to Southampton and put in Preece's charge for practical training, laboratory experiments, and lectures: Preece would be assisted by Dr Bond of the Hartley Institute in the High Street (opened in 1862 by Lord Palmerston). Eleven young men arrived at Southampton early in the summer of 1867. Preece saw that they were satisfactorily lodged and soon had them working on the construction and repair of lines, operation and maintenance of telegraph instruments. They spent four days each week on outdoor work at the railway's depot at Bishopstoke (later to be known as Eastleigh) and at other times attended the Hartley Institute.

Preece showed considerable imagination in his dealings with those young men. He had not forgotten how he had felt at their age and had no illusions about the difficulties which lay ahead of them in India. Such young men could count on a welcome in Southampton and Preece was able to arrange a full social life for them during their four to six months' stay, including, of course, cricket

at the Antelope ground, boating, billiards, fishing, picnics in the New Forest, and dances and theatricals at the Carlton Hall and Philharmonic,

wrote one of them, continuing,

Kindness and hospitality were met everywhere and Mr. Preece was not only a clever coach but a good and genial friend.

A result was that rarely would one of them miss a session at Bishopstoke or be absent from one of Preece's lectures. In reporting to Colonel Robinson at the end of August on that first batch Preece recommended that their period of training be extended and that future groups sent to him should come better prepared in practical mathematics. That first eleven were sent off to India, via the Red Sea route, in mid-January 1868, to arrive in Calcutta six weeks later.

Early in May 1868 a second group arrived at Southampton. There were fourteen of them, of whom six had apparently not been examined on their theoretical training by Sir William Thomson, who had taken over from Professor Tyndall. Preece set an interim examination at the end of three months and reported that eight had passed, and put on record that

they have all afforded me much satisfaction . . . nothing whatever has occurred to mar the pleasure I have felt in having them under my tuition.

He picked out a few for special comment, including

Mr. Ayrton [who] has remarkably distinguished himself by his untiring assiduity and his remarkable mathematical attainments.

(William Edward Ayrton was appointed, when twenty-six years of age, to the Chair of Physics and Telegraphy at the Imperial Engineering College formed in Tokyo in 1873, for some years the world's largest technical university. There he became a great friend of Professor John Perry and they collaborated in electrical developments and inventions and in educational projects for many years: Ayrton was elected a Fellow of the Royal Society at the same time as Preece, in 1881.)

Preece set examinations every three weeks to check each student's progress and since six of them were due to be examined by Professor Thomson early in October he included some of Thomson's subjects, only to find that those subjects had been neglected: one or two were confident that they could learn all that was needed in a week or two. Preece did not think they could and therefore sent a special report to the India Office anticipating, and to some extent excusing, their failure. He wrote:

It is impossible for me to speak too highly of their general behaviour and their conduct while with me . . . they have afforded me the greatest satisfaction in everything with one exception . . . they have been idle.

He made it clear that his adverse criticism did not apply to their practical work and attendance at his lectures: he drew attention to the inherent abilities of each and suggested that one or two had over-rated their preparedness and thereby set others a bad example. They duly received a shock at their poor showing in Thomson's examination but were given a second chance and Preece was able to report soon after that they were all working 'with the greatest zest and assiduity'. Two had, however, been expelled from the class and petitioned the Secretary of State for India to be allowed another chance. Preece had reported the least favourably on those two. One had surprisingly, in view of the physical requirements postulated on the printed application forms, a paralysed right hand and Preece could not but feel that such work as would be required of him, parti-cularly in such a climate, would be beyond him. He pleaded success-fully for the second on the grounds that he had shown great zeal in his practical work and had been sufficiently punished by the severe check he had received.

When the students for 1869 reached Southampton their academic examination had been disposed of but each had been advised that he was not therefore entitled to an appointment but must attend a practical course of instruction

Under Mr. Preece . . . to produce a certificate from that gentleman testifying to your proficiency in the working details of your profession before you will be considered qualified for admission into the service.

Preece's examinations always included theory for he held that there was 'very little distinction indeed to be drawn between a practical and theoretical course of telegraphy'.

More students were sent to him during the next two years. His final report, in November 1871, was on a batch of fourteen: there-after candidates were trained at the newly opened Royal Indian Engineering College, Cooper's Hill.

Many of the seventy-two young men who passed through Southampton did remarkably well: very few were failures. Two were knighted; four, in turn, became Head of their department; some went to important work in other fields throughout the East; others fell victim to disease and assassin while carrying out their duties at lonely frontier telegraph offices. Although officially designated Secretary of State's Nomination Assistants they were always known as 'Preece's Lambs', a sobriquet 'revered by those who bore it'.

13

STATE TELEGRAPHS

ROWLAND HILL has recorded that he received in 1852, when Secretary to the Postmaster-General, a private communication of a Captain Galton's proposal that the Post Office should manage all telegraphs; not a particularly original idea since governments were in charge of such systems as had been developed except in the British Isles and the United States. Hill thought favourably of the scheme, which was sent to the Board of Trade where Lord Stanley was president. Four years later the first detailed plan for such a takeover was drawn up by Mr F. E. Baines of the Post Office, who had earlier been a clerk in the Electric Telegraph Company: he was given official permission to send his plan to the Treasury. Lord Stanley became Postmaster-General in 1860, at the time when two of his officials, F. I. Scudamore and E. Chetwynd, were working out the details of organizing and operating a Post Office Savings Bank. With that new service successfully launched, Scudamore was promoted Receiver and Accountant-General of the Post Office. In 1866 Lord Stanley, who agreed with organizations and individuals lately making representations that the State should control electric telegraphs, asked Scudamore to report on the feasibility of this, whether the public would gain thereby, and whether a large expenditure beyond the purchase of telegraph companies' existing rights would be entailed. Scudamore, a small pink-complexioned white-haired man, remarkable for his enthusiasm, good temper and seemingly boundless energy, reported emphatically in favour.

He listed current public grievances: that many offices were open for inconveniently short periods, and were often a considerable distance from the business centre of a town; that there was no telegraph in quite important towns although elsewhere competing

"The moving power"

F. I. Scudamore; from F. Preston, *Electro Plates*, 1875

companies had offices near each other. Under competition the companies had not expanded as they might have done. Charges were exorbitant and transmission of messages tardy and inaccurate. Scudamore instanced the better and more popular service in Belgium, and Switzerland, whose governments were responsible for telegraphs. He compiled a list of towns in England and Wales with populations over two thousand to show that only a third were well served, and a fifth, with an aggregate population of half a million, had no service. He concluded that were telegraphs combined with the postal service hours of availability would be increased, charges could be reduced, and money orders could be sent by telegraph. He estimated that the main companies' property and rights would cost £2·4 million, with £100000 to be spent on extending the service; and that a net annual revenue (surplus) of £130000 would accrue. He proposed that offices be opened in all the towns he had listed, a minimum charge of 1s. for 20 words, address free and irrespective of distance, be introduced, and that all post offices be empowered to receive telegrams to be sent by post to the nearest telegraph office. He was sure that the

Post Office would have to bear no expense not amply covered by revenue.

Though it seemed clear that shareholders would be willing to sell their holdings if a good price could be got, companies' officers prepared to resist the proposed takeover. The chairman of the E.T.C. contended that extending telegraph facilities to small towns would involve losses, that village post office staffs could not work the telegraph, and that the companies could, if they consolidated, do better than the State. The main companies were the E.T.C., the British & Irish Magnetic, and the United Kingdom (which had introduced in 1861 a 1s. rate irrespective of distance; four years later those companies agreed that 1s. charge should be restricted to distances below 100 miles). They offered special rates for press messages which they supplied through their own Intelligence Department under the control of C. V. Boys of the E.T.C.

Much of the agitation for a transfer of telegraphs to the State came from the larger newspaper organizations, which objected to the editing by, and the charges for, news from the companies' Intelligence Department. Boys also compiled a daily news summary, the *Morning Express*, which was telegraphed to the provinces. One of Preece's responsibilities was to see that such 'I.D.' messages sent to Southampton were distributed to those who had paid for the service.

A Bill was presented in 1868 'to enable the Postmaster-General to acquire, work, and maintain electric telegraphs', although it did not propose to grant a monopoly to the Post Office. Preece obtained a copy and, sensing that the E.T.C. was by then only concerned with getting a good price for its property and rights, thought he could usefully draw the L. & S.W. Railway Board's notice to the Bill's provisions. He wrote:

Southampton April 17th 1868. *The Government and the Telegraph*. I forward herewith a copy of the Bill introduced by the Government for the purpose of acquiring the Telegraphs. It appears to be very crude in its present form. It is merely permissive in its present character. The object of the Government is evidently to maintain Electric Telegraphs for the purpose of forwarding and receiving *public paid messages* only and not to interfere in any way with the Railway Company's use of telegraphs for the working of their traffic. But the Bill or the published views of government officials scarcely develop this idea. They apparently desire to possess the power with respect to telegrams which they now have with respect to letters. The Government in their point of view must be the only 'Telegram-Carrier' in the country. They propose to acquire this position however by very questionable tactics. They contemplate taking the different Telegraph Companies in detail and when they have obtained one or two insolvent companies on easy terms they expect the prosperous ones to surrender. They have however omitted the Railway Companies whose interest in the telegraph service of this country both pecuniarily and intrinsically is second only to that of the Telegraph Companies themselves. The only provision in the Bill respecting Railways is Clause 7 which provides that any Railway Company possessing a telegraph open to the use of the public or possessing any beneficial interest in such telegraphs can compel the Postmaster-General to purchase their rights.

The South Eastern and Taff Vale are I think the only Railway Companies in the United Kingdom in the entire possession of a telegraph for the use of the public. All others are worked under agreement with the Telegraph Companies and in the majority of cases these agreements are of the most diverse and complicated character. The E. & I. Telegraph Co. alone have 158 working agreements with different Railway Companies and every one of these Railway Companies have a certain interest in the establishment of a telegraph on their line whether it be opened for the use of the public or not.

I regard the working agreement between the Electric and International Telegraph and the London and South Western to be of such a character that the L. & S.W. Railway have a very deep interest in the nature of the telegraph facilities offered by their line. I estimate this interest *at the present time* to be worth £4,257 per annum. I say *at the present time* because the value of telegraphy is rapidly extending. It is almost in its infancy and it must receive enormous expansion and the effect of our working agreement is such as to render the Railway Company interested in its growth. I should say that the value of the Telegraph Company's rights upon the L. & S.W. Railway is equivalent to a rental of £5,000 per annum.

Whatever Bill the Government introduce or pass should certainly be such as to compel them to compensate the Railway Companies for the expense that will be thrown upon them by having to undertake the maintenance and management of their own lines as well as the loss of the beneficial interest which most of them already possess in the application of their telegraph to the use of the public.

It may be said that the Government will undertake the maintenance and supply of telegraphs for the Railways and not only acquire the rights but accept the business of the Telegraph Companies. This is not provided for nor is it either feasible or probable. The Government could not become contractors and engineers as the Telegraph Companies are. The Government could not undertake those joint working arrangements which are found so beneficial at small stations. A Telegraph Company's Clerk can book trains and assist in the general work of the station. He is to all intents and purposes the servant of the Railway Company. It could not be so with a Government official.

The Government may acquire the rights of the Telegraph Companies to send public messages leaving them to fulfil their agreements as regards maintenance with the Railway Companies and to continue their business as contractors and engineers but this is neither possible nor likely. The right to send messages is inseparable from the present business of the Telegraph Company and the Telegraph Company could not dispose of one without giving up the other.

The Government must therefore absolutely acquire all the rights of the Telegraph Companies and then deal with the Railway Companies separately and independently and proper clauses should be inserted in the Bill compelling the Government to compensate the Railway Companies for the interest they lose in having their partnership with the Telegraph Companies dissolved and for the extra expense they will incur in having to manage their own telegraphs. The Government have evidently not considered the magnitude of this transaction nor can they be aware of the enormously involved and complicated arrangements existing between the Companies.

Supposing the Bill to pass I think the Railway Companies should endeavour to resist the undisputed right of way (which is however not now sought though it was included in the original notice in the *London Gazette* Nov. 15th 1867 – but will certainly follow) over their lines for the erection of telegraphs and endeavour to enter into contracts with the Government to erect and maintain wires for the purposes of the Government. In fact the Railway Companies should acquire as far as telegraphy is concerned the same position that they now hold with respect to the conveyance of mails. The inconvenience of having two separate and distinct staffs of men under different management upon those lines of railway which already maintain their own wires is very great and it must become infinitely more so when every line will have its own telegraph staff as well as that of the Government.

In conclusion I would urge (1) that the interests of the Railway Companies generally are inseparable from those of the Telegraph Companies and that in purchasing the rights of the Telegraph Companies they must also purchase the interests of the Railway Companies. (2) That this measure, if it is to be a measure, should be complete and final in its character – that the Government should be compelled to purchase every Telegraph Company and to compensate every Railway Company whose interest is affected. (3) That the Railway Companies should strenuously oppose the interference of the Government in the internal management of their telegraphs or other business. (4) And if they are to be permitted to come upon their lines it must be in a very different position to that assumed by the Telegraph Companies. The Telegraph Companies are to all intents and purposes the *servants* of the Railway Companies but the Government would rapidly attempt to assume the position of masters. The Government should only be admitted as *servants*.

Matters turned out much as Preece foretold and, following determined attempts by the companies to retain their business in large centres, leaving the Post Office with the costly process of providing lines to scattered communities, a second Telegraph Act had to be passed in 1869 to grant the Post Office a monopoly, and to increase to £8 million its grant for purchasing the companies' undertakings and railways' interests. The transfer was made early in 1870 and by the end of 1872 £1 560000 had been spent in renewals and extensions. The telegraph companies and railways had driven such hard bargains that £6 640000 had gone in purchases. Rowland Hill had commented in 1869:

This important measure is now on the point of being carried into effect but I must regret that it should be at a cost . . . so enormous as to make it very doubtful whether it can be self supporting . . . and almost certain that, save at further loss to the revenue, correspondence by its means cannot be cheap.

There was no one at hand to dare to tell him that he too had miscalculated thirty years before on uniform penny post, and of the considerable loss to revenue which that service occasioned: even as he wrote, although gross revenue had doubled, net revenue had not yet regained its 1839 level.

The Post Office introduced a charge of 1s. for 20 words irrespective of distance, address and delivery within a mile of the receiving office free. A clause in the Act was obtained by the newspapers which was far more likely to decrease working surplus: it limited to 1s. the charge for 100 words transmitted between 6 p.m. and 9 a.m. and a similar charge for 75 words during the remaining nine hours; charge for the same message to an additional address was not to be greater than 2d. Nor was this the last of the bounty distributed by the Post Office: officers with twenty years' company service not employed by the Post Office were to be paid an annuity of two-thirds of their company pay at the transfer and those of lesser service *pro rata*, while those employed by the Post Office were to count as State service each year they had served with the companies. Mr R. S. Culley, Chief Engineer of the E.T.C., was appointed Engineer-in-Chief of the new Telegraph Department and Preece became Engineer in charge of the Southern Division, which added Rochester, Canterbury, and Dover to the area he had been controlling.

* * *

The International Telegraph Company was formed in 1853 to lay cables across the North Sea: two years later it was incorporated into the E.T.C. so the Post Office at the transfer thereby acquired cables to Germany and Holland, which it leased to the Submarine Telegraph Company already working cables to Belgium and France. The 1869 Act had inadvertently omitted the Channel Islands, which Scudamore regarded as part of the domestic milieu. Channel Islands cables, as we have seen, had been worked till mid-1861: some of the original company's board formed a Jersey and Guernsey Telegraph Company Limited and took over Preece from the original company as Engineer, with shares in the new Company as part payment for his services.

An extension Bill to the 1869 Telegraph Act was drafted to include the Channel Islands, while a Select Committee under Lord Hartington, Postmaster-General, looked into the matter. The Channel Islands Company directed Preece to appear on its behalf. Before he was called to give evidence, on 5 July 1870, a member of the committee named Bidder claimed that Preece, 'as head of the new Telegraph Department', had, in the interests of the Channel Islands Company, behaved irregularly. Preece acknowledged that he was a large shareholder in the Jersey and Guernsey Telegraph Company for which he was acting, was an officer of the public Telegraph Department, being Engineer of the Southern Division from which the

Post Office would be laying a new cable to Jersey and Guernsey, and that he was professional adviser to the Post Office in some matters. His advice had not been asked for or communicated concerning the cable. On his withdrawal Bidder apologized to the Chairman who reproved him for giving inaccurate information to the committee and for making an unjustifiable imputation, and told him he should have apologized before Preece was called.

A cable was laid from Compass Cove, Dartmouth, to Guernsey at the end of October that year. Preece was to have superintended its laying but was excused because of 'domestic distress'. His wife, who was twenty-one when he married her, bore their first child, Llewellyn, fifteen months later (that Llewellyn arrived on St David's Day must have been regarded by them as a most propitious omen). In August of the following year Arthur appeared; three sisters followed him, the youngest of whom had been born that autumn. There can be no doubt that this succession of annual pregnancies (not unusual in the community at that time) had imposed a serious physical strain on a young woman who could not be described as robust.

Preece's two brothers, George Edward and John Richard, had followed him into the telegraph business and George now took his place on the cable-laying ship. That was undoubtedly courageous of George, and he must have been tested when the ship encountered such heavy weather that it had to run for shelter and several days passed before laying could begin, for George had been one of the telegraph engineers on the P. & O. steamer *Carnatic* in 1869, of which he wrote to his brother William, 'This last trip has given me a sickener of the sea.' The party had travelled overland to Suez to join the *Carnatic* (the Suez Canal was opened later that year). Within a few hours of leaving Suez for Bombay the *Carnatic* was wrecked on a coral reef in the Red Sea three or four miles north-west of the uninhabited island of Shadwan with a loss of thirty-one lives. Latimer Clark sustained a broken collar-bone and had to return to England, leaving George in charge of laying a cable through the Red Sea to join with India. Preece's Addiscombe friend of 1853, now officially engaged on telegraphic development as Major Champain of the Indian Army, was also aboard; he had steadied the passengers in the presence of a comparatively indecisive ship's captain. A postscript to George's letter read:

I could not have believed it unless I had seen it that people could have been under such circumstances as cool and plucky. Fancy hours in a broiling sun above your knees in water! Champain is a brick *secundus nulli.*

When George reached Bombay a few weeks later he was able to get in touch by telegraph with their younger brother John Richard, who entered telegraphs in 1861 and seven years later was posted to Persia by the Indo-European Telegraph Company as an assistant traffic manager. One of William's 'lambs', W. E. Ayrton, in charge of telegraphs in Bombay, was able to lend George testing instruments to replace those lost in the shipwreck.

George also commented in his letter to his brother:

I hear from Jane [their eldest sister] that your exact position is uncertain as regards Government, and that probably they will retain you, in that case try and keep your place warm for me, it would be a nice thing to fall into.

As we have seen, William was not called upon to vacate a place but George, in August 1870, was given an appointment as clerk in the Engineer-in-Chief's office.

*   *   *

Divisional Engineers were covering the same regions as the postal Surveyors, a grade which from the early eighteenth century had supervised postal services, making all necessary alterations of postal arrangements, and was now being called upon to introduce a telegraph service.

This strange work they had first to learn themselves and then to teach to the postmasters. Without their active co-operation there must have been a breakdown. . . .

Scudamore called a conference of Divisional Engineers in November 1870 at Westminster Palace Hotel to discuss progress, and share experiences, in expanding the telegraph service, on which task they had been urged to a frenetic pace by Scudamore who, in his determination to make public telegraphs a success, despite expensive changes to his original plan, had spared himself least of all. A joint conference of Surveyors and Engineers followed to give them an opportunity to get to know each other and to discuss how best they could co-operate where their responsibilities overlapped. Preece emphasized the need for superintendents of telegraph instrument rooms to supervise circuits also: he had lately found that the Gloucester office had been sending messages to Plymouth via London when a circuit via Bristol was available; through want of system, quantities of news were being transmitted needlessly. He stressed the advantage of a regularized relief system for telegraph clerks and the desirability of investigating complaints locally without delay. He described his 'process' – which was adopted as standard procedure – whereby every morning each office reported first thing to its head office, and those head offices to him, that lines were in working order. Faults occurring during duty were reported to the officer responsible for the maintenance of that section, recorded in the office diary, and a copy of each entry sent to Preece. At the transfer he had 190 offices in his division: he had since opened 360 more, necessitating the erection of over 1000 poles and running 5000 miles of wire. To give receipts for telegrams handed in had been normal practice but Preece told the conference that at race meetings he did not do so: customers there were used to sending telegrams, the few who asked for receipts were given them.

Generally the public asked for them and I should be very much inclined to say what the navvy said of his wife who was thrashing him very severely, 'It does not hurt me and it pleases her.' We shall soon be rarely asked and in a short time they will be dropped out of sight and memory altogether.

To assist the surveyors Scudamore had formed a staff of telegraph instructors who were allocated areas of the country where they were to teach rural postmasters to operate telegraph instruments. Some postmasters resented that additional demand on them and threatened to resign. Most, however, cheerfully attempted to reach a standard, within a set time, of sending eight words a minute and receiving five, for which a guinea would be awarded. That coin was gained in one area by a chemist over seventy, an equally old postmistress, and, at thirteen years of age, the daughter of Chipping Sodbury's post-master.

Towards the end of 1871 Scudamore (who had largely been

responsible for the halfpenny postcard introduced in 1870) began to look at the possibility of a sixpenny telegram. He asked his Division Engineers to make certain traffic calculations. Preece wrote to him privately:

I understand that your idea is to reduce simply the tariff at once from 1/- to 6d. without making any change in the mode of charging and without any limit in the number of words in the address. Is it not worth while considering the advisability of limiting the number of words *including* the address to twenty for 6d. If so we might estimate the value of each message at at least 10d. Such a reduction would satisfy the public and would be far more remunerative to the Department for while it would scarcely diminish the percentage of increase due to the sixpence it would largely increase the profit to the Department. I have some recollection of your shadowing such a probability in one of your evidences.

Moreover it would give the opportunity of assimilating the method of charging of both inland and foreign telegrams and prevent the present break of gauge. It appears to me most desirable to establish uniformity particularly now that you have joined the Telegraphic Federation and more than that it is worth even altering our form of message to bring it in unison with the rest of the world – an alteration that was much discussed years ago by the Telegraph Companies and would have been adopted if the system of charging and the absence of free address had admitted of it.

I am also afraid that 80 messages per hour is too high a limit for those long underground circuits but I will look into this more carefully. I fear that the wires Culley has used are too small for high speeds.

The foreign form of message would give the signature at the bottom which is so much demanded by the public.

Scudamore replied:

We should gain nothing by limiting the addresses to ten words. They only average eleven and a fraction at present and the public would look upon the limitation as a nuisance. My proposal is, Addresses free, First ten words 6d., each additional five or part of five 3d. Eighty messages per hour is a low rate for good Wheatstone working. When the wires are in good order and we have got the work we can do 150 to Manchester. We have consistently made one Wheatstone beat four *Morse*.

The Wheatstone was an instrument transmitting Morse code automatically by means of manually punched paper tape: it was parti-

Died. October 19ᵗʰ 1875.

Sir Charles Wheatstone; from F. Preston, *Electro Plates*, 1875. The Wheatstone automatic telegraph used for press messages reads: WHEATSTNE

cularly suitable for distributing press messages since a number of tapes could be punched simultaneously.

* * *

R. S. Culley, sixteen years older than Preece, had been very much his senior in the E.T.C. and in the order of things Preece would accept him as his chief, but Culley was due to retire in another eleven years and Preece, looking around, saw as his nearest rival Edward Graves of his own age who had joined the E.T.C. just after himself. On the telegraph transfer Graves had been appointed Midlands Divisional Engineer: his negotiating ability was oustanding and that 'economy' was his watchword was widely known ('which he put before efficiency', Preece, much later, could not resist writing). Preece decided that a tentative inquiry of Scudamore as to his own standing vis-à-vis Graves was worth while. He received a reply from Scudamore.

March 22nd 1872. My dear Preece, It is not at all necessary that either Mr. Culley or I should express any opinions as to the relative positions of Mr. Graves and yourself. Officers of your position are in the Post

H

Office to be held of *equal* grade and when questions of promotion arise with respect to them their merits and past services are taken into account before their *term* of services thought of. I shall carefully guard myself against thinking Graves above you or you above Graves.

In dealing with men of lower position length of service is taken into account and promotion goes to a qualified senior, but with men in the position of Graves and yourself, the promotion goes to the fittest man. Ever yours truly, Frank Ives Scudamore.

Nor was Preece alone in wondering about his future in State employ; that problem was more urgent for thousands of telegraphists whose hopes had been kindled and increases in pay deferred by the companies, with a promise that all would be well when the telegraphs had been nationalized. Scudamore had promised revisions of pay and regrading of posts notwithstanding that his estimates of future profits had been based on the continuance of wages at company levels: he had to grant graduated increases immediately after the transfer because of the companies' arrested increments. Scudamore knew, as did the telegraphists, that the State dare not pay its employees markedly lower than fair private employers.

Spending all the hours he could remain awake, Scudamore increased stations and extended routes to meet unprofitable public demands and he became exasperated when in the autumn of 1871 impatient Manchester telegraphists began a strike in concert with their colleagues in Edinburgh, Glasgow, and Liverpool, and a few northern and Irish offices, which he had endeavoured to prevent by broadcasting a telegram:

London 18th November 1871. To all telegraph stations. Mr. Scudamore wishes the following notice to be written large and hung up in every Telegraph Office and the purport of it may be communicated to any member of the Press seeking information on this subject: I do desire very earnestly as a real friend and brother officer to warn you against putting faith in the conflicting and exaggerated statements which are being transmitted to all parts of the country with respect to the Telegraph Department.

I beg you to put your trust in me as a man who has never deserted his brother officers and has no intention of doing so. Anyone who tells you that the Chancellor of the Exchequer of the Treasury has even the faintest sign of hostility to you or has had any opportunity of doing so is a liar and is merely seeking to lead you away for some private advantage of his own.

If you have patience and confidence in me you will find that you will be fairly dealt with. If I detect anyone engaged in spreading false reports with a view to disaffection I will recommend him for immediate and severe punishment but anyone who adheres loyally and faithfully to his work will find me a firm friend. (signed) Frank Ives Scudamore.

The strike had got under way despite his assurances, so he sent telegraphists from the South of England to maintain services, and followed up with a letter:

To the Telegraph Staff. I recently warned you that I would recommend for severe punishment any of your number whom I found to be endeavouring to promote disaffection. I have now found myself compelled to suspend from pay and duty (pending the decision of the Postmaster-General) a few persons who in spite of this warning have endeavoured to bring about a strike. Full and fair enquiry will be made as to the guilt of those who are implicated, and any explanations which they may have to offer will be impartially considered, but I cannot doubt that the Postmaster-General will visit with very severe punishment those officers of a Government Department who shall be proved to his satisfaction to have committed so grave an offence.

I wish to point out to the Telegraph Staff generally, that the persons who have been suspended, instead of furthering the attainment of the object which you all have in view, have really done their utmost to delay the attainment of that object.

As you know, my ordinary duties are very arduous and now that I have in hand, in addition to those duties, the formation of an Establishment for many thousands of persons of all grades, and scattered throughout the whole Kingdom, I cannot afford to give any portion of my time or attention to other matters. But during the past four or five weeks, those persons, by their persistent agitation, and by the calculation of conflicting and false rumours from day to day, have compelled me to occupy myself in taking steps to detect their proceedings, and to render it impossible for them to carry out their scheme. They have thus very seriously delayed the completion of the task which you desire should be completed. I will do the best I can by personal exertion, to remedy the ill effects, to you, of their misconduct, but I must ask the great body of Telegraphists, who, I am sure, are too sensible and loyal to approve of such proceedings, to aid me by openly and steadily discountenancing them for the future. (signed) Frank Ives Scudamore. Second Secretary.

Immediately awards of increments of half-a-crown a week for telegraphists in receipt of £1 or more and two shillings for those below £1, and an amnesty being promised, the strike soon ceased. In the Postmaster-General's report to the Treasury for 1871 the only strike referred to was:

Telegraphs. . . . There are many events, too, such as the strike of the Warwickshire labourers, which occur suddenly in some small place, and compel the Department to send off, at a very short notice, a highly skilled force capable of meeting the public demand for news.

His report was reassuring on: Mixed staff of officers.

From the first day of the transfer, the Department entered on the experiment of employing a mixed staff of male and female officers; and there has been no reason to regret the experiment. On the contrary it has afforded much ground for believing that where large numbers of persons are employed, with full work and fair supervision, the admixture of sexes involves no risk, but is highly beneficial. It raises the tone of the male staff by confining them during many hours of the day to a decency of conversation and demeanour which is not always to be found where men alone are employed. Further, it is a matter of experience that the male clerks are more willing to help the female clerks with their work than to help each other; and that on many occasions pressure of business is met and difficulty overcome through this willingness and cordial co-operation.

Before very long, to the detriment of Scudamore's earlier promise of profits for public funds, telegraphists were graded more favourably, better paid, and with a higher, fixed proportion of supervisory posts to staff numbers – the latter a persistent Treasury system which has ever encouraged 'empire building'.

*   *   *

William Monsell, Postmaster-General 1871–3, soon found himself on the wrong side of the Treasury and suspected it was because the Prime Minister, William E. Gladstone, had overruled them in favour of the Post Office in several instances (he confessed this in a letter to the Secretary to the Post Office, John Tilley, in October 1872) since he had been in office and had then turned down his claim that

Surveyors should have their salaries increased in the light of the extra, telegraph, work they had undertaken, an increase which each postmaster had already received. The Treasury suggested that the number of Surveyors should be increased. Monsell minuted:

to increase the number of Surveyors by only one would cost more than to give them all round the additional £100 recommended. Besides it would be inconvenient; and above all it would leave what they feel to be a grievance unredressed.

This was one of several cases he brought to Gladstone's notice at that time. Gladstone replied on 21 October 1872 from Hawarden Castle, Chester, concluding:

I am anxious to avoid a renewal of polemical correspondence in a matter already rather *brûlante*, as I think it is always better made the subject, within a Government, of the last rather than the first resort.

I must in conclusion admit that according to my recollection the Post Office always had a good character with the Treasury and that where there is a vast *business* to be conducted much confidence must be placed on those who have to carry it on.

Without doubt the Treasury were greatly perturbed by large increases in estimates of funds necessary to purchase and extend the telegraph service, which had been less than £3 million in 1866. Scudamore needed more money for expansion and, well aware that the Treasury would balk at supplying more than the £8 million already granted, drew over £800000 from the Post Office Savings Bank funds for that purpose without engaging the specific attention of Sir John Tilley, Post Office Secretary, or Monsell to his action. Thus new offices continued to be opened in their hundreds. Scudamore's transaction was brought to light by the Public Accounts Committee in 1873. Treasury triumph was complete. Scudamore was to be summoned to the bar of the House of Commons to be censured for his excess of zeal. Mr Gladstone ruled:

The conduct of Mr Scudamore may be a very proper subject for animadversion, but Mr Scudamore is no fit subject for the censure of the House. It is the political officer who stands between the permanent officers and its censure. Mr Scudamore has committed a great error but that error is balanced by still greater services and upon the merits of this case I refuse to censure Mr Scudamore.

Parliament authorized £1¼ million to cover telegraph extensions. It also voted £20000 to Scudamore for his outstanding services. His exertions had affected his well-being and he was allowed to resign his post on health grounds but in September 1875 the indomitable little man was off to Constantinople to reorganize the postal services of the Ottoman Empire. By now the Treasury was in stringent control of the Post Office finances and maintained their grip ('stranglehold' was the usual word in the Post Office) for more than forty years. The scandal was bound to have a lasting effect on the Post Office administrators and executives: it put a bias on Preece's activities even if it cannot be proved directly to have affected his career.

14

DUPLEX WORKING

AFTER the transfer of telegraphs to the State F. E. Baines travelled throughout the British Isles and sent in detailed reports to Scudamore on local trade and industries and on telegraphic traffic and staff performance; he also indicated what circuit changes seemed advisable. He co-operated when in the Southern Division – in 1871 and 1873 – particularly closely with Preece and paid him the compliment of making him joint signatory of reports from his Division. When Preece was in Penzance with him in May 1873, J. G. Uren, the local postmaster, asked Preece if he would give a lecture there on the electric telegraph, in which Cornish curiosity had been stimulated. Preece excused himself on pressure of work but handed over full notes of a lecture he had recently given in Southampton to enable Uren himself to give a talk.

As great as a need for public appreciation of telegraphy was a forum, Preece felt, for telegraph engineers and manufacturers, thus he was a leading figure in the formation of the Society of the Telegraph Engineers which held its first general meeting, 28 February 1872, in the lecture hall of the Institution of Civil Engineers. Dr C. W. Siemens, F.R.S., British representative of the German telegraph manufacturers, was elected President. Preece – who said he had not come prepared to speak, but did so on three occasions – held that the Society, which had arranged to meet fortnightly except during the summer months, would fill a wide gap and claimed that practical telegraph working brought to light problems which would not be discovered by experimenters. R. S. Culley gave a lecture on the Wheatstone automatic telegraph. Preece, invited to comment, pointed out that 'in telegraphy, as in everything else', what they gained in one direction they lost in another. The automatic telegraph

The Surveyor General

F. E. Baines; from F. Preston, *Electro Plates*, 1875

had gained accuracy and speed, but to punch tape involved delay: anyone going into a public office should feel that his telegram would be sent within five minutes. Hand-signalling speed was 30–35 words a minute; 60–70 words, the average rate of working of the automatic system, would mean doubling clerks to produce the tape, and clerks, they knew, 'could not live on nothing'. The Post Office none the less would probably adopt Wheatstone's automatic; he would like to see also brought into service 'Hughes's beautiful apparatus' (a telegraph with a 'piano' keyboard whose receiver printed incoming signals in roman type).

The Society arranged a 'soirée' at the Royal Albert Hall in June, with an exhibition of telegraph instruments, and Preece was unanimously elected to give a short talk there on telegraphy. Before his public lecture he addressed London telegraph staffs on 'scientific education', when he advised them to attend any lectures available, and to read, observe, and reflect on their subject: he recommended his practice of always carrying a notebook – a lifelong habit of his – and reminded them of 'Captain Cuttle's sage remark, "When found make a note of"'. He presented a paper at the Society's meeting on

27th November, *Lightning and lightning conductors*, a continuing interest of his: he was elected to its council and his brother George, who had already contributed several articles on submarine telegraph cables to the Society's *Journal*, was appointed secretary.

Preece was also instrumental in launching, on 15 November 1872, the *Telegraphic Journal* and edited its first few numbers. It comprised technical articles, including a series for students, correspondence, and information on contracts and patents. The *Journal* later became the *Electrical Review* and he wrote in an article to commemorate its fortieth year of publication:

I . . . for a short time edited it . . . but the transference of the telegraphs . . . from private companies to the State threw such a burden of work upon my energies that I had to clear away all other work.

The School of Military Engineering, Chatham, called upon Preece to give four lectures on telegraphy at its autumn 1873 session. First he reviewed its application to railway working during which he paid tribute to the Royal Engineers officers who acted as Inspectors of Railways on behalf of the Board of Trade, concluding with

the best of all teachers – superior to all the theory in the universe – stern experience.

In his next two lectures he described commercial and Post Office practices, various instruments and their uses (including Wheatstone ABC for the country 'postmaster and his wife', consisting of a clock-face with one hand, surrounded not by figures but the letters of the alphabet; moving the hand to point to selected letters operated a hand in unison at the distant instrument). His last lecture was on naval and military uses; he referred to telegraphy during the Indian Mutiny and the Franco-Prussian War, and to United States Army practices. He ended:

I am conscious that my lectures have been too general to be of much value. They have been wanting in illustration. The fault has been in the subject. But I trust their effect will not be altogether uninstructive. My object has been to impress upon you the truth that telegraphy is primarily the child of experience, and that, under your present constitution, if you ignore the experience of others, you will waste very valuable time in acquiring, perhaps too late, experience yourselves.

He remembered his potentially military studies at King's College and when, as a result of the enthusiasm he had engendered, an army company of voluntary telegraphists was formed to do practical work at weekends he agreed to serve as its Captain. The War Office soon put a stop to that irregular movement and quashed his temporary commission.

About that time he joined the Canute chapter of the Rose Croix Masons (the 5th Earl of Carnarvon was Sovereign Grand Master): he was installed as a Prince of the Order in Southampton in June 1875.

Again his family increased when at the end of 1872 his sixth child, Frank, was born.

★　　★　　★

That all was not well with the finances of the Telegraph Department was, meanwhile, sensed by some of its senior engineers. Culley went to Buxton in June 1873 for a course of treatment at its thermal baths for neuritis of his hand: he continued, nevertheless, to deal with official work during that spell. Preece wrote to him on 18th June,

I wanted to see Scudamore yesterday about Army manoeuvres, and he would not see me! He is evidently *en rage* against the department all round. *Sic transit gloria* telegraphic.

Culley commented, in his pencilled reply,

I agree with *Sic transit.* It was a great blast of trumpets about a questionable arrangement – nevertheless after all we have a great system – but money has been no object. You have seen the House got as much information as usual last night – what fools they are!! They can't ask their questions properly. So much the better however.

[19th June: Mr. Dillwyn asked the Chancellor of the Exchequer whether the inquiry re certain funds under the control of the Post Office employed on extensions to the telegraph service which on 21st March he promised to institute had been concluded and when would notice be given of the result. He was told that the matter was with the Committee of Public Accounts and they would decide in what form their report would be submitted to the House.]

Don't think much of F.I.S. not seeing you – I have been denied 3 times and vowed I would not go again unasked – but I think I was wrong – he is sorely badgered – I daresay he has his hands full at the office.

Preece had ended his letter:

I have got chicken pox in the house and Bo (Llewellyn) has gained his first prize at school. I hope to see it bestowed on him tomorrow.

Culley congratulated Preece on his son's success, adding,

but don't make the boy work, don't let him if you can help it. I wish we could see each other oftener. I don't see why we should not. I mean to visit Graves soon.

Preece had reported that he had just spent 'two pleasant days' with Graves. He also had reported that

Oliver Heaviside has written a most pretentious and impudent paper in the *Philosophical Magazine* for June. He claims to have done everything, even Wheatstone automatic duplex! He must be met somehow. Of course your paper before the Society will do good and it ought to be the first read.

They were awaiting the first number of the Society of Telegraph Engineers' *Journal* with the text of a paper which Culley had given on telegraphy. Preece asked:

Have you any objection to my writing a simple paper for the *Telegraphic Journal*, simply theoretical and historical?

Heaviside had written a short review of duplex telegraphy (by which signals are transmitted simultaneously in opposite directions over a single wire):

according to the very practical author of *Practical Telegraphy*, this system has not been found of practical advantage.

(Heaviside's reference was to R. S Culley and his *Handbook of Practical Telegraphy*: Longmans Green were just then pressing for a new edition and Culley had asked Preece for his opinion on proposed additions.) Heaviside stated with a throw-away line – 'in a very simple manner which it is unnecessary to describe' – that he had duplexed Wheatstone's automatic transmitter and with hand-operated transmitters had found it 'not at all a difficult matter to carry on *four* correspondences at the same time' (that is, quadruplex, two trains of signals simultaneously in each direction).

Culley noted:

O. Heaviside shows what is to be done by cheek. This we see every day –
look at Thomson among the great, brings forward the tangent and sine
scales on galvanometers as new. He does not read his *Handbook* it is
evident. He claims or is supposed to have brought out lots of other things.
We will try to pot Oliver, somehow. Pray write in the *Telegraphic
Journal*, but try carefully your experiments first.

Preece wrote:

I must publish my leakage plan (of duplex working), if it does not prove
to be successful it is at least unique and pretty.

He had been arranging tests from November 1872 of that duplex
method. A colleague, David Lumsden, had reported most unfavourably on its effect on the London–Bristol circuit. He wrote that
he only learnt when signals went wrong at London that Preece's
system was being used at the Bristol terminal, and concluded,

when any changes or experiments are being made it would be better that
we should be informed of the fact.

(David Lumsden had become an E.T.C. clerk at Leith at the age of
twenty. He was senior clerk at Edinburgh in 1858 when Culley was
Superintendent there; two years later he was working in Amsterdam
at the terminal of the cable to Holland, for six months under an
arrangement by C. F. Varley (Chief Engineer) in 1866, when the
Wheatstone automatic telegraph, used on that cable, created a revolu-
tion in telegraph technique. Culley and Lumsden made a number of
improvements in its working, for which they were paid by Wheatstone. Culley appointed Lumsden his scientific assistant in 1866 and
after the Telegraph Transfer he became Submarine Superintendent
and Electrician.)

Preece challenged Lumsden's conclusions sharply but pointed out
that he did not know or wish that his 'leakage' plan should be tried
on the London–Bristol wire. He asked Culley that his comments
should, however, go no further,

for a deal of mischief is done by intemperate remarks – a failing I am
sorry to say I have given way to too much. The fact is I have no faith
in Lumsden's judgement.

Culley pencilled on that letter his agreement with 'intemperate'
but added:

I don't like not to be able to know what a man thinks either – nothing makes me so savage.

He regarded impulsive comments as

a pleasant habit at the time – but bad in results, yet better than never speaking your mind.

He did not doubt that Lumsden's report was substantially correct though he allowed that Lumsden would not be sorry to see Preece wrong: 'Arcades ambo – ye are.' He thought it would be difficult to find a better man than Lumsden:

he is very persevering and hard working but a wee prejudiced. He seems loyal also and not flighty as some are.

Culley then added a few perspicacious suggestions for improvements to Preece's duplex technique.

* * *

Clearly the effect of duplex working was to double the carrying capacity of a wire: wires represent the largest capital outlay in a telegraph system, thus duplexing could make a considerable reduction in costs. Doctor Gintl, a director of Austrian telegraphs, was the first to bring such a system into practice – in 1853 between Vienna and Prague. Currents do not actually cross each other on the line but mutually interfere in such a way as to disturb the electric balance which independently exists at either end.

Carl Frischen, of Hanover, quickly improved the system and patented it in England in November 1854, but was forestalled by Stirling Newall who had patented a similar system the previous month. Newall's was tried successfully between Manchester and Altrincham, but on the longer-circuit Birmingham–London static charges seemed to necessitate expensive equipment to overcome so his system was abandoned. Preece had taken out a patent in 1855: during that year he reported that experiments on loops at Liverpool justified a trial between Liverpool and Manchester; a later trial between Southampton and Cowes was more successful. He had not, however, tried one of the methods, 'leakage', in his patent. He recalled these experiences in a memorandum to Culley on 4 January

1873 and promised that he would test his leakage system on the next Sunday,

the better the day the better the deed.

We shall be doing right in encouraging Stearns [an American inventor who was coming to see Culley] and behaving well to him. He would check everything already done at the same time.

If Eden's [system] is better I'll chuck my own like a shot. I think my own is cheapest and simplest, no rheostat, no bridge, but simply a constant coil and an adjusting screw.

I think my work in 1855 deserves a little more notice than that I took out a provisional specification for I exhausted the subject worked hard and knew nothing of Siemens' and Newall but only Gintl's plan.

A letter from Siemens's Westminster office six months later explained why his duplex system had been abandoned despite six such apparatuses working on the Continent in 1854, increasing to sixty-four the next year.

That duplex telegraphy was not more rapidly introduced in former years than it is at present and will be in future, we believe had the only reason in circumstances that it did not formerly appear necessary to get out of a telegraph line the greatest possible amount of work and also the telegraph personal [sic] was not yet of such perfection as to establish the most rational service possible. We always believed that the greater development of telegraphy will have to look for all possible means to augment the number of messages on a given line, and then will be the natural time when Duplex Telegraphy must find its way and larger introduction.

Joseph Barker Stearns had, in 1868, experimented successfully with a duplex system on the New York–Boston line. He obtained an English patent in 1872. He asked £2000 a year for the Post Office's use of his patent. Culley concurred with Preece's suggestion of £1300, as the system would save £25250 a year: £1600 was finally agreed (the sum paid to Wheatstone for the use of his patents), but that was after Preece had thoroughly tested Stearns's system.

Preece's promised articles began to appear in the *Telegraphic Journal* (vol. 1 No. 11) in July 1873. He explained that such telegraphy had been dormant in England for seventeen years and had recently received great attention because of Stearns's success in America. He himself had applied Gintl's scheme to Bain's chemical telegraph in 1855.

The 'Stearns' Key

J. S. Stearns; from F. Preston, *Electro Plates*, 1875

Experimentally it worked beautifully but when essayed in practice it failed to answer thoroughly. This was due to many causes [including] the line circuit was varying every minute of the day hence frequent compensation and adjustment became necessary. Rheostats were scarcely known in those days, and means of adjustment were difficult. The effects of static induction upon land lines were not known. Magnetic inertia, or the effects of electro-magnetic induction on apparatus were not understood.

He described later improvements culminating in Stearns's system, where instead of maintaining equal current values at the terminal stations equal potentials were used.

It now remains for me to explain the third method of duplex working which has been adopted practically, and which is less known than any of the other methods because it has not been published before this, although it was worked experimentally, in the year 1856, between Southampton and Cowes. Our busy practical engineers have, as a rule, so much work to do, that they have no time to write and publish accounts of all the trials and experiments upon novel plans and new apparatus which they make, especially when their results are not entirely successful.

Consequently many new kinds of apparatus, modes of working systems and plans which have been thoroughly thrashed out are, years after, brought out as new inventions, for the want of this publication. Duplex telegraphy was thoroughly exhausted in 1856, and with our then means it proved a failure. It has now, thanks to Mr. Stearns and to our improved means, proved a success, not, however, so much by the reproduction of exploded plans as by the introduction of methods which are as novel as they are ingenious. . . . I never published the leakage plan, as much from want of opportunity as from want of real practical success with our then means. It is now thoroughly practical and in use.

A partial leak to earth is introduced at a point along the line and the resultant difference in current on each side of the leak is used to operate a duplex system.

In England we are peculiarly liable to great variations in the resistance of our lines, not only from the excessive moisture of our climate, but owing to the special means which we have taken to prevent the escape of currents from one wire to another on the same pole, which occurs either with indifferent insulators or with broken and defective ones. This is due to 'earth wiring' or the erection of iron wires on every pole, to allow the leakage at once to pass to earth without interfering with any other wire.

Preece went on to give the resistance variations when, on a wet day, on a line 280 miles long, the reading in ohms constantly fluctuated between a maximum of 2947 and a minimum of 1611. Apart from physical difficulties there was also the problem of patents and where any combination of apparatuses was involved there existed the possibility of infringing a patent, a frequently recurring incident which did much to handicap development: for instance, C. F. Varley soon brought a claim against Stearns alleging he was infringing on an earlier patent of Varley's.

That year Stearns came over from the United States accompanied by his wife, teenage daughter and baby son. Preece arranged for him to start trials of his system. The London & South Western Railway allowed W. E. Langdon (Preece's assistant on the railway – all circuits west of Southampton at that time were run along railway routes) to participate.

Not all were in favour of this method of doubling wire capacity: Staff Superintendent A. V. Tubb wrote,

It would never make way with the female staff as they cannot talk or reply [exchange short friendly messages with a distant operator], I don't think the males would like it either. You will never get on without a little friendly talk.

Culley pencilled on that letter, 'This is a confession', but would not accept it as a valid objection. Preece assured him that such an experienced officer as Tubb would be in favour of duplex working. Culley hoped that Preece's own experiments would be fully successful, 'it would be great fun to show them [Stearns and the American Telegraphs for which he worked] a better system than theirs'. Preece soon recognized, however, that Stearns's system stood up to working conditions better than his own. As a result the Postmaster-General's report published in 1874 included:

Telegraphs. . . . The greatest improvement last year was, perhaps the application of the so-called 'Duplex' system to many of the principal wires. By means of this apparatus (the perfecting of which is largely due to the American electrician Mr. Stearns) a telegraph wire can be worked simultaneously in opposite directions; and thus the transmitting power of about 70 wires, varying in length from a few miles to some hundreds, has been practically doubled. The principle of duplex working has, I believe, been known for a long time; but it is only within the last year that it has been applied successfully to British telegraphs.

Preece invited the Stearnses to stay with him at Southampton. Stearns wrote (12 September 1873) from London to him:

I know you say what you *think* and it is a great joy to have *you* think well of anything I may do . . . how Mrs. S and I enjoyed my visit of a week with you and your dear lady. Surrounded by six of the sweetest of children – in the pleasantest of homes.

He wrote again on 24th December, just before leaving for the Continent with his invention:

Many thanks for kind words from Mrs. Preece and yourself. Had Arthur Harold S been old enough to toddle about the floor and push over or be pushed over by Benjamin Franklin P we should have been only too happy to spend our Christmas in the Happiest Home in England. As matters stand we must bide our time and hope to see the two future electricians playing in a happy home in New England. . . . That your lives may be

I

long, happy, and useful is the sincere wish of your 'American Cousins' Joseph B. and Amanda E. Stearns.

*   *   *

With the New Year Agnes bore her seventh child, Percy John, but at the cost of her own life. Preece was distracted with grief and, leaving the children in the care of his eldest sister Jane Elizabeth, fled to Carnarvonshire.

Stearns wrote from Vienna in mid-February:

I have not written for a month past . . . believing you'd be better without letters. But how are you my dear fellow . . . how long did you stay in Wales? What are you doing to keep your thoughts from dwelling too continuously upon your loss? Write, or study Astronomy or Entomology or anything that you can make a *fad* . . . [we are] leaving for Italy in a day or two. I already long to be back in Old England (if I cannot be in New England) before the hawthorn blossoms. I count that man blest whose Mays and Junes are passed in England – in the country – not in London. . . . Remember me to the little ones and to Mr. Langdon and Mr. Sivewright.

Preece decided to move to London, in many ways as convenient a centre for him as Southampton. He rented a terraced house similar to – and not far from – that in which his mother was living: No. 10 Queen's Road (renamed Queen's Grove in 1938), on the north-west edge of Primrose Hill.

The Primrose Hill house, near though it was to the homes of his mother and sisters, proved inconvenient: it was too far from Preece's work with the L. & S.W.R. and the access that railway gave to his Southern Division. He therefore looked for a house close to that railway and no further from the City of London. By the end of October he had moved into Gothic Lodge, Wimbledon Common, with his unmarried sister Jane Elizabeth and his seven small children.

He obtained a twelve-year lease on Gothic Lodge, a detached house 'where the road from the village dips down into the valley', built by John Lawson in 1785 and at one time occupied by Captain Marryat's mother: a noted horticulturalist, she had brought from America in 1819 three swamp cypress seedlings; she planted one of them in the garden, in which a spring flows beneath its gravel top-soil. For many years Kew Garden officials made annual visits to measure the tree's growth. Preece purchased Gothic Lodge when the term of his lease expired.

He carried on with his work as strenuously as before but his pleasure in its performance was eclipsed by the shadow of his sadness as he mourned Agnes. He wrote little for the technical press and neglected the professional societies of which he was a member to spend all the time he could spare to help his sister and his children to settle in at their new home.

15

ESCAPE INTO EUROPE

CULLEY, appreciating that detailed information on European telegraph developments and a closer contact with those concerned was becoming increasingly important but could be obtained only by personal visits, determined to send Preece on such a mission. The resulting challenges and changing scenes would, he was confident, also do much to restore Preece – for whom he had a warm regard – to his erstwhile zest for life. He engaged a linguist, J. H. Stanton, to accompany Preece and the two of them crossed the Channel on 1 September 1875 with instructions that they were not to miss opportunities for sight-seeing. By this time Llewellyn was nine and a half years old and Arthur, a sturdier lad (who grew to resemble his father) was eight years old. They were always asking questions. Preece, who was not given to private correspondence, nevertheless decided to make notes of his journey to post to Jane as often as possible for her to read to them. Most nights he got out his pen and pot of ink to write and make little sketches of what he had noticed (although he also included information from Baedeker's guides). He wrote well over 20000 words to produce a lively, ingenuous record and concluded his epistles:

I have always had the boys before my eyes and I have been anxious that they should learn . . . that a proper use of the eyes and a . . . record of what the eyes see afford not only amusement, instruction and delight to oneself but impart the same benefit and knowledge to others.

Here, shorn of guidebook information, repetitions, and some generalizations, is Preece's journal.

1st Sept. The 8.30 L.C. & D. train from Holborn Viaduct is a capital train stopping only at Chatham and Canterbury. Our boat left Dover at 10.50

and though the sea looked like a millpond, our little steamer with its flat bottom and round section rolled like a Dutch doll . . . only boat accommodation for 60 so what would have become of the 138 other passengers in case of accident God only knows. The South Foreland lights lit by electricity are very brilliant and we could see them all the way across. Cape Grisnez is also lit by electricity but the men on the steamer, *Wave*, say it is not so well done nor seen so far. We left Calais at 2.00 a.m. We seem to have left one world behind and tumbled into another. We are received by military swells on the quay, military swells abound at the station. The station master looks a worn-out Marshal of France and even the porters in their dirty blouses look like decayed generals. We are all as we land asked our names and nationality. The Marshal at the gangway said to one of our travelling companions in French, 'What is your name?' 'What the devil is that to you,' replied our John Bull in English. 'Eh bien,' said the military swell, 'you are an Englishman – pass on.' The porters move the luggage in great elongated vans so heavy that they can scarcely move them and Stanton and I had to put our shoulders to the wheel to make one truckful move. We could have had anything we liked in the buffet but contented ourselves with beautiful coffee and bread-and-butter – rather an unusual meal at 1.30 a.m. At Blandain, the frontier town, we were all bundled out of our carriages at 5.00 a.m., like a flock of sheep, and taken before the douaniers (more military swells) and locked up in the station while the carriages were searched by the Belgians. (I am quite proud of our volunteers after seeing the Belgian army.) This examination of baggage is a nuisance and a farce: it quite spoils one's rest which has already been disturbed a needless number of times by the examination of tickets both at stations and by the guard when the train is in motion. The latter practice is very dangerous and startling. You are just dozing off when the door is suddenly opened and an unshaven military swell comes in demanding, 'billets sivous plait'; he stinks of bad tobacco and retires into outer darkness as mysteriously as he came.

In Belgium you could fancy yourself in Dorset – until the blue blouses and the sabotted females appear in the fields. The women appear to work as much as the men – perhaps more.

After a cold bath and a change at the Hotel de l'Europe in Brussels we breakfasted and sojourned forth as fresh as paint. All the shops opening, women going to market, and milk carts flitting from house to house. Women sell milk out of these little carts which are drawn by DOGS! The dogs pull with great energy and seem to like their work very much: they draw vegetable carts, wheelbarrows, ladders on wheels. Sometimes you see men and dogs both at work and in every case that I watched the dog seemed to be the more willing labourer. They are very fine animals, something between a mastiff and a Newfoundland. I can well remember the time when hawkers used to come to Carnarvon driving dogs *in tandem.*

It is very amusing to see the women here walking about without any covering to their heads, without stockings and wearing only wooden sabots on their feet.

2nd September. I visited Brussels about 12 years ago and then I thought it the most beautiful city in the world. Whether the place has really changed or whether my ideas have changed I know not, but now it strikes me as second rate. I think the latter is the case for London is spoiling us for everywhere. London is rapidly becoming the most beautiful city in the world. Its squares, its parks, and its embankent are unequalled. There is an apparent absence of energy in Brussels. A great many shops are to let. Its park is not very much bigger than Russell Square but has fine trees and statuary. Every statue, however, has had its nose knocked off by roughs during political riots and now you see each Hercules, Venus, and Cupid with a false nose clumsily stuck on. We went to see the Wirtz collection: his pictures are very wonderful but very horrid. Murders, massacres and death should never be depicted on canvas. Pictures should show the pleasing side of nature. We went to another gallery at the Ducal palais. Visitors to foreign places think of scarcely anything but picture galleries. Stanton is picture mad – I am not yet. Stanton affects to be very learned – I have my doubts. He knows every painter – when he sees his name, which reminds me of how much I astonished T in the Isle of Wight by knowing every carrier – simply because I read their names on their carts.

We were seized upon at the Wirtz gallery by a conventional British snob – a horrid parasitic Englishman who dropped his H's and stuck to us so pertinaciously that we had difficulty in shaking him off. He was evidently a counter jumper or a servant out for a holiday but he made himself out to be a Warwickshire county swell. Belgians smoke the vilest tobacco all day long it smells like dirty brown paper. Curious to see attached to all scaffolding where men are at work a *cross* of rough laths tied to the end of a beam – intended to drive away those evil spirits who cause workmen to fall.

All Government buildings are well protected with lightning protectors. Just opposite our hotel window is the Museum surrounded with a cloud of these fine thin rods that tower twenty of thirty feet in the air. Stanton, who speaks French like a native, is disgusted at my walking about with

map in hand ferretting my way about as though I were in London. He
does all he can to eschew the excursionist. Amusing to see Belgian officers
strutting in the park like peacocks, in shoals, to hear the band play and
to ogle the *haut ton* who congregate there every afternoon. It is their
Kensington Gardens. In the evening, after an excellent table d'hote we
went to the Zoological Gardens to hear a concert by a splendid band
belonging to one of the regiments of the 'Grand' army. The gardens are
poor and the animals few.

3rd September. The Cathedral was not a patch on our cathedrals. I spent
most of the day in the Telegraph office where I met with great attention
and where I found myself a bit of a swell for it appears that my name is
very well known on the Continent. In our insular pride and conceit we
think our English telegraphs the first in the world but in many points of
system and order the foreigner licks us hollow. When a convenient wet
day arrives I have a great deal to write about Belgian telegraphs.

In the evening we went to the theatre and saw 'Tour du monde en
80 jours', a roaring farce (to us) in 15 acts.

4th September. We left Brussels at 9.35 a.m. reaching German territory
at Herbenthal. We had passed along the valley of the Verdre through
most picturesque country reminding me forcibly of the beautiful valleys
of North Devon excepting that here and there were large cloth factories,
the refuse from which made the river mucky and dirty.

One feature of the Belgian railways is that along the banks they have
in many places wire fencing for miles along which pear trees are cultivated
in espalier fashion bearing quantities of fruit. Another peculiar feature
of the French and Belgian railways is that the signalmen on the line
signal to each other and to the drivers by horns from which most doleful
sounds are emitted. We entered Germany and the change was like a
transformation scene in a pantomime. The change between England and
the Continent is not to be wondered at for they are separated by a broad
sea, but here there is nothing to separate territories but an imaginary line
upon a map. Men, manners, costumes, houses are all different. On the
platform at Herbenthal are two telegraph poles about ten yards from each
other, the one Belgian the other German – they are entirely different in
form, fittings, and character. And the fussy swaggering Belgian with
French kepi and wasp-like waist is transformed into the stolid sober
German with broad cap and pipe in mouth.

The Rhine at Cologne is crossed by a bridge of boats and a magnificent
bridge carrying both road and rail. The stream runs very fast and the
water is very dirty. Cologne stinks, there is no drainage to the place.

Narrow and numerous streets have their gutters connected by artificial means into running streams – like Truro – and into these flows all the refuse from the houses. In the morning they are clear and bright – in the afternoon they are filthy and dirty.

The policemen wear the regular Prussian helmet – which is very becoming and quite classical. It is curious to see the different costumes worn by the peelers in different countries. The French wear cocked hats and look terribly fierce, the Belgians light jaunty kepis and look very stagy, the Germans look like our own men but more martial.

We saw 'Der Freischutz' at the opera, capitally performed. S. told me – as though I didn't know it – that the music was by Weber. I told him that *Paradise Lost* was written by a man called Milton. Though he beats me at pictures about which he really does know something I lick him in music about which I really know very little. He is a capital companion and we get on splendidly.

5th September. We took a guide and visited all the churches. When there are no galleries to see travellers go to the churches. I annoy Stanton by paraphrasing Johnson and saying, 'Sir, one church is like another church . . . I like to see men and women. Sir, let us go to the Rheinaustrasse.' All the churches were full and I must confess I do not like entering a church sightseeing when people are there worshipping.

We visited the Zoological Gardens; they are very fine. All (the animals and birds) have plenty of room to thrive; if they knew it the struggle for existence with them is over but no one is happy in the lot set for him and we all want to make our own beds and lie on them. Cabs and buses in Cologne are execrable – the former great heavy lumbering diligences drawn by the most villainous worn-out knock-kneed quadrupeds fit only for the knacker. The drivers have a wonderful habit of cracking their whips which startle the occupiers and the wayfarers but which do not have the slightest effect upon the horses.

I was much disappointed with the modern appearance of the houses in Cologne. The German houses of the drawing books are not to be found on the route we are taking. Our guide – an aged being with one eye blind and the other nearly so – pointed out one which belonged to an old burgomaster whose wife died and was buried with all her jewels on her fingers and perhaps her bells on her toes. Some robbers knowing of her wealth stole to her tomb at night but to their surprise and alarm found her alive and kicking. They cut away like mad as you may imagine and so allowed her to escape. She went to her home and rang the bell. The servants shrieked and screamed and told their master that his wife was at the door. He said he could believe that his horses would come to his bedroom but not that his wife could come to life. She heard this, went to the stables, released the horses who did go up and his wife followed. They lived together for seven years afterwards and had three children and now to this day the two horses are to be seen in the bedroom. I saw them looking out of the window of the top storey of a modern house, looking very unhappy for they are of stone. This is the story I gathered from the ancient guide but there are one or two others about those horses equally wonderful and perhaps equally truthful.

Dogs are to a small extent used as beasts of burden. The poor dear things I do pity them so. They seem to work so willingly and so kindly that I would like to release them all and give them a good dinner.

The coinage is a terrible nuisance; English, French, German and Belgian money is in circulation and you have to bear in mind the relative value of each. Marcs, twenty to a Freiderich's d'or, have recently been introduced by the German union. We were quite amused to see girls acting as porters – lugging portmanteaus about in a wonderful style. However it is very exceptional for even a German was surprised to see it.

6th September. We left Cologne for Berlin in a train crammed with people. Here, where everybody is smoking, the carriages are marked 'Zum nicht Rauchen', for *non-smokers*, and not in our milk and water way, viz. 'smoking is not permitted in this compartment'. One of our 'companions due voyage' was a Russian on his way to Astrakhan, who smoked incessantly the whole way. He used little cigarettes which lasted him just ten minutes, so that he must have lit at least fifty of them. He had the old sulphur matches so that he gave us fifty very unpleasant sniffs. It is a great mistake to imagine that only English travel first class on the Continent. Everyone who can afford it does so. The effects of my journey with Sanger were entirely upset by submitting to the horrid discomfort of second-class travelling. [Preece had visited telegraph offices in Ireland a year before, in company with Sanger, divisional engineer for that island.] At Oberhausen we passed close to Krupps great works and each side of the line looked like the neighbourhood of Wolverhampton or South Wales. I was surprised to see in many places no fencing whatever to the railway. We stopped at Dortmund – once the headquarters of the famous Vehmgericht – so vividly illustrated in *Ann of Gierstein* – the greatest secret tribunal that ever existed. Next at Hamm which curiously enough is a great depot of Westphalia hams and sausages – the country around is very English in its character. We soon entered the mountains – which are wooded on their tops – and there came a change o'er the spirit of my dream. The English-looking cottages disappeared and up arose the German toy house – exactly like those the children build in bricks. Farmhouses, barn, labourer's cottage are all built on the same model and only differ in size. Their intensely red roofs are very conspicuous in the dark trees.

We emerged through a wonderful defile or gap in the mountains and crossing the Weser reached Minden where we dined. Here we saw for the first time strange national costumes and the women in the fields were clothed in picturesque red petticoats, white sleeves, and dark bodices. Thereafter the country was flat and uninteresting. No birds were visible excepting the ubiquitous crow and an occasional magpie. Once my Russian friend pointed out an eagle but it might have been a big hawk. However, I chose to believe that it was an eagle and I am inclined to be in raptures over my first sight of the king of birds out of a zoological collection but my pen is tired and so am I. I will however finish what I have to say about this journey for we have not much further to go. We sometimes saw bullocks ploughing, sometimes horses, and occasionally *cows*.

I think I must have slept through Hanover. When I awoke my fine companions were all asleep. Men can't talk all day – the Russian would perhaps have done so but the good dinner at Minden drove him into the arms of Morpheus and didn't he snore! We passed through great fine forests to Stendhal, thence over the Elbe through Shorhausen, the birthplace of Bismarck, and along a great flat plain reminding me very much of the Delta of Egypt where grazing land, sand flats, and peat bogs succeeded each other monotonously until we reached the great fortress of Spandau.

(Preece had travelled to Suez in 1873 to advise on Indian railway telegraph equipment. On his outward journey his stop at Gibraltar was long enough for him to suggest the first practical solution to the problem of duplexing long submarine cables: de Sauty, the local superintendent of the Eastern Telegraph Co., followed his advice to succeed, from 27 April 1873, in working duplex over the 365 nautical miles of cable to Lisbon.)

It was moonlight when we reached Berlin. The great column of Victory loomed through the dull light. The tall, majestic houses, the grand triumphal arch of Brandenburg looked like a set piece in grand opera and the magnificent Unter der Linden, where our hotel was next to the palace of the Queen of the Netherlands, was bright with lamps and gay with shops to give us an imposing and impressive idea of the capital of Germany.

We took a carriage and a guide [next day]; there was not much to see, a mediocre museum and picture gallery and no churches. Out guide was a dragoon who had been through some of the wars and had lived in England – a very smart fellow and intensely Prussian. Stanton told him there was nothing in the Palace to see. He drew himself up and said, 'If the Emperor of all Germany is nothing then there is nothing to see.' Stanton said at the Tivoli Gardens that he couldn't drink beer for it made him fat. 'Ah' said our guide, with a wink to me, 'you are not fat yet.' (N.B. S is very fat).

When the first impression of Berlin wears off the truth forces itself upon one that it is all brick and stucco and when its excessive modernness disappears it will require an immense amount of energy to keep it up. Curiously enough that which we call a gas-cock or a water-cock are here called 'hens'.

8th September. I went to the Telegraph Office where I was very well received and welcomed. I find they have translated several of my articles and papers into German. My visit will form the subject of a big report when that wet day arrives. Table d'hote is at 4.00 p.m. They do not understand dining in Berlin – soup, fish, meat, vegetables, game, sweets are given in any order and in strange confusion. In Brussels one arose from dinner fresh and light, here you feel heavy and gorged. People come in and out during the whole time and nothing is regular and methodical as in Paris. I am sorry to see that the Berliners also use poor bow wow as a beast of burden but I have not seen many of them. Traffic in the streets is not concentrated as it is in London. Shops are striking from having their whole windows one solid piece of plate glass without partition or division. The men are very polite to each other and take off their hats in the most approved style and there is a decided absence of smoking in the streets among the better classes.

Our hotel is palatial and very cheap though the dinners are not altogether to my taste. It wanted a stronger stomach than mine to relish them. Stanton who has the digestion of an ostrich pegged away at everything but poor I with broken down digestive organs was forced to fly to Cockle [a popular proprietary medicine, Cockle's Antibilious Pills] to eradicate the effects of an ill-assorted German menu.

Our Guide luxuriated in the name of Carl Francis Stuart Weber and his son is in Teheran in Seimens's employment. I felt a sneaking liking for the fellow when I found his interests were telegraphic and he turned quite obsequious when he found I was a telegraphic swell. The Berliners burn nothing but peat and wood. Coal is scarce and very dear. There are great stores of wood apparent everywhere and the canals are full of barges laden with peat.

We left Berlin at 9.00 a.m. and reached Dresden a little after noon. The country between is flat, stale, and unprofitable. As we approached the valley of the Elbe hill and dale supplanted sandy waste and woody plain. The women in the fields wore no shoes. Stanton asked me why. I didn't know. 'Because' replied he 'they didn't shoose.' He had me there. The environs of Dresden are very much alike those of Bath or Leamington and there is a nice park with its Rotten Row and restaurants – the accompaniment of every Continental public resort. People have become far more German and less English but still costumes and fashion remain the same. Railways and telegraphs are levelling the world. Shops show precisely the same things as those in London and the young ladies are just as tightly closed in about the legs as they are in Brighton.

10th September. We spent all morning in the far-famed picture gallery. It would repay the time and cost of the journey from England to see Raphael's *Madonna de San Sirto* alone. Of course there were the usual number of saints in very uncomfortable positions; Sebastians who are made pincushions of . . . Martins who are being dissected. To me it seems a pity that such splendid artists should have wasted their powers on such uninteresting subjects: the Dutch artists, however, have not done this but have given us faithful pictures of Dutch life and places. I spent the evening in the Telegraph with a young German who speaks English fluently and who has been ordered to attend upon me! He took us around and about the suburbs and gave us some fine Saxon beer – splendid stuff. Dresden is unquestionably the prettiest place we have been to. One feels inclined to stop here a month. Berlin, Cologne, and Brussels palled. The boats on the river have no rudders but have long oars sticking far over the stern.

I quite long for the boys to be old enough to travel about with me and to find them speaking French and German. They will have to do so by hook or by crook. It is miserable not to be able to speak the language in these delightful places. Everything looks so bright and fresh and beautiful this morning. We breakfasted in the open air, a delicious breeze blowing off the river. I have been much amused by seeing the little boys here of Bo's and Artie's ages wearing Wellington and Hessian boots.

I underwent this morning the same trial as poor Susannah – who is so frequently depicted by the old masters – I was surprised in my bath. While I was sousing and invigorating myself with delicious cold water from the Elbe in walked the buxom chambermaid with my letters. Stanton says I was far more confused than she and that I was suffused with blushes. Perhaps I was for the situation was novel. We paid a final visit to the glorious gallery and I spent some time in the Telegraph Office. We left for Prague at 12.40 p.m. which we reached at 7.30 p.m. The line follows the river valleys. Down the river float immense rafts of telegraph poles commanded by three men who guide them with long poles that reach the bottom of the river. The ferries are very dodgy – the boat is transferred from one side to the other by the force of the stream alone. The man in charge simply steers with a long oar astern. At Milligrund we entered Bohemia and found ourselves in Austrian territory. Again the only change visible was the uniform of the men and the character of the telegraph posts. At Bodenback our luggage was examined and we had to change carriages.

Every station in Austrian territory has a gunpowder magazine which is carefully protected and in the neighbourhood of which no one is allowed to smoke. Fancy such a state of things in England! All notices in the stations and even the names of the stations are written up in two languages – German and Bohemian – and in our carriages there are three languages – the third one we took to be Hungarian.

12th September. Prague. The Jews' quarter is very striking and there are about ten thousand of them with a self-governed town to themselves. They are like those you see in London and their chief trade appears to be 'old clo'. The oleander and the acacia flourish – the former is in full bloom and all the avenues and even the hedges are of the latter. Every shop is indicated in the two languages: one large shop had over it 'THEE RUM JAM' what it was I don't know.

The place is inundated with Austrian soldiers in every possible uniform, white, blue, green, grey, brown etc. Many of them look very like our volunteers and are very smart, lithe, active young fellows. The policemen wear swords and have brown Garibaldian jackets and elegant wideawakes with feathers cocked in them. They look very nice.

The smells are like those of all German towns very nasty. Our 'hotel d'Angleterre' is very comfortable and well kept: our dinners have been excellent and far superior to those of Berlin which fetched me up a bit. One of the quaintest places we have seen is the old Jewish burial ground in the very heart of their quarter. It is disused because there is no more room for bodies and those that have been buried are heaped so high that they have formed a regular mound. Gnarled and twisted elder trees grow in fantastic shapes all over the place and harbour spiders in myriads. The

Jews have a curious custom of expressing their respect for the dead by placing stones upon the tombs. The result is that the place looks as though all the boys of Prague have been pitching stones into the place for years, all of which have alighted on the tombs.

At the palace of Wallenstein – a grand old mansion – we met Prince Ludwig (brother of the Emperor) and his wife. Ludwig is a fine tall handsome fellow and his wife with a waist like a wasp.

The foot pavements are very prettily paved with coarse mosaic work and nearly every street has a different pattern. The effect is very nice and seems to last well. Each stone is about $1\frac{1}{2}$ inches square and they are of black and grey.

The further we get from England the less is Sunday respected. Here shops are open, business goes on in the usual way; the girls may put clean clothes on but there are no signs of reverence or devotion. On the contrary it seems a day of pleasure, frivolity and gaiety. The restaurants, gardens, and theatres are crammed. How different at home! And how thankful we are that in this respect at least we are not as other men. We did not do 'as the Romans do' for beyond driving about for four hours with a very good guide and sauntering out in the evening, we read and wrote, and then to bed.

13th September. We walked the town and re-examined several places that we saw yesterday, visiting the museum – where there are some fine meteorites that fell in Bohemia – looked at the Bohemian glass, which didn't tempt me, ogled the young ladies who are not particularly attractive.

Watchmen paraded the streets at night and signalled to each other with a kind of morse alphabet by smartly striking their iron-shod heavy sticks on the pavement. It had a very disturbing influence on our rest for it was a peculiar and unusual sound. First you heard a – · · · close under your bedroom window, and then not so loud at the end of the street, then fainter in the distance, and fainter still until the mind made you believe that you heard it murmuring away for a long time.

The journey from Prague to Vienna was uninteresting. It was night, we were in the last carriage which shook so violently as to make sleep entirely out of the question. The night wore wearily along and Stanton and I tried to enliven it by vile jokes and to pass it away by learned discussions on art etc. Stanton – who is a capital hand at that game – I mean sleeping – at last slept and I was left solus. I saw the sun rise over the plains of Moravia as the day brightened I saw labourers – long pipe in mouth – wending to their work. The women with handkerchiefs over their heads were plying their household cares. Partridges were startled from their drowsy sleep and hares scampered over the downs. Here and there crosses and crucifixes were visible and on the top of one hill were three crosses, an evident representation of Christ and the two thieves.

Still no national costumes! I have seen more national German costumes in one day in the streets of Southampton than I have in the whole of my run through the Fatherland! The weather turned cold, a great change from the delightful heat we have had. Our hotel 'Hof Erzhezog Cart' is in the very heart of the city – an old fashioned square-built house with a court in the centre – in a very narrow crowded street. It is comfortable and has a high reputation. The omnibuses are like those at Prague, simply execrable. The rings and main thoroughfares are supplied with tramways which are much better. The police wear swords and kepis and are very smart fellows. We went in the evening to the Opera to see a new work 'The Queen of Sheba' – a Wagner kind of thing very heavy and monotonous without one single air but with very fine instrumentation.

15th September. Of course we went to the Belvidere, the picture gallery. Stanton would not be happy unless he ventilated his love of pictures. He mugs up the guidebook on the sly. Every picture is the best he has ever seen and as he finds me incorrigible he pours forth his knowledge to the guide who regards him with due awe. On a flower piece by Van Huysum the dew drops were so beautifully done that it was only by trying to wipe them off with my finger that I convinced myself that they were not real dops of water. Over three doors I saw some capital plaster casts of animals and fixtures. I was rather surprised to see them among the pictures but when the guide pointed them out as paintings on canvas I did not acknowledge my mistake or I should never have heard the end of it but I took the precaution to find out that I really was sold. There really are some splendid pictures by the great masters and though I do make fun of my ill-used friend Sebastian and of the plump partridges who Rubens calls 'the Graces', I am obliged to acknowledge it is a great treat to see such power in a brush when guided by skilful hands. We bought pipes – no one comes to Vienna without buying a meerchaum pipe – dined at Sackers, saw 'La Juive' by Halevy at the Opera, magnificently put on.

16th September. A great feature of Vienna is the sumach avenues which are now in full bloom; even the chestnut has come into second bloom but the heat of the summer has scorched up the leaves. All rooms are heated by stoves seven or eight feet high and three feet square. There is a small fireplace at the bottom and the stove is apparently a receptacle for heated air. Immense stores of wood they burn are to be seen about. They are said to be very warm and economical. A strange absence of flies and other insects. I expected to find such a country of stinks swarming with them. Perhaps they prefer, as I do, the sweeter air of old England. The uniforms of the soldiers is various and pretty. Most striking are the Hungarian dressed in light blue, their trousers being *tight fitting drawers* with a row of buttons all down one side.

In the church of the Augustines the lovely monument to the Arch-duchess Christina by Canova to my mind possesses all the poetry of all the old masters condensed. I was obliged to turn away for my heart came up to my throat and even now while I think of it I cannot restrain the sympathising tear. It not being a picture, Stanton did not think much of it. We went to the Luhtenstein gallery but the sight of two or three 'pincushioned pilgarlicks', as I call the blessed Sebastian, drove me away and I left Stanton to enjoy his pictures without his scoffing companion.

We went to the Imperial Library. Our guide pointed out a Koran written four hundred years before Christ and Vasso's manuscript written three hundred years before Christ! He is a very smart active little man with the cheek and impudence of a cockney boy. He speaks English thoroughly with a strong Yankee twang. He was for some years in the United States Navy and speaks German, French and Hungarian. He knows everyone and everything and his information is of course very reliable as you have seen. He has conferred quite an honour upon us by being our guide. He makes up his cigarettes and smokes them in our faces with the excuse that talking makes him dry and smoking makes him wet. He will do anything, go anywhere, and while he won't let anyone else rob us he takes good care to rob us effectually himself. Some big Austrian swell was in one place; he wanted me to see him so up he walked, took off his hat, the swell did the same; they entered into an animated conver-sation, parted with bows: 'there' he said to me, 'that is Herr von Some-thingorother who dines at the Emperor's table nearly every day. I know him quite well.' The rascal! I saw the old boy was very much surprised at his impudence but was too polite to kick him before me.

While Stanton went to Schonbrun to see palaces and pictures I went to the Telegraph office to pay my respects to the officials and to arrange for my visit in forma. I then went to the cathedral which is used as a thorough-fare even when service is going on! The interior is lofty and imposing but the gimcrackery about it takes away all reverent feelings as our grand buildings generate. Half way up the tower is the *Fire Watch*. Men – who strike the quarters of the clock – watch with telescopes which move on graduated frames in such a way as to record and mark the exact position of a fire so that by telegraphing all the firemen are directed to the proper spot at once. My favourite hero, Eugene of Savoy, is buried here. I took a stroll in the Park to see the men and women and the boys and girls and enjoyed myself thoroughly watching the Viennese at play. We dined at Sacker's again and went to the Opera again to see 'Massancello', beautifully done. We start tomorrow morning at 6.30 for Pesth and Buda, returning here on Sunday.

17th September. We left Vienna in a small steamer which took us about six miles down the Danube to a deserted spot where the captain ran us ashore and a sailor boy jumped on land and ran a hawser round a tree: a most mysterious operation to us. Was it murder and piracy? There were 60–70 passengers to about six men so it couldn't be that. Was it an accident? No – everybody was perfectly unconcerned, so we determined to wait and see the result. Presently a large steamer crept gently out of a creek and with a great deal of manoeuvring on her part and ours we got alongside each other and changed ships. It had been quite clear when we started from Vienna but as the sun rose its warm beams converted the river into a thick mist and delayed our journey. The big steamer the *Budapest,* started from a different point to us and was equally delayed, hence the mysterious operations on the banks of the Danube. The boa_t

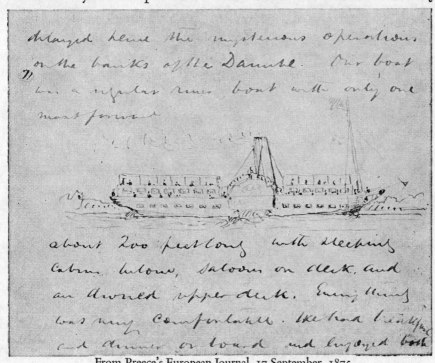

From Preece's European Journal, 17 September, 1875

about 200 ft long, with sleeping cabins below, saloons on deck, and an awned upper deck belongs to a company with the sole right to navigate the Danube with steam. The river divided itself into numerous channels leaving islands of various extent. The captain had often to thread his way through by sounding. Two men stand on each side of the bow with long thin poles with which they feel the bottom and a man above shouts out the depth to the captain who steers accordingly. We often touched bottom. When the river gets too low the steamers cannot ascend higher than Gonyo, about halfway between Vienna and Pest and in winter they are stopped by ice. The traffic on the river is very large; native boats of all kinds are constantly plying about and rafts of timber float down the stream. The men on these rafts, with their broad-brimmed hats and 'petticoats', look just like Chinamen. The banks are teeming with people but the villages on the final part of our journey are out of sight for they are built out of reach of the inundations which are common.

We were the only two Englishmen on board and we became the observed of all observers. We had two native Magyars on board, a woman in short petticoats and *top boots* and a man in *petticoats* – in reality it was a petticoat to each leg (which they tuck into their top boots when they go into town). The river was bowling us along with great

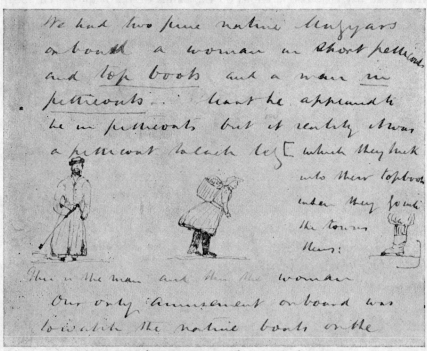

From Preece's European Journal, 17 September, 1875

rapidity: it runs about four knots and is very dirty. Theben, a grand and splendid castle completely commanding the river reminded me very much of Tintagel. Somewhere about here our Richard Coeur de Lion was incarcerated by a villainous Austrian noble but I cannot find that the exact place is known.

If a month ago anybody had said to me, 'on the 17th. September you will be on the Danube in Hungary,' I should have been astonished but now that I am here there seems to be nothing surprising in it. I am as comfortable as though I were on the Thames. I am only vexed that no stirring adventure occurs, that the Danube won't play the fool, that our steamer won't sink, that no one will fall overboard so that the two Englishmen might jump overboard and save some fair one's life, that the Hungarians won't rise in insurrection and give us a chance of seeing some fighting, that brigands won't come and take us prisoners and so on, but no! – everything is like it is on board a Gravesend steamer.

We saw no new birds but peewits abounded in thousands and thousands; two kinds of crows were abundant – our old black friend who cawed in good sound English and a grey gentleman, like those I saw in Egypt; lots of cormorants plied their busy trade and gave indication of abundance of fish, the sandpiper flitted about in flocks and sparkled in the sunshine as they moved with one mind; the note of the curlew relieved the stillness of the air, and ducks stretched in one long line across the sky. One great feature of the river was the hundreds of corn-mills moored in the stream and worked by the force of the current that flowed by them. Two barges are moored side by side with a great waterwheel between them which worked the machinery in the small mill house erected on the barge nearest the shore. The quantity of corn they grind must be enormous.

Of insect life we saw only wasps, which flew aboard in shoals. One butterfly came aboard which I very nearly caught for Aggie but while I was chasing it with my hat a German collared me thinking I was mad and going to throw myself overboard! We saw plenty of cattle browsing on the banks and cooling themselves in the river but they were very small, light and poor – like sickly Alderneys with long horns. Pigs and geese were plentiful and also horses – a light arab breed. Occasionally in the woods we saw improvised huts which the woodcutters erected for shelter . . . they looked much like Red Indian wigwams.

We gloried in the moonlight for two or three hours before reaching Pesth at 9.30 p.m. having steamed 175 miles in fifteen hours. The latter part of the journey had been very picturesque; villages abounded clustering around their churches; the old women were descending the banks to obtain water, the young women were washing reeds and clothes at the river's brim, the men were mooring their rafts and their flat bottomed boats for the night, cattle were being driven down to drink, and geese were being driven home to roost. Children were playing on the banks and in the water. As the night advanced fires and lights sprang up, and as the steamer approached, rafts and barges sent up a light by torch to give notice of their presence.

18th September. Our hotel 'de l'Europe' is an old house comfortable but badly managed, facing the river and commanding a delicious landscape of Buda. On the extreme left is a high rocky eminence, as high as the Downs about Shanklin, surmounted by the citadel. On another eminence in the centre of the picture is the Royal Palace and on the extreme right mountains covered with vineyards, the intermediate portions being filled up by the river, the fine suspension bridge, and the town.

Capital streets and excellent shops but everything, including fashions, the same as everywhere. The fine national costume is as scarce as that of the Highlands or of Wales. Coachmen of some private carriages are quaintly dressed with the Spanish turban hat and hussar jackets of dark green cloth. The sweeps are in uniform! Fire brigade men swell about in gorgeous attire of bright light blue infantry uniform. Policemen carry swords and are distinguished when on duty by an armband of the national colours. Long lizards were playing about in the Palace Gardens. I am happy to say that there is no visit to picture gallery, cathedral or church to chronicle, for Budapest is destitute of anything of the kind worth visiting. Our guide tried to inveigle us into a museum and into various buildings but we were resolute. We went to the public gardens on an island laid out as a park with restaurant, baths, etc., where there were five military bands performing – magnificent as are all Austrian bands. Our guide had been a waiter at the Civil and Military Club in Regent Street. He was new to his work. He had in his pocket a manuscript guide which he had translated from Magyar into German, then into French, then into English. He read portions to us and I am bound to say that though I at least listened attentively I failed to catch a single idea or the meaning of a single sentence.

19th September. We left Pesth at 7.50 a.m. to return to Vienna at 2.00 p.m. – a hot, tedious, uninteresting railway journey. In the neighbourhood of Presburg we saw vineyards and maize fields. The acacia grows wild in these parts and the vines are trained up poles like hops, in fact we mistook them at first for hops. Although this is Sunday all the platelayers are at work on the line, and the labourers busy in the fields. There is no indication of Sunday anywhere although in Vienna many of the shops are closed. After dinner we took a drive in the Prater where all Vienna and his wife and family mustered to the tune of military bands *ad nauseum*. Gaiety, gaiety, gaiety, all is gaiety. On such a day I long to be at home slashing away at the inevitable leg of mutton, wondering where Bo stows away all his meat and Prissie all her pudding, inhaling the fragrant weed under the verandah, and taking my forty winks in my own armchair; but above all marching with my little crew to church to praise God from whom all blessings flow and to keep his commandments which are unknown in these irreligious parts.

20th September. I spent the whole day in the Telegraph Office and gave the officials a regular twister. They wanted it for they are the slowest coaches I have ever seen. In the evening we again went to the Opera, and saw 'Martha' – very well done indeed, certainly the Opera House of Vienna has been one of the greatest treats we have met during our evening entertainments. Vienna certainly is a charming place and it bears away the palm among all the places we have yet been to. It has the reputation of being a very dissolute place but if it is, it is very well veiled: I do not believe it is worse than other places. It is essentially a city of palaces and the very picture of what a capital should be. We leave to-morrow at 7.00 a.m. Oh these horrid morning trains and long journeys – we shall not be in Trieste until 10.00 p.m. – 15 hours! Ugh!

21st September. I forgot to mention that we noticed in Hungary large quantities of beetroot under cultivation. We now find there are no less then 270 large sugar refineries in Austria and that sugar is one of the principal exports from Trieste. Beet produces seven per cent of its weight in sugar. This information was obtained from a very intelligent German who was one of our companions du voyage to Trieste and who spoke English capitally. Other Germans popped in at one station and out at another but none afforded us amusement except a lady who was full of life and fun and for an hour amused the Germans directly and us indirectly.

We left Vienna at 7.00 a.m. The slow trains take 22 hours to travel the 370 miles to Trieste. We took 15 and this to us in England would be slow work. The line is unquestionably the loveliest I have ever travelled over, one long exquisite panorama. At the head of the pass (Semmering) women sold flowers. I bought two crosses of a rare alpine flower, the Edelweiss. Here there is a monument to the engineer Carlo Chega, and richly he deserves it. The distance from one foot, Glognitz, to the other, Murzzuschlag, is 25 miles and we took two hours to do it. It is like going up one side of Snowdon [this was twenty years before the railway was

built from Llanberis to Snowdon summit] and down the other only all
the hills, even to their summits, are covered with pines. The railway
sweeps and curves and dances about among the hills and is simply
indescribable. It was worth coming all the way from England to see. The
morning which had commenced cloudy and dull became a wet afternoon
and mist and clouds gave a different and more interesting aspect to the
ceaseless panorama. Thus we passed Graz, the capital of Styria, passed
villages protected in the middle ages by a castle soaring upon the top
of a hill whose ruins added picturesqueness to the scene. The valleys are
most richly cultivated with maize, *pumpkins*, flax etc., and strange little
water wheels are seen with floats on their circumference working in a
trough of water. Bullocks are used very largely as beast of burden and
the soft-eyed gentle cow browsed on many and many a green patch that
displayed itself on the side of some pine-clad hill, carefully watched by the
shoeless hatless native.

22nd September. After a good night's rest Richard is himself again though
a little shaky about the eyes. Our hotel, de la Ville, overlooks the harbour.
An American man-of-war the *Congress* lies in the roads. Here you see
no seaweed and the tide is scarcely perceptible. We drove to Miramar,
the summer residence of poor Maximilian; his Tudor castle as a sight is
the only thing in or near Trieste. Bullocks almost the only beasts of
burden are lying about in hundreds; they seem very well cared for but
slip about terribly on these stone-paved streets and quays. The only
universal thing that has appeared in all our journeyings is the household
fly; here is abundant, very impudent and most persistent in his efforts to
alight on your nose. I am afraid our insect troubles are commencing.
Hitherto we have been very free.

23rd September. We were up at 4.30 a.m. and left Trieste at 6.00 a.m.:
though both windows were open and it was before daybreak, dressing
was a Turkish bath operation. The line for many miles skirts the Adriatic
sea. Scattered along the coast are sweet little harbours full of fishing boats
and life. As we approach the frontier the beautiful cypress began to dot
the landscape with its dark heaven-pointing form. We crossed the
frontier – the dried up bed of a river – near Cormons with a certain
amount of formality. The train stopped on one side of the bridge and
dropped an Austrian soldier, crossed the bridge, stopped again and picked
up an Italian one. We had entered the plain and its vineyards in which
rows of fruit trees are planted at some distance apart and the vines trained
in graceful festoons about them. The vine leaves are just being tinted by
autumn and look like Virginia creepers laden with grapes. Our compan-

ions were two Italians: one was a fat pale-faced short middle-aged individual who did nothing but smoke and sleep. He would light a long cavour cigar and before he had half smoked it he would be sure to fall asleep and the end would fall out of his mouth. When he awoke he would light another – the result was that the carriage floor was strewn with half ends of cigars. The other was a young handsome man who read nearly the whole way. I was anxious to see what he was reading: it was Jules Verne's *Journey to the centre of the earth* in Italian. Curiously enough on our journey to Cologne a Frenchman was reading the same book in French and I also saw it in German somewhere else. I do not think it is in English.

It is quite pretty at the small stations to see the young Italians in their picturesque dresses offering baskets of fruit for sale. Their longing black eyes are most impressive and I fear I ate more grapes than were good for me. The women even do duty on the line and you see them with their official hats and flags acting as signalmen and gatemen. We have again entered the land of military swelldom. Tight waists are as fashionable as with the Belgian: the gens d'armes is a splendid swell. He wears a cocked hat and a sword and has such a magnificent moustache which he twists and turns with magnificent airs.

We reached Venice dusty and dirty at 2.00 p.m. As we glided in our dank hearse-like gondola through the silent waterways past decaying palaces and along deserted canals a feeling of sadness and melancholy came over me – something like the impression produced by a very solemn piece of music – which has not departed. Our present hotel d'Italie was once the palace of some noble family. In the evening we were regaled with some excellent music by some gondoliers; and we wandered into the Piazzo where a military band was playing. It was still very hot and when were turned to our room we found two enemies – a horrid stink from the canal and *mosquitoes*. Buzzing and humming about us all night. Poor Stanton has suffered worse than I have. I am only attacked about the arms but his face and neck are a caution to see. My arms and hands are a mass of spots just like those the youngsters suffer from at home. Which confirms me in the opinion that the gnats of Wimbledon and the mosquitoes of Venice are one and the same family.

24th and 25th September. We ascended the campanile of S. Mark (Stanton didn't, he is too fat and lazy). We circumnavigated and internavigated Venice in a gondola. We did all that became travellers and we retired each night pretty well done up and reckless of the assaults of our enemies.

A feature is the water-carriers, old men and women who prowl about all day with great baskets strapped to their shoulders containing great flasks of water sometimes surrounded by smaller flasks of syrup and spirits. I am writing with wearied eyes by means of a wretched light so that I dare not attempt a villainous sketch to try and convey an idea of an imbecile water-carrier. Hawkers flit about in picturesque attire selling fruit, fish, or baked pumpkin (and nice it looks, but to be carefully eschewed by the wary traveller). Others sell bread, and cakes, and sweets, and all kinds of things. And then there is the inevitable Jew with his old clo' shop and his fat wife and his black-eyed daughter, and then the long-robed sleek-faced priest slinks along like a culprit out for an airing.

The canals in the morning are always clear and clean owing to the night breezes and the tidal current – for the tide rises from two to three feet – but in the evening vegetables and refuse of all kinds flit by slowly generating odours to which those of Cologne were sweet. And in this water all the washing and cleansing is done! We went among the lagoons that surround Venice in our gondola. We saw some fishermen hauling in a big net. We went and helped – by looking on carefully. Some twenty brown-legged Venetians hauled away and secured to their immense delight about a fish apiece. When this was over two pretty little black-eyed tawny urchins about as old and as big as Percie clambered over the boats and came to us cap in hand. We each put something in. One little beauty flew back to his father's boat, disappeared to count his gains, jumped up with such an expression of exuberant joy and clapped his little hands with unfeigned glee. On comparing notes afterwards of our impressions of Venice I asked Stanton 'what had left the deepest impression on his mind'. 'The little boy's joy' said he. 'Ah' I said, 'nature is better than art this time. So much for the old masters.' 'Brute' replied he. I could dilate on Venice for hours but the flickering dip, the heavy head for I have a bad cold (bad luck to it) and the weary eye warn me to shut up.

26th September. We left the Queen of the Sea at 8.25 a.m. It was Sunday but there were no signs of the day of rest anywhere. One of our fellow passengers was an old Englishman who had spent the greater part of his life in Canada in making a fortune: he made the time pass pleasantly and knew all the country we were passing through so that he was as good as a guide. He was an art enthusiast and was going to Milan which we reached at 4.00 p.m. to do some shopping! After a wash and a dress we took a stroll into the town. It was gratifying to find that there were signs of Sunday. All the shops were closed and the people were decked in their Sunday best. The women wear no hats or bonnets. The number of dwarfs and deformities amongst the women was most remarkable and there were many cases of goitre – the first we had come across.

27th September. Of course we did the cathedral and the principal churches and the pictures. There is only *one* cathedral in the world – the exterior is in Salisbury and the interior in Milan. I ascended the roof and was richly rewarded with a view of the city and the plains of Lombardy: the roof is however horribly disfigured by lightning conductors which stretch across the skyline as badly as the telegraph wires in London. Wretches had knocked off the arms and legs of the beautiful marble figures and I must confess I was horribly tempted to walk off with the foot of a pretty little angel which was loose but I left it for some other sacrilegious heart.

The prettiest thing in Milan is a statue to Cavour who stands in proper modern costume on a pedestal upon which the loveliest possible figure of Italia – of course improperly dressed – is inscribing his name. Stanton cannot understand my rapture over this. I say it generates an idea. I see before me all Italy weeping over the loss of her greatest son and inscribing his name indelibly on the scroll of fame and personified here by youth and beauty which is unquestionably the condition of the country. Stanton who falls in raptures over an incongruous assemblage of ugly mugs coolly witnessing the murder of a crooked damsel, says 'Pshaw', and turns up his nose.

The poor soldiers in this hot country are actually wearing their greatcoats. The country is poor. They had a large quantity of greatcoats in stock so they served them out as summer uniforms to a large portion of the army rather than go to the expense of purchasing new uniforms – cruel, but perhaps wise economy!

The public gardens are very nice. Our hotel, Cavour, overlooks them. They are prettily laid out with plenty of water running through them in ponds and cascades and rock work. I noticed many specimens of deciduous cypress but not one like ours. I was quite delighted to see the police still dressed in tall black hats with a band of shining leather, surtout coats, and long sticks. It reminded me of our great police force of two in Carnarvon.

Opposite our hotel, to fill a gap as it were in the houses, is a piece of scene painting representing the front of a magnificent house. I was anxious to know what it meant and our silent guide – for we couldn't get one who could speak English and the man we had pretended to speak German but Stanton couldn't understand him – took us into a private house where the garden at the back was exquisitely finished off with scenery representing some Italian mountain views with villas and waterfalls – like the Coliseum of old. Fortunately there was nothing going on at the Scala so we were prevented from going to the opera on a Sunday but we went in to see it today and saw a ballet rehearsed and a very funny sight it was.

28th September. We left Milan at 9.40 a.m. for Como which we reached at noon. Como is the birthplace of Volta, one of the fathers of electricity. We took steamer on the lake in the afternoon. We were told the surrounding mountains were over 7,000 feet high but they do not look higher than those of Wales or Scotland; in imagination Snowdon looks like a giant to these alpine hills. At Bellagio Stanton with his accustomed laziness remained down below while I ascended a lovely wooded hill with an ancient castle at the top from which I surveyed all three arms of the lake. The village is a kind of Italian Clovelly and abounds with woodcarvers who work in olive. I bought a stick and a paperknife. Everybody brings something away and I could not be exceptional though I have steadfastly refrained from buying anything, for my luggage and my purse is limited.

29th September. We crossed the lake after breakfast, in a light shower of rain, and leaving our small boat took carriage to Portegga at the head of Lake Lugano. The sun was bright and we had such a rainbow! A rainbow that was composed of all the rainbows I had ever seen in my life before condensed into one. We took steamer for Lugano. The women carry grapes, coals, vegetables, and even children in a kind of knapsack basket, and they wear no shoes but the veritable old sandal. We stopped the night at Lugano. Being in Switzerland and at the foot of a mountain my mountainous soul soared to reach the top. That lazy Stanton would not stir twenty feet above his mother earth so there being time before dark and, armed with my Baedeker, alone I determined to scale the monster's side! I found my way without difficulty but a little boy offered his services and with his aid I went perspiring at every pore in the hot sun but repaid at every step with fresh beauties. After over two hours hard work I reached the top and there I found a German clergyman who spoke a little English, who pointed out all the spots to me and there I saw for the first time the snowclad tops of the alpine giants and the sun set in all his glory behind the mighty Monte Rosa. Oh what a sight was that my countrymen! The clouds vying with the mountains in their fantastic shapes to add glory to the scene. Both the German and I sang for joy. It was worth living for and as I descended – with rather more ease than I ascended – the stars began to peep out from the glorious blue vault of heaven, the lizards rustled away from our path, the cicadas rattled away at their evening song, and all nature declared the glory of God.

I arrived very late and found poor Stanton dinnerless and in an awfu[1] funk at my absence. He had pictured my fall down some precipitous cliff and was contemplating a search for my remains.

30th September. We left beautiful Lugano at 9.00 a.m. and drove in a carriage and four! A carriage and *four*! Through another lovely pass to Luino on Lake Maggiore where we took another steamer for Arona. At Pontetreso the road goes absolutely *bang through the houses.* There is no street at all but an arcade which is the road. At Fornasette we crossed the frontier again and had to go through that ridiculous formality of examining baggage. We were spared this on entering Switzerland. At Luino is a very fine statue to Garibaldi to whom they pay so high a compliment as to leave the pedestal nameless. Stanton can't see the poetry of this. What higher compliment could they have paid Garibaldi?

Stanton has been asleep for some time, and who accuses me of stealing from Baedeker because I write so much, has suddenly awoke and said 'Go to bed-you-cur.' He thinks that so good as to deserve a note.

I forgot to mention that at Lugano our hotel had been an old monastery and there was a church adjoining. It was said to possess some fine frescoes. I went to see them but was driven back like a thunderbolt. Stanton in alarm wanted to know 'What is the matter?' '*He* is there' I said. 'For heaven's sake who?' asked he. 'Pilgarlick' I replied.

At Arona I saw the Diligence arrive from Sierre after a twelve hours journey over the Simplon. It seems as much an object of antiquity as a stage coach though many of them still exist.

We had a magnificent view of the snow-capped peak Monte Rosa on our way to Novara. It was at least fifty miles off and yet it looked close by – the atmosphere was so clear and the light so bright. There are few things more delightful in Italy than the abundance of fruit. Peaches, figs and grapes are sold at every station and at every corner for a mere song. The figs are simply delicious. They are so cold that you would fancy they must be kept in ice: twopennyworth is enough to make you ill. Threepennyworth would give you diarrhoea and fourpennyworth cholera morbus. I must have taken sixpennyworth more than once with great relish much to Stanton's horror and my own surprise.

We arrived at Turin too late to see the town but after dinner we paraded some of the arcades and streets to see the Sardinians at home – which is the open air. It was the same tale – band playing, men smoking, women ogling, gaiety and frivolity everywhere. We went to bed very early for we had to rise very early for our long long journey on the morrow.

2nd October. We left Turin at 9.00 a.m. and ascended the valley of the Dorn to Mt. Cenis; the rough rugged sides of the hills – though the valleys teemed with population and vineyards and maize fields abound – were more like the pass of Llanberis blown out to gigantic porportions than the soft luxuriant wooded sides of the Semmering pass. We passed through miles of tunnels which played bo peep with the mountain landscapes. Of course Stanton was asleep. When we were halfway through Mount Cenis tunnel I lowered the window to smell the air and see what was to be seen. The scowl of virtuous indignation on Stanton's face was a sight! I saw the end before us like a pale green star. The air was quite pure. It is pumped in at every twenty yards by water power. On the other side we crossed the frontier and bade farewell to lovely Italy.

The Italians are a peculiarly excitable, demonstrative talkative race. To see an Italian in a rage is a sight. His arms fly about like a windmill and his face is contorted like a squeezable india rubber doll. They are very sober, thrifty, and industrious. We never saw a single drunken or even a man approaching inebriety. The women work as hard as the men and they are to be seen indiscriminately intermingled in the fields and vineyards. Indeed one sees more women than men at work. They are said to be dirty but they are always washing. At the brink of every lake and at the edge of every river shoals of women are seen washing – yet it is said that every Italian has two suits. The one which he wears he never washes and the one which he washes he never wears. It is the fashion of the country to wear moustachios and imperial only, a la Victore Emmanuel, and as the men as a rule are a hairy race and only shave occasionally their faces are usually covered with short stubbly stuff which is not conducive to cleanly appearance.

We saw no monks, and the priests in their broad three-cornered hats and long gabardines looked a homely healthy lot. They seemed quite 'hail fellow well met' with the people and smoked and chatted and laughed with the best of them. Indeed the Italians as far as we saw them looked happy and contented and in truth they have everything to make them so. We saw no beggars! Their money is, however, remarkable. They have no gold or silver. It is all paper except the centissimi, five of which equals a halfpenny or soldi, they are in copper. We never entered a theatre in Italy – they were all closed – a disappointment but the opera season had not commenced.

We arrived at the Grand Hotel, Paris after twentyfour hours of tiresome, sickening travelling in a carriage chockful of smoking Italians and excitable French.

And here my diary must end.

16

CROSSING THE ATLANTIC

EARLY in 1877 Preece received a request from the South African Government to visit that country and reorganize its telegraph service. He asked for arrangements to be made for his secondment only to be told that he was to go the United States. He recommended that James Sivewright, his assistant in Southampton who had co-operated with him in writing a textbook on telegraphy, should travel to South Africa in his stead. As it turned out Sivewright spent the rest of his working life in South Africa with marked success – in 1890 he was appointed Commissioner of Crown Lands and Public Works and three years later was awarded a K.C.M.G.

In April Preece left for the United States in company with H. C. Fischer, Controller of the Central Telegraph Office in St Martin's-le-Grand. 'At last I have crossed the Atlantic' he wrote to his sister Jane on 26th April from New York City: the crossing by the Cunarder (steam and sail) R.M.S. *Abyssinia* had taken twelve days. Preece had determined to send home a 'regular diary' for Jane to read to his children but the voyage had been so rough that he had been unable to write on board: that did not prevent him from praising the Cunarder –

a noble ship of 3,376 tons . . . a floating hotel . . . I have never seen a P. & O. ship to equal her

– he dreaded the return trip and regarded the voyage

a pain and a penalty on me for some past sins. It ought to blot out a lot!

A gale had blown during the first night out of Liverpool; it abated and the vessel stopped at six o'clock in the morning in fog. Preece went on deck

CUNARD LINE

ESTABLISHED 1840.

British and North American

ROYAL MAIL

STEAM PACKET COMPANY.

SALOON PASSENGER LIST,

R.M.S. "ABYSSINIA,"

Liverpool to New York,

APRIL 14, 1877.

and found the Captain sounding to find out where he was. He found out and we reached Queenstown at 9.30 . . . a few of the poor pale passengers appeared at breakfast.

During the storm that night Preece had, typically, improved the unpleasant hour by opening his pocket watch and timing the roll of the ship, which he determined as 16 seconds.

To my surprise Fischer weathered the storm all right and he made a breakfast which simply made my eyes open . . . it did not take many days for my form to improve. . . . I think I have eaten as much in ten days at sea as I should do in ten weeks at home. There is little else to do. A cup of tea and a 'cracker' is brought to you at 7 a.m. Breakfast comes at 8.30. Luncheon – always the meal of the day – at noon. Dinner at four. Tea at 7.30. Supper at 9.30. When I tell you that I never missed one meal and that every one was a good one you may imagine what the effect of the sea on my wretched digestive organs must have been.

Of my fellow passengers I was first struck with a handsome melancholy looking man who came on board with two charming little girls about 10 and 8 years old. They were in very deep mourning. Some mysterious sympathy told me at once that he was a widower. He had just lost his wife in Paris. She was in apparent perfect health but one day after dinner she took a nap and never woke. . . . He is a very nice fellow. We cottoned together quite wonderfully.

. . . He was however, a terrible Yankee. When he last crossed the Atlantic he travelled in a White Star Ship. The Captain was driving his ship against a severe storm as he thought recklessly, so he said, 'I went to him and I said to him, Captain I guess you'll be in hell before you know it.' His children are charming little things, smart and precocious as all American children are, but polished by three years' living in Paris. There was nothing on board more touching than the affection and the attention shown by Plumb (such was his name) to his little girls. We were great friends. I was the 'old Bear' and many a romp we had after we had secured our sea legs.

While it was blowing a very strong gale from the NW against which the ship was labouring very much – enough to frighten Fischer – the steward said very coolly 'this little knocking about won't last long'. It didn't last very long, but it gave us a terrible night during the most part of which I sat with Fischer cheering him and reading to him – poetry of all things and to his amusement, amongst other things, 'The Wreck of the Birkenhead' which he thought very appropriate. We were very glad when morning came, and I early went on deck to watch the grand and magnificent waves cut off into spray and mist by the driving wind. The deep dark blue – almost blackness – of the Atlantic is very striking, and where it is broken up into foam by the screw it becomes gloriously beautiful. I watched it for hours with my polariscope and obtained the most beautiful effects. There was a very snug place behind the steerage house where I could do this in comfort and where I was not always alone. It was there where I compared the face of the ocean to the face of my companion. Such is life. 'E'en in our ashes live their wonted fires.' Crossing the Atlantic even in a storm can be made very pleasant if you have your sea legs and somebody else has hers.

Breakfasting in a gale is a very trying operation. While you are balancing your coffee cup in one hand, you have to secure your meat with the other, and while you are occupied with the one, the other – in spite of fiddles – may be depositing itself on your neighbour's lap. Dinner is even more trying for you have more things to look after. One of the funniest sights in the world is to see a whole dinner party trying to balance their soup plates. It is almost impossible to avoid either dipping your nose in hot pea soup or greasing your beard with the same.

One of our amusements on board was to watch the heaving of the log to see how fast the ship was going. It was done every two hours and varied from 10 to 14 knots according to the direction of the wind. A sandglass, which ran for 14 seconds was used and the length of line paid out over the stern during this time gave the rate at which we were moving. To the end of the line is fixed a triangular piece of wood called the log which catches the water and remains fixed there. It is a primitive but really most accurate mode of measuring the speed of the ship. A · noon on the 17th we reached Lat. 50° 14' Long. 21° 09' and had run during the 24 hours 251 miles – a very good run in such a sea. Towards evening the wind strengthened again and it became cold. We turned in with the ship pitching and tossing and rolling, creaking and groaning and moaning as badly as ever. Nevertheless, I had at last a good night's rest.

In the morning of the 18th the wind changed to the SE but it was cold and still blowing very fresh. Talking of cold at breakfast Plumb said that 'in New York it was so cold in Winter that it freezes off the cast iron tail of a monkey'. Some of his expressions were very quaint. One man 'lied like thunder', another 'was as sharp as lightning'.

During the day the wind went right around the compass and, curiously enough, during our run across it actually went around the compass seven times. The weather was wet and the day was very uncomfortable but towards evening it settled a bit and two or three of the ladies ventured on

L

deck. The children also turned up and we had a great romp. I made myself a bear in my great ulster and it was great fun to run after the children who rolled about splendidly on the unsteady deck. At noon we were in Lat. 49° 19′ Long. 28° 39′ and the distance run was 294 miles.

On the morning of the 19th I amused myself by taking observations of the sun with the sextant and by observing the variation of the compass at noon by the sun. The compass does not point true north in England. It varies about 24° from the true pole. This variation changes right across the ocean sometimes reaching 30°, but it is only about 7° on this side. If we went on we should at last find a place where the magnetic pole and the true pole are the same. I wonder if the boys can make this out and understand it. The way the variation is taken is very simple. At noon the sun is, of course, true south. A long pin is fixed on the glass of the compass in its centre and the shadow of this pin falls on the rim of the compass card showing exactly the difference between the two. If there were no variation the shadow would, of course, fall on the N line, but as there is a variation it fell on N 17° W.

Plumb's appetite was certainly a caution – one of his favourite dishes for supper was a raw red herring and for breakfast tripe and onions. I ventured on both, but paid the penalty.

There was the wife of an American clergyman on board – Mrs. Hilliard – who had 2 children, her sister and her maid with her. She was very nice looking and I showed her much attention. She was the invalid to whom I had given up the Saloon at Euston and for which she was very grateful, but she sickened everyone by her lackadaisical ways and the attention she almost demanded from all. It was steward do this and steward do that all day long. She had a nice little boy who was the pet of all the sailors, one of whom made him a capital boat and which I spent a whole morning in rigging much to the delight of the children and their mammas. This boy was always all over the shop. How it was he didn't go overboard or tumble into the hold or the engine room I cannot make out. The constant cry from Mrs. H. was 'Oh where is my boy!' 'Mr. Preece will you kindly see if Haire is all right.' 'Where can Haire be?' Everyone got sick of Haire and his mother. She required more attention from the deck steward than all the other ladies put together. We bet she would give him no fee. While all the other ladies gave 10/– she only gave 4/–. It was the finest joke in the world to see 'old John', the deck steward, look at his fee and then at us. We roared.

At noon on the 19th. we were in Lat. 47° 29′ Long. 35° 50′ and had run 306 miles. We were now 1,342 miles from Liverpool and were approaching the banks of Newfoundland. Signs of life began to show themselves. Little birds – the Great Northern Diver – popped out of the water, flew over two or three waves and then popped in again. Some of them rose to the surface evidently frightened by the ship, shook their little heads, gave every indication of fear and then disappeared. We passed through a very large shoal of porpoises – hundreds of them gambolled about – they were so close that we could see them distinctly in the water. It was a very pretty sight. They took the tops of waves just like a horse takes fences. At last I saw a whale! One passed close to the ship blowing away every now and again beautifully. The effect was just like a cloud of spray thrown up when a shot strikes the water. Some people prognosticated that we should have bad weather as if we hadn't had enough. Sure enough it came on to blow again 'like steam' as the Yankee said. We shipped during the night some very heavy seas which came through a companion and flooded our gangway. Fischer was very frightened and I didn't at all like it. We went 14 knots all night and to our extreme mortification instead of having been passing through extreme danger we found that the Captain was delighted at having such a splendid 'breeze'! He carried on sail all night, but I found he had been up himself.

There was an American lady on board – Mrs. Briggs – a perfect picture of a typical Yankee girl. I shifted her chair for her and asked her where I should place it. She said, 'I'll sit right here I guess'. Fancy such a speech from an English girl. She was very young and remarkably lively. She covered a comb with paper and made it into a kind of harp producing therefrom remarkable music. Our last evening was smooth – the deck quiet, so we danced. She danced beautifully. The English ladies were shocked. Mrs. Fletcher, this Mrs. Briggs and a German lady were the only ones who had their sea legs. The less I say about the German lady the better. I am assured by all my friends on board that I shall have a shot through me or a bowie knife into me before I am many days in New York. She is the wife of a Yankee lawyer. If you have not had an unpleasant telegram ere you read this you may conclude that I am safe. Or, if I have hired an assassin and disposed of the Yankee lawyer and bring home a German wife, do not be much surprised!

We amused ourselves on board when we could by playing quoits and shuffle board, but they were uninteresting games and difficult to play on a rolling and heaving deck.

While the ship was pitching so heavily during the night I went and sat with Fischer. You would have been amused to have seen us in our pyjamas bewailing the heartlessness of the Treasury in curtailing our expenses when on board ship. . . .

The temperature of the water is taken every four hours as a rule, but when ice is expected it is taken every hour or even less. The water which had been 51° had fallen at 8 a.m. to 46° and at 10 a.m. to 40°. It became very cold. Ulsters and warm things were in greatest request. Birds became more abundant. The sun appeared and cheerfulness was on the increase, but in the afternoon another very heavy swell came on and we had the prospect of another bad night – a prospect that was fully realised.

I was remarkably struck with the way in which the temperature of the air followed the temperature of the water. We could at once tell the currents we were passing through. We had touched the Gulf Stream once and doffed our great coats, but we were now on the polar stream again and we donned them once more. My bath in the morning which was the greatest luxury on board was an infallible indication of the coming weather. There is no doubt that we owe our balmy climate in England to the Gulf Stream.

Sunday, April 22nd, was ushered in with a heavy swell still, on which speedily was followed by rain and more wind, and eventually by the curse of trans-Atlantic travelling – a fog. That horrid fog – we were in it for two days. We couldn't see a ship's length before us, yet we pegged on as hard as we could pelt and in the next 24 hours made 332 miles – the fastest day's journey of all. The fog whistle – a deep drone like the lowing of 10,000 buffaloes – kept on every two or three minutes and literally murdered sleep. Once the fog lifted a little bit and there within a cable was a brig passing us at a rapid pace. One turn of our wheel would have sent us right through her. Escape from collision is a simple question of chance. The ocean is illimitable and a ship a mere mote. The probability of two motes meeting is infinitely small. Luck was with us. The safety of the Cunard line is said to be due to luck, but our American Captain on board said to me sententiously 'Luck, Sir, is leaving nothing to luck.'

We had service at 10.30. It was read by the Doctor of the ship in the saloon. I am sorry to say that it was little more than a farce. Two hymns were tried and utterly failed. The whole morning service was read except the Communion. It was a great pity. A short impressive service would have been acceptable for we were in real danger. I was very sorry that we had no icebergs. There is no doubt that we were not far from the ice. The temperature of the water showed it, but it did not come near enough for us to see it.

At noon on Monday, April, 23rd, our Lat. was 40° 58' Long. 62° 41' and distance run 313 miles. The fog had cleared away in the morning, but we were again into it in the afternoon. A lady once asked Captain Judkins – now retired from the Cunard service – if it was always foggy off the banks of Newfoundland. 'How can I tell, Madam,' he said, 'I do not live there.' Another ship of the Cunard line was confined in Halifax by a fog. An anxious and impatient passenger pointed out to the Captain that it was clear overhead. 'We do not go that way' he said.

The sensitiveness of the Americans to anything said derogatory to their country and institutions by the British press or English folks was often ludicrously exemplified on board and it gave me many opportunities to chaff and tease the Yankees. The Britishers at my end of the table were in the ascendant and we gave it to the Yankees pretty hot, but all in good part. They can stand chaff very well and retaliate with fine force. If I had only kept a diary I might have retained many smart things said by the Yankees. They maintained that 'I guess' was a quaint old English idiom retained in all its purity and that the frequent use of 'Sir' in conversation is justified by Boswell's 'Life of Johnson'.

We occasionally indulged in American notions. Cocktails for instance which is an appetiser – a substitute for sherry and bitters. A good story was told of a man who always took two cocktails, his excuse being that when he took a cocktail 'he felt like another man' and he was obliged to take another for the other man.

The fog continued all Monday night, but cleared up about sunrise. I went on deck and saw in the great distance the whole horizon marked with great masses of fog banks, and as their tops were just tipped by the rays of the rising sun they looked just like the snow capped Alps. At noon we were Lat. 40° 22' Long. 69° 57' and only 180 miles from Sandy Hook. Our run was 332 miles. For the first time the water became smooth. The cold fled and the sun came out in all his glory. Coats were off and we entered quite a different climate. All the patients came on deck and we became quite a cheerful party. Sweeps were made for the number of the pilot that would board us. The moon came out in all her loveliness and the evening turned out clear, bright and beautiful. We dissipated in the saloon upon a German bowl of punch and we danced on deck. It was a delightful evening. Just at dark we sighted the Pilot who boarded us whose number was 21. An American gentleman won £5. 5 and my German friend 35/–. He brought us newspapers and we learnt the sad war news. At 1 a.m. we passed Sandy Hook and at 2 a.m. anchored off Staten Island. Of course we were too excited to sleep and we couldn't if we wished for the cessation of the engine and the stoppage of all noise was now as unbearable as the row itself was at first. So we were up at daylight and found ourselves lying off a small Isle of Wight studded all over with Swiss Chalets and Florentine villas. We were in the Hudson River. On the other side was Long Island glorying in all the beauties of budding spring and before us was the magnificent bay of New York – a splendid almost landlocked harbour large enough to anchor all the fleets in the world. New York itself was just visible, its spires and towers filling up the landscape. How thankful we were to see it at last, and now that we were safe how little we cared for the dangers and troubles we had passed through! We landed at Jersey City at 9 a.m. after having been visited by the Quarantine Medical Officer and inspected by the Custom House gentlemen.

Thus ends my first trans-Atlantic trip. Though unpleasant as regards the weather and unprofitable as regards anything done, it was amusing as a study of life and valuable as an experience of ships, 'of they that go down to the sea in ships and occupy their business in great waters'. A ship is a perfect little world. No one can be on board for 10 days without exposing in some way or other his or her weaknesses and peculiarities. Defects cannot be kept in. In the same way good traits come to the front....

17

THE NEW WORLD

A FAIRLY crowded programme of visits to telegraph companies had been arranged for Fischer and Preece during the two months of 1877 they were to be in the United States and Canada: they expected to manage some sightseeing and, indeed, their hosts made sure that they did. Taking no more time on their first morning than needed to check in at the Fifth Avenue Hotel, they went along to the Western Union Telegraph building.

Preece noted during those first few hours that

everything partook of the motion of the ship and I found myself occasionally staggering too and fro like a drunken man.

FIFTH AVENUE HOTEL, N. Y.

His first surprise came at lunch with William Orton, President of the Company, and one of his Directors:

fancy luxuriating in strawberries and cream and munching the rich luscious banana . . . in this enormous continent the various seasons are going on the same time. . . . The south is now pouring its fruit into the North and fresh vegetables abound.

In his letters home Preece described the plan of New York City, the size of which had taken him by surprise: 'it appeared interminable'. He referred to Broadway as

a very fine street and the chief artery of the place. . . . All the shops are there and all the people . . . shop along it. . . . There are more Germans in New York than in Cologne. My informant said twice as many but I have learnt to take Yankee figures cum grano salis. German is very much spoken and lager bier gartens abound . . . most remarkable to hear the inhabitants in their buses and cars coolly discussing venality and dishonesty of their governors, aldermen and rulers. The streets are vilely paved and on my expressing surprise at this a gentleman in the car said, 'We pay for it, Sir, but the money instead of being spent in paving goes into the pockets of our Corporation.' We crossed the Hudson from Jersey City in one of their magnificent ferry steamers. . . . One of the most prominent objects was two lofty piers to support an enormous suspension bridge between New York and Brooklyn which will be the most stupendous work of the kind in the world. . . . A suspension chain or rope has been taken across but the bridge is still under construction.

Decidedly the most striking feature in New York to my professional eyes is the poles that disfigure the streets in every direction. How such an enormity can have been perpetrated is simply incredible. Hideous crooked poles carrying 20 or 30 wires are fixed down the principal streets and sometimes three different lines of poles run down the same street . . . sometimes the mass of wires crossing a street form a perfect cloud. The wires are coated with kite tails, cloth waste . . . hideous. Oh, for our British parliament to legislate here awhile.

At breakfast at nine o'clock next morning he looked at the menu and, confronted with a list of seventy items to choose from, confessed 'it was a puzzle to know what to eat' so, typically, he decided to spend the next few mornings 'attacking the list in detail and trying everything, especially if American' and started off with 'pigs' feet breaded': he pronounced coffee 'admirable' and bread 'exquisite'.

Breakfast

BROILED

Beefsteak	Tripe, plain	Pickled Tripe	Veal Cutlets
Calf's Liver	Smoked Bacon	Mutton Chops	Lamb Chops
Mutton Kidneys	Pig's Feet breaded	Ham	Pork Chops

FRIED

Pig's Feet breaded	Oysters with crumbs	Pickled Tripe
Calf's Liver	Sausages	Clams
Sausage Balls		Pork Chops

STEWED

Clams	Veal and Mutton Kidneys	Oysters
	Hashed Meat	

FISH

Fried Codfish, with pork	Salt Codfish, with cream	Hashed Fish
Broiled Salt Mackerel	Smoked Salmon	Digby Herrings.
Broiled Shad	Fried Smelts	Fish Balls

EGGS

Omelets, plain, or with parsley, onions, ham, kidneys, or cheese,
boiled, fried, scrambled or dropped

COLD MEATS

Roast Beef	Corned Beef	Tongue	Ham

POTATOES

Stewed	Lyonnaise	Fried	Baked
Fried Indian Pudding	Oatmeal Mush	Dry and Dipped Toast	
Boston Brown Bread	Muffins	Rice Cakes	
Graham Bread	Graham Rolls	Cracked Wheat	
Corn Bread	French Rolls	Hominy	
English Muffins	Buckwheat Cakes		

Coffee, Chocolate, Oolong, Green and English Breakfast Tea

BREAKFAST from 7 to 11   LUNCH from 1 to 2

DINNER from 2 to 5, and at 5½ precisely, table d'hôte.

TEA from 6 to 9   SUPPER from 9 to 12

DINNER ON SUNDAYS, 2 and 5½   BREAKFAST, 8.

HOURS FOR CHILDREN AND SERVANTS

BREAKFAST, 7   DINNER 1   TEA, 6

NO RESERVED SEATS AT BREAKFAST

Fischer and he were not surprised to find that all they needed midday
was a 'cracker' and a glass of lager beer 'until dinner at 6.30 p.m.
which is another sumptuous meal'. He had heard that Americans

rushed in to dinner, bolted their grub as quick as lightning and then
skedaddled but I have seen nothing of a sort. They are very fond of ice
and drink an enormous quantity of cold water. Iced water is put in
your bedroom at night and brought in in the morning. It is given with
every meal and after every drink. Ice is very abundant and cheap. It is
carted about in great solid blocks and deposited upon the pavement like
logs of wood, or stone.

He quickly appreciated the advantages of their decimal coinage,

calculation is very simple compared with ours; conversion to English
value very easy . . . multiply by two, knock off the last figure

to get pounds – he admitted that dividing by five would give the
same result.

Although Fischer and Preece had to spend days on end preparing
questions and transcribing notes on the organization and techniques
of the telegraph companies they visited, Preece still managed to find
the time to compile a journal of his journey in the United States and
Canada, sending home 27000 words in several instalments. Many
things caught his attention, including such incongruities as 'Take
Hobensark's worm syrup and liver pills' daubed along rocks on the
edge of Central Park with, immediately below it, 'PREPARE TO
MEET THY GOD'.

Preece saw much to admire in New York. He commented:

The New Yorkers have a rage for trotting horses and they turn out in
shoals in light-wheeled vehicles and light harnessed nags who trot at a
pace that is wonderful to see. Racing is the order of the day and the roads
are lined with loafers who smoke and lounge to watch the trotting. Collisions and rows are frequent and the police have frequently to interfere.
The police are very fine stalwart fellows in wideawake hats and light
blue uniforms and outside the park are very well mounted on fine
horses. Bobby is as much an institution in this country as he is with us. . . .
In the evening we went to a Sunday concert at Booths where singing
was interspersed with reading 'Sheridan's Ride', 'The May Queen' and
'The Charge of the Light Brigade' being very well given. Sunday here
has very much the aspect of Sunday at home . . . the congregation at

church was just what we should have seen at home and the crowd in the 5th Avenue is what we should see in Portland Place were it three miles long. The continental appearance of the place that struck me so much at first is principally confined to the lower and older portion . . . and disappears as we come to the residential and fashionable quarters. Indeed, the 5th Avenue reminds me of Glasgow and the churches are like the highly decorated Gothic structures that we find scattered about the new parts of Notting Hill and Kensington. They are principally built of a dark brown stone which has a rather sombre appearance but the architectural details are very good indeed.

Monday April 30th. We spent the whole day 'from early morn to dewy eve' in the Western Union Office ferretting out facts for ourselves. It is unfortunate for us that there is a very heavy lawsuit on just now between the two great rival companies respecting the invention and ownership of the quadruplex apparatus. Everyone's attention is occupied in this case and we have to look out for ourselves. It has however this advantage that what information we do get is reliable. I went into the court for a short time to see their practice. It differs but little from ours. The judge and counsel are not made guys of with caps and gowns but sit in plain everyday garments. Edison the inventor of the quadruplex system was the witness under examination and he remained under examination eight days. Orton told me in England of him 'that young man has a vacuum where his conscience ought to be' and he is known here as the Professor of Duplicity. The evidence that I heard implicated officials here in a way that, thank Heaven, is impossible in England. I would not for £50,000 have my name bespattered as Prescott's was. The patent is taken out in the joint name of Prescott and Edison. Edison was asked if Prescott invented any part of the apparatus. 'None, Sir.' 'Did he invent anything?' 'Never, Sir.' 'Then what has Mr. Prescott to do with it?' 'I never could have got it tried if I had not associated Prescott with it as joint inventor', and so on and so on. This is a big case and will last several months.

Our hotel is a long way from the centre of business 'down town' as they call it – nearly three miles – but the 'cars' and 'stages' enable us to ride cheaply and well. The cabs here or 'carriages' as they call them are really carriages. They are nice, commodious, comfortable and well horsed. But they are frightfully dear. They charge a dollar where in England we pay 1/–. We have only taken one as yet. . . .

The 'cars' are our favourite mode of locomotion. The regular formation of the streets of New York renders the construction and working of horse-drawn tramways easy. They insersect the city in every direction from E to W and from N to S. Several different lines pass our hotel door. We get from here to the Western Union office for 5 cents (2½d.) The cars are precisely the same as our 'Trams' and they are very much used. Indeed they are frequently crammed to suffocation especially in the evening when everybody is coming 'up town'.

The omnibuses are called 'stages'. They are roomy and comfortable but they carry no outside passengers or conductor. The driver controls the door with a long strap and each passenger has to place his own fare inside a glass box which is locked but which the driver can see. When we went in one first the driver after a little while rang a bell which we did not understand and after some time a passenger came in and relieved us from our dilemma. . . .

Sunday May 6th. I went to Brooklyn to hear Ward Beecher preach. I could not rouse Fischer. He is without exception the loudest snorer, the heaviest sleeper and the laziest fellow in the morning I have ever known. I had to breakfast at eight for it was necessary to get there early. Today happened to be a special day – May day – the commencement of a New Year. Eckert went with me and secured seats. Brooklyn is a very large place – having over 400,000 inhabitants – and because it has 233 churches it is called 'the City of Churches'. It is separated from New York by the East River which is crossed at several points by steam ferries. Ward Beecher's church is called Plymouth Church. It is a plain simple red brick building barn-like and chapel-like. Its interior is simple to a fault . . . and seats at least 2,000 people. . . . The place is filled quickly and hundreds were turned away from the doors. At the N end was a very fine organ and below it a platform upon which a high backed carved oak armchair was placed with a little octagonal table by its side carrying a magnificent basket of flowers. In the front of the platform was a reading stand decorated at its foot with arum lilies. Two other stands of flowers were on the platform. While the crowd was streaming in Beecher quietly walked to his armchair with his greatcoat on and sat down as though he were one of the congregation. He had no white tie or any garb on to distinguish him from anyone else. He was dressed in plain black frockcoat, turn down collar and black tie. He is about my own height. His light grey hair is brushed off his face and streams down his back like Scudamore's. Curiously he reminded me much of F.I.S. but his features were totally different. He has a hard bold impudent look about him, and his heavy massive jaws show him to be more an animal than an angel. There is nothing of the pastor about him – none of that piety and affection beaming from the eye that one associates with one's vicar. He looks a man of the world or an actor dressed out to play a part. I do not like him at all. The service commenced with singing the 'Te Deum' which was sung well by a choir of fifty voices. We then had an extempore prayer and a hymn. Ninety-seven persons were then publicly admitted as members of the church, all standing up and agreeing to certain covenants which Beecher read, and 65 more went through a preliminary profession of faith. Of this last batch 18 were baptised and 'named' by the reverend gentleman, each handing him a card with his other name and devoutly kneeling at his feet as he touched their foreheads with water saying '(Mary) I baptise thee in the name of the Father and of the Son and of the Holy Ghost.' The ages of these young Christians varied from 10 to 25. . . . Christening is by no means a general practice in America. They seem to have regarded it as a British institution which needed reformation or total abolition. He preached on the Signs of Heavenly Life and his principal object appeared to be to throw discredit on the description of Heaven given in the Bible. It was a very curious sermon. The Bible he said teaches through the imagination 'it never defines, it never describes by clean right lines' – 'it never gives bills of items for us to check and scrutinise'. His illustrations were quaint and peculiar, snowflakes, dandelion seeds, soap bubbles were like our ideas of heaven. 'Kings were poor weak things, at least we democrats think so.'

He once or twice raised a positive laugh. He spoke with a strong nasal twang. . . . I was disappointed with him. He is a pastoral mountebank and his sermon was dangerous twaddle.

In the evening we dined with Eckert at the Windsor. . . . We had a very good dinner and spent a very pleasant evening. Eckert is the nicest fellow . . . President of the Atlantic and Pacific Telegraph Co. – the active opponents of the Western Union Co. – and a fine specimen of a determined, energetic, self-willed American. There is very bitter feeling between the two cliques and it will require delicate management for us to keep clear of it.

I ought to add that after service in Plymouth Church we drove through the park of Brooklyn – a beautiful natural park larger and prettier than New York Park and saw all the Brooklyners parading and promenading, trotting out their trotters and airing their new spring costumes. There is a magnificent boulevard right across Long Island from Brooklyn to the Beach about five miles long, which is the drive, and a magnificent drive it is.

May 8th. We proceeded early by the 'William Orton' to Sandy Hook to examine the Marine Department. Ship signalling is quite an institution here and very extensively carried out. The two rival companies have signalling stations on Sandy Hook and each does a large business. Sandy Hook is 20 miles from New York. We should have had a very pleasant excursion if the weather had been nice but it was dull, raw and cold. Sandy Hook is the American Shoeburyness and we experienced great civility from the Ordnance folks. I fired a 160 pounder by electricity and saw the shot strike the water three miles off. Their electrical appliances for measuring velocities are very beautiful but they come from Europe. Two miles off is an automatic buoy which, as it rises and falls with the waves, compresses air within it that periodically escapes and blows a whistle with a low melancholy wail such as that which would be uttered by a Brobdignagian bull when suffering from a toothache. . . . This is a new thing and likely to be much used. . . .

Home sweet home! How my mind flies to the nursery to see the lions feed and where my young barbarians are at play. I fancy I can see you now (Sunday evening 7.30) presiding at the piano and Penny singing away at the top of her voice (with hideous grimaces) her gentle hymns while Percy pretends to accompany her and Arty breaks in a wrong key. Bo lying on the hearthrug making attention his bread and industry his butter. The worst of it is as far as my picture is concerned that it is now with you really one o'clock on Monday morning and the only hymn that is being sung is a chorus of snores in the night nursery.

May 10th. Poor Fischer who laboured under the prevailing impression that I do not love work and that it would be all leather and prunella with me has fairly put up his back today. Perhaps he had cause. A record of my day's work may be interesting. Up at 6 a.m. writing till 9 a.m. – then breakfast – 10–11 a.m. inspecting automatic fire alarm apparatus with General Shayter, Messrs. Iver and Watkins – 11 till noon with Prescott, Pope and Gerritt Smith discussing technical qualifications of staff – noon till 3 p.m. examining manufacturing and repairing shops – 3–5 p.m. examining working of duplex and quadruplex circuits in Instrument Room – 5–8 p.m. dinner etc. – 8–10.30 p.m. again in Instrument Room examining press circuits and night arrangements.

We really have not lost an hour since we have been here and I do not think Fischer has ever worked so hard in his life before. 'Look here' says he, 'you may well like it – I don't and whats more I won't.' He doesn't like my early hours at all. Few do. If it were not for them you would not hear much from me I guess (!)

May 12th. We devoted the day to an inspection of the Atlantic and Pacific Telegraph Co's head office – which we found all activity, bustle and work. Towards evening however the inevitable approached. Beef-steak and veal performed their accustomed duty. My head gave way and I went to bed about 7 p.m.

May 13th. Here was a pretty kettle of fish. I had promised to go to church with the Misses Orton and dinnerless, supperless and breakfastless with a splitting headache I went. Their church – the Church of the Apostle – is an ugly red brick building outside but a really fine copy of an old Norman church inside. Suffused with a dull light dimmed by coloured glass windows it had a very impressive and reverend effect. It was very well fitted with a homelike congregation. The reading desk, pulpit and communion table were all within the altar rails. This was the only departure from an English church. It is Episcopalian. . . . The singing was excellent . . . I was very much impressed with the way in which the clergyman – a very earnest looking real pastor – desired the thanksgivings of the congregation for the safety of the *City of Brussels* which had been announced to him just before church time. The announcement was news to the congregation and it was received with such a deep burst of sup-pressed emotion by them that the tears fairly started from my eyes. The anxiety about that ship has been most intense and this scene brought up very vividly to my mind the dangers of the deep and the thankfulness I shall experience when I enter Christchurch [the Wimbledon church near Gothic Lodge] again. We had an excellent sermon – ten words of which were worth a million of Ward Beecher's.

May 16th. I met General Shayter, on the Fire Alarm Commissioners and went with him to inspect the Fire Alarm arrangements of the City. It was a blazing hot day. Summer heat suddenly enveloped us . . . the temperature sprang up to 87° in the shade. The Fire Alarm business is wonderfully perfect. The moment a fire is spotted an alarm is raised at the corner of every street – ringing bells at a central station in such a way as to indicate the exact spot raising the alarm. The alarm is distributed from the central station to the fire stations and within a very few minutes four engines are on the spot pegging away at the fire. The same current that distributes the alarm releases the halter that holds the horses and these horses are so beautifully trained that they rush at once to their proper places at the engine and truck. At one station the alarm was raised for me. The horses were released, the men were in their places, the horses harnessed up and the driver ready to start in 8 seconds! On one occasion this same company were playing their engine upon a fire 1 minute and 40 seconds after getting the alarm. It is difficult to picture the perfect discipline and training of the men and horses or to realise the rapidity of movement which method and order aided by mechanical and electrical appliances can secure. Fortunately for us fires are rarities in London – here they are frequent. We have seen two or three in the distance and the engines gallop by frequently but we have not been near one yet. . . .

May 17th. During the day we sweltered in the Western Union building and during the evening we attended a lecture by Professor Bell on his telephone. We heard an organ distinctly that was played in New Brunswick 32 miles off, and conversed with a man there. Cyrus Field and I spoke and were answered clearly. It is a very wonderful performance and I am simply lost in amazement not so much at the performance itself as at the simplicity of the apparatus employed in producing the phenomena.

May 18th. Another blazing day which I spent at a place called Menlo Park with Edison – an ingenious electrician – experimenting and examining apparatus. He gave me for dinner *raw ham*! tea and iced water!! It is nearly 30 miles off. The railways here have no fences and they go bang through the streets of the towns. The whistles have the most horrid howls – more like an elephant's trumpet than anything else. The stations have no names and there are no porters about. Everyone has to look out for oneself. We nearly missed our station and as it was had to jump out while the train was moving. At level crossings the only notice put up is – 'Look out for locomotive' – the *up* and *down* lines are reversed as compared with ours. They also drive on the opposite side to what we do. The country we passed through was like home except that the hedges are mere wooden posts and rails. The chestnuts and lilacs are in full bloom and nature is clothed in brilliant green. I saw a few gorgeous butterflies flitting about and red and blue backed birds – what they were I do not know. Our old friend the common housefly is the only insect I have yet met of my acquaintance. He seems to be found everywhere. I got back in time to see some experiments of Bell's and succeeded about 10.30 in getting some dinner!

May 19th. Professor Bell came and breakfasted with us and we had two hours' interesting telephonic talk. I hope to bring home with me a complete set to astonish the weak nerves of the Britishers. I spent the rest of the day inspecting the out-of-door work of the W.U. with their construction superintendent. It wasn't pleasant work with the temperature above 90° and a wen on my throat. Whether it be the heat or the iced water or the change of living or anything else I cannot say but a most unpleasant tumour or abscess or both or carbuncle has come up on my neck and has caused me much trouble.

May 20th. I had to remain in all day with poultices on and in the evening called in a doctor who out with his lancet like a shot and ripped it open. The discharge relieved me muchly.

May 21st. My neck better but I had to remain in all day and was glad of it to enable me to enter up notes and write home. We start our peregrinations on Wednesday and right glad I shall be for I am sick and tired of New York which has become quite unbearable in this awful heat. We had a succession of visitors yesterday who hearing of my trouble came in to sympathise.

May 24th. We left the 5th Avenue Hotel at 8.30 and in crossing over to Jersey City in the Ferry boat we were delighted to see the British shipping displaying their bunting to celebrate the Queen's birthday. The Queen is a great favourite in America and it is wonderful to hear the enthusiastic way in which they speak of her. If she were to come over here the Americans would place a new Empire at her feet.

A very sudden change has taken place in the weather. It was quite cold. The thermometer has fallen 40°! and greatcoats were in request. The climate is very subject to these sudden changes and people have to be very careful. The gates of our ferry boat were very pretty. They were on the 'lazy tongs' principle opening and closing like the children's soldier toys. The people here speak of a train as we do of a ship. The collectors cry out 'Passengers for Philadelphia *all aboard*'. If there be an accident the train is *wrecked*.

. . . We patronized the Pullman Car and found it very comfortable. Indeed it was an express train and every car was a Pullman. There were two drawing rooms and several private rooms and smoking rooms. We could perambulate the whole train. A boy – a cheeky fellow – wandered up and down first with newspapers then with novels, after that with magazines. Anon he appeared with fresh fruit – very nice and grateful especially the bananas – then with fresh sandwiches, cigarettes and French chocolate. Finally he appeared with iced water which would have been more grateful if the weather had been hotter.

We crossed the Delaware at Trenton – famous for one of Washington's victories (how these Yankees hallow every spot that has been stained with their brothers' blood!) – and entered Pennsylvania. The line skirted the Delaware for some distance and we passed through very English scenery. To see such English fields and woods and hear such English spoken one can scarcely realise the fact that we were three thousand miles away from home. We reached Philadelphia at 12.30. We were accompanied by Van Horne, one of the W.U. General Superintendents – a dry old stick

M

but a very pleasant communicative companion. He was our guide. The General Superintendents are the great officers at the Telegraph Companies here and they unite in their persons the executive duties of Secretaries and Engineers-in-Chief. They are very much respected. There are four of them: 2 in New York, 1 in Chicago and 1 in San Francisco. . . .

Of course we did the Telegraph Offices at Philadelphia; the W.U. and the A. & P., and the Philadelphia Local Telegraph Co. Local telegraphs in America are developed to a marvellous extent – everyone seems to have a private wire and everyone seems to telegraph.

We wanted a light 'duster' or thin overcoat for travelling so we went to 'Wannamakers' a large store which was once a railway station, where everything on the face of the earth is sold and where 950 people are employed. It was a small Crystal Palace managed à la Whiteley.

May 26th. We left Philadelphia at 7.30 a.m. – much to Fischer's disgust. . . . I do not like these railway cars. There is as much difference between them as there is between an omnibus and a private carriage. You cannot rest yourself to sleep. If the car is full you are very crowded. . . . Railway working is very strange – there are no signals – the stations have no names – no bell rings to announce departure, the guard carries no whistle. The engine emits forth tremendous clouds of smoke from soft coal. Our conductor was an extremely polite respectable old gentleman who acted more as the captain of a ship than the guard of a train. He shook hands with most of the passengers as they came in and seemed on pretty familiar terms with all. At Newark we entered Maryland. We were now in the Slave States and darkies began to multiply. The country became uncultivated but we passed through woods where wild flowers, ferns and other plants were numerous . . . we crossed the Susquehannah which here falls into Chesapeake Bay, a magnificent inlet of the sea which we skirted until we reached Baltimore which we did at 12.30 p.m. – entering the town down one of the main streets. We commenced with our settled plan of seeing the Telegraph Offices first. . . . We left Baltimore at 8.15 and arrived at Washington pretty well tired out at 9.30. . . . As we drove to Willard's Hotel the Capitol shone beautifully in the bright moonlight – looking grand and picturesque. . . .

May 29th. We were up at 5.45 a.m. to prepare for a long journey to Cincinnati – which we should not reach utill 5.30 the next morning! These distances are tremendous and far exceed one's conception of distances at home. Indeed the time consumed in travelling will materially shorten our proposed journey. Americans travel mostly by night and hey have every inducement to do so. All express trains run by night and they are provided with magnificent sleeping cars. . . . We were accompanied by Mr. Stewart the Superintendent of the Baltimore and Ohio Railway. . . . We passed through a country rich in reminiscences of the Great War. Harper's Ferry where John Brown was captured and hung. The Shenandoah Valley made famous by Stonewall Jackson. Bridges torn down and never rebuilt. Houses still loop-holed or shelled out. Churches demolished and factories still in the dilapidated state the war left them. At Harper's Ferry we had the most graphic description of the capture of John Brown from the mouth of a railwayman who was present. 'Wall – you know' he said, 'I was standing just here when Colonel Lee (afterwards General Lee) he came round that air corner with national troops at the double and then John Brown and his men wented themselves in that air store place – which I guess we still call John Brown's fort – Lee – he stands afore his men you know and says "Men not a shot – we must not kill our countrymen". Well you know they took a long ladder and they ran it up agin that air door twice, and at the second bout they busted it and rushed in. John Brown's men fired and you know they shot one man in the eye and another in the arm and they fought like devils. The officers you know tried to restrain the man but Lor bless you it war no use. Several was killed you know. One man jumped over this wall into the river and swam to that island and there for two hours they were popping at him as they would at a dog afore they killed him. Another man you know swam under that air bridge and it war a long time afore they killed him. All taken and a good job too' – and so he went on telling me all about it in the most interesting way. . . .

Perhaps with a little experience and with tired limbs one might enjoy the comforts of a sleeping car . . . but with the strangeness and novelty of our position sleep was banished. The horrid dull bray of the whistle . . . the lurid flames of forest fires – the ceaseless roar of the rattling wheels and the persistent shaking of a poor permanent way made the night a very uncomfortable one and we were thankful to reach Cincinnati at 5.30.

Our hotel was the Grand Hotel and conducted on the true American principle. The hall is surrounded by various establishments useful to the traveller. There is the hair cutter to cut and brush your hair and shampoo you. The tailor to mend your clothes or supply you with new ones. The tobaconist to supply you with weed to smoke or to chew. The railway ticket office to supply you with tickets or register your luggage. The telegraph offices – for both rivals are in nearly every large hotel – to flash away your wants. The bookstall to supply you with stationery, books or papers. The druggist to supply you with medicine or with scent. The bar to supply you with drink. Indeed as you have to look after yourself for everything the task is made as light as possible by these numerous conveniences at your feet.

Cincinnati is *quite a big* manufacturing place and looks as you approach it not unlike Sheffield. We thoroughly inspected the Telegraph Offices and, there being some work going on, we thoroughly inspected the lines. I told the W.U. Superintendent that I was glad I had lived long enough and travelled so far to see how many kites could deposit their strings and tails on the wires. It was a wonderful sight. In one street there were literally thousands. They cannot get them off. Burning is dangerous. They have to submit. . . . Of course Cincinnati has its park but it is principally famous for its breweries. We went over one where they consume 180 tons of ice every week. . . . The Ohio is crossed here by a magnificent suspension bridge said to be the longest in the world. I crossed into Kentucky and saw from it a splendid sunset and several of the great quaint river steamers either departing or returning. It is a source of great regret that we are unable to take a trip down the Ohio or on the Mississippi but circumstances have made it impossible. We should have to stop a year here to see all we want to see.

May 31st. We had to rise – to Fischer's great disgust – at 6 a.m. and we left for Chicago at 8 a.m. The refreshment stalls at stations are very similar to ours and certainly as bad – oranges, stale buns and cakes in glass cases, dirty bottles arranged in rows . . . cigars in seedy boxes and so on, strew the shelves and counters. . . .

And here we are in Chicago – the Ultima Thule of our journey. . . .

June 1st. Immediately after breakfast we went to the W.U. office and presented our credentials to General Stager, Vice-President and General Superintendent of the Company. . . . Stager is a pleasant genial charming fellow. He received us most warmly. He introduced us to everyone, took us all over the building, and then drove us about the city. He was present during the Great Fire [of October 1871 when much of the city was destroyed] and showed us its course and extent. There are still traces of it left but generally upon its ashes have sprung up the most magnificent city in the United States.

June 2nd. I spent the whole day with Professor Elisha Gray examining his telephone – a very remarkable instrument but not so wonderful as Bell's though more promising as a practical working apparatus.

June 3rd. Sunday. I am sorry to say that I didn't go to church but having a great deal of writing to do both of us stopped in and wrote. We had an early dinner at the Stagers who has a wife and a small family of two daughters – grown up, both nice looking and very agreeable. The one plays the piano wonderfully – reading perfectly at sight – the other doesn't play but makes up for it with her tongue. Callers called in, in the afternoon – amongst the rest the Belle of Chicago Miss Bickford. Such a beauty – my stars! And such a chatterbox my eyes! . . .

June 4th. I spent the whole morning in examining the Western Union Manufacturing Company manufactory and in the afternoon went through the store and supply department. . . .

June 5th. The Baltimore and Ohio railway is not a favourite railway in Chicago. It is considered the very worst in America. The Chics did not at all like my rapturous approval of the B. & O. road so Mr. Pullman (the Pullman car originator) brought out a magnificent new hotel and drawing room car and with a few friends took up a trip along the lakeshore to Milwaukee. In order to counteract the effects of the Philadelphia and Frederick ladies upon us Miss Stager was detailed to Fischer and the Belle of belles Miss Bickford to me! My eye and Betty Martin! Here was an attack! To defend oneself for six or seven hours against all Chicago. Of course I gave in at once and acknowledged that however nice the B. & O. road was that to Milwaukee was much nicer, and however beautiful the Maryland beauties were those of Illinois were much more beautiful. This was cowardly but who could withstand such an onslaught. . . .

We spent three hours in Milwaukee where we met . . . the officers of the North Western Telegraph Company – the third large telegraph company of the United States – the ladies making calls and we attending to our business.

June 7th was spent in calls and saying goodbye, but in the morning early – too early for Fischer – I went with Stager and a party of doctors to see the stockyards where they kill and cure 1,500,000 hogs every year. It was a wonderful but sickening sight. Hogs were being killed at the rate of three per minute and in three minutes they were cut up and ready for curing! I found a cocktail a very necessary antidote to the horrors of the morning. . . .

On leaving Chicago we skirted the lake for some distance which lay before us like a calm and beautiful sea. As we were to pass a whole night and the greater part of the day in the train we secured two berths in the sleeping car. This is the favourite through line to New York and there were four sleeping cars on the train. From Chicago to Detroit we pass through Michigan by the Michigan Central Railway, at Detroit we enter Canada and proceed by the Great Western Railway to Niagara. From

Niagara the train proceeds by the Erie Railway to New York. Between Chicago and Detroit we had supper in a sumptuous dining car. . . .

June 8th. We crossed into Canada by a ferry about 4 o'clock in the morning at Detroit. The whole train was taken over the river St. John, about one mile wide. . . .

At last we have found a railway protected with signals. The Great Western has distant signals – semaphores – the first we have seen.

It was amusing to see the piles and piles of wood heaped up at the stations for the use of the locomotives. The freedom and independence of the Conductors are also striking. They are the biggest swells on the train. Our lordly swell beckoned to me from one carriage to another. I thought there was something wrong. 'Have you this man's ticket' said he, pointing to Fischer. I had, and I showed it him meekly.

June 10th was devoted to writing and to an examination of the falls from every point of view on the Canadian side.

. . . Hucker, the Manager of [an important telegraph repeating station at] Buffalo [22 miles off] came over to see us and he used an expression which is common. Speaking of his position as a translating station he said, 'We get abused right straight along.' The birds twitter about here quite beautifully and the fireflies are very pretty. . . . Ferns are very scarce. I have gathered one and mean to try and bring it home but I fear it is a hopeless task. The robin here is as big as a thrush and quite a different bird to ours. It has however the same red breast which is all it has in common.

Our hotel is an extremely comfortable one and reminds me very much of the George, Menai Bridge. Indeed the whole place reminds me very much of that locality. And now farewell Niagara! You are very grand and very beautiful. Nature has been very kind to you but man spoilt you by making too much of you as indeed he does with most of his pets.

. . . We left Niagara at 10.30 a.m. passing between the two ports that guard the river within half a mile of each other, the one American and the other British. The scenery about was an amphitheatre of wooded hills and productive vales. . . . Our steamer was a pleasant passage of $2\frac{1}{2}$ hours across Lake Ontario. . . . We exhausted the Chief Telegraph Office of the Montreal Telegraph Co. – the largest Company in Canada and their Superintendent Mr. Dwight – a charming fellow – guided us about the place. Of course we were taken to the park – Canada has parks! – to the Law Hall, the University, the School and other places. The school is a wonderful establishment – a South Kensington Museum in miniature – where objects or art in painting, statuary, etc., are bought and copied simply to educate by eye. Education here is very good and very cheap. Two dollars a month would educate the son of a gentleman. I wish they would bring Toronto to England.

June 12th. We left Toronto at 7 p.m. by train for Kingston – a town at the end of the Lake and the commencement of the river St. Lawrence. It was a very great success to get Fischer to travel by night. It was the result of false information; we had hoped to have slept at Kingston but we did not arrive there till 2 a.m. and our steamer arrived at 3.30 a.m.! We were left on the wharf high and dry for an hour and a half and we had the pleasure of seeing night fade into day, Aurora gently trip into existence, old Sol peer above the horizon and all the awakening of the 'busy hum of incense breathing morn'. The novelty of the scene made Fischer quite chirpy. . . . Our steamer – the *Spartan* – a regular river steamer of the American pattern and a floating hotel left at 5 a.m. We couldn't get any berths on board – it was so full. . . . Breakfast at 7 a.m. seemed to clear my brain for though I had not slept a wink I felt as fresh as a daisy. There was a very pretty effect of colour on the water which I could not account for at all so I asked a Western Yankee standing by my side if he could account for it. 'No Sir' he said, 'I cannot but I have laid up a heap of thinking about it', meaning evidently that it had puzzled him as much as me.

. . . We reached Lachine where the steamer stopped at 6.15 and got to Montreal by train at 7 p.m. We passed only one raft of timber – it was too late for them. They come down earlier in the year, but it was a very interesting sight. The men who have charge of these rafts build a hut on the raft where they live while descending the river. That trip down the river was the cheapest trip I think I have ever had. We travelled 172 miles and had two excellent meals, breakfast and dinner for five dollars. Hotel touting in Montreal is driven to a system and a nuisance. Five men run on these boats every day and pester the passengers with their cards and their touts. It costs one hotel – the St. Lawrence Hall – 1,500 dollars a month to keep up this game for it involves the employment of three men.

. . . We spent a very pleasant day with the officials of the Montreal Telegraph Co., who after showing us all we wanted to see, lunched us at the club, drove us about the town and suburbs and gave us a game of whist in the evening.

. . . Montreal is very well protected with a fire alarm system. We were fortunate enough to hear an alarm raised and to follow the whole proceedings even to the victory over the fire. It was intensely exciting. A fire broke out in the upper storey of a house in the principal street (St. Jacques) and within two minutes of the discovery men and hose were on the spot. There are no engines in Montreal. The water service is so good and the pressure so great that it is only necessary to attach a hose to be able to direct the water anywhere. Several hoses arrived and in less than half an hour the fire was mastered – not however without destroying the roof.

We left Montreal at 7 p.m. by steamer for Quebec. . . . It was very crowded but we had taken the precaution early in the day to secure 'State Rooms'. The scene at departure was like that at Liverpool on the departure of the Cunard or at Southampton on the departure of the P. & O. boat. . . . The Montreal people are very hospitable and what with champagne and cocktails Fischer was very merry. F. is very amusing when in this condition. It develops itself in music of a demonstrative character. The German [Fischer was born in Hanover in 1833 and in 1856 joined the E.T.C.] when inebriated becomes musical, the Frenchman fantastical, the Britisher combative, the Irishman argumentative and so on. F. wasn't drunk but he was amusing. After a very brilliant sunset and a good long peep at the populous and pretty banks of the river we turned in early.

June 16th. We left Quebec at 8.30 p.m. crossing the Ferry to Point Levi where we took the Pullman sleeping car on the Grand Trunk Railway. Anything more beautiful than the illuminated rock is this lovely moonlight I have never seen. We kissed farewell to Quebec and the St. Lawrence and snuggled into our berths but at 2 a.m. we were roused up at Richmond to change cars and at 5 a.m. we were again turned out to be inspected by the U.S. Custom House for at Island Pond we crossed the frontier and took breakfast.

We were kept at Island Pond two hours! Poor Fischer was disconsolate. 'I want rest' said he, 'Three blessed nights this week have we been out of bed and I want rest.' I regard this week as a great triumph. By travelling three nights we have gained three days . . . at 1 p.m. we reached Portland the capital of Maine. It is a law now in Maine that no intoxicating liquor can be sold and no one for love or money can get beer, or wine or spirits. Fischer was disconsolate. The loss of three nights rest and no beer was too much. We searched Portland through and all we could get was ice cream – ice cream soda, Ottawa beer (a sweet pop) – ginger ale – syrup drinks – tea – coffee, etc. etc. We were glad to leave Portland which we did at 5.30 p.m. . . . to reach Portsmouth at 7.30 p.m.

June 17th. Portsmouth is one of the oldest towns in the States and is more like an English town than anything I have yet seen though I do not know any English town so pretty. Its streets are all lined with trees and nearly every house except in the business streets is detached in its own garden which for shade are kept full of trees. The houses are pretty English villas built of wood. They are painted white, while the venetian blinds are painted green and these colours mixed with the green leaves give the place a picturesque cooling effect. It is the only seaport of New Hampshire but its sea business is small. It is a naval station and they build ships here. It is really three miles from the sea on the Piscataqua River. . . . There are 9 churches and chapels and two daily and three weekly newspapers! Why Carnarvon, a town of the same size can scarcely keep one weekly going. Newspaper printing is a mania in America and few towns however small are without their dailies. The *New Hampshire Gazette* published here is the oldest American paper continuously published. It was started in 1756.

I made an early dinner with the Stearns and met Stearns's youngest brother and Mrs. Stearns's mother – Mrs. Edmonds. I spent a very pleasant afternoon indeed. In the cool of the evening we wandered about exploring the quaint and pretty streets and wondering where all the pretty girls came from. There appeared to be ten girls for every man here. I heard an excellent sermon and some capital music at a church close by. After the quietest day of rest since I left home we retired early feeling thoroughly restored. How little I ever contemplated dining in Stearns's own house yet now that I am here it appears perfectly natural that I should make an afternoon call. One of the strangest features of this journey is that though at times I am very homesick I never feel separated by over three thousand miles. The cable annihilates the idea of space. . . .

June 19th. . . . We left Portsmouth at 7.23 p.m. for Boston. It is a very amusing at these American stations to find no porters at all. Everyone has to carry and attend to his own luggage. The engine rings its own bell at entering and departing from the 'depot'. . . .

June 20th. We commenced with our usual practice of pursuing business first and pleasure afterwards by inspecting the Telegraph Companies' Offices. . . . We went over to Bunkers Hill and ascended the monument – at least *I* did.

June 21st. After inspecting the Fire Alarm telegraph – considered the best in the country, I spent the greater part of the day with Bell in his laboratory experimenting and examining telephones. We left at 6 p.m.

Our visit to Boston was a great deal too short and too hurried . . . it is a grand old city magnificently situated and full of interesting places. . . .

We arrived at Fall River at 7.30 where we joined the steamer *Bristol* for New York. We had taken tickets and state room before starting. A man in the train exchanged our tickets for the keys of our state rooms so that we had nothing to do but to carry our own luggage and walk straight into our cabins. The *Bristol* is the most magnificent river steamer in America. It can and has carried 2,500 people. It frequently in the summer takes 1,500. It is quite palatial. Such saloons and galleries and decks. It is in fact simply a gorgeous floating hotel. We had however a very nasty night in it. It was a very thick fog. The horrid fog whistle gave out its hideous and depressing sounds until the early hours. It also thundered and lightninged above – a very strange combination with a fog. By the bye they make their own gas on board so that we were to have capital light in our cabins which was a comfort. . . . We passed Hell Gate and then down by the East River round the Battery to the Hudson side of the city where we landed at 7 a.m. We were glad to see New York again. It was like coming home.

The Cunard liner R.M.S. *Bothnia* left New York for Liverpool on Wednesday, 4th July, completing the 3112-mile voyage in ten days in markedly contrasting conditions to those of the outward journey; Preece recorded 'a very pleasant voyage'. His name is not to be found in the list of 250 saloon passengers because of a printer's error, but in a four-page souvenir the *Bothnia Illustrated Times* (vol. 1 No. 1, mid-ocean July 11th 1877) is recorded under 'The Entertainments' that 'Besides the volunteer singing on deck, which has become quite spirited of late, two capital entertainments have been given in the large saloon, which has, on each occasion, been crowded to its full capacity . . . Mr. W. H. Preece drew shouts of laughter by a stump speech' and is named among the eleven passengers who formed a chorus of male voices on both occasions. 'A chorus of twenty ladies sang very sweetly "A Cup of Tea" from *Genevieve de Brabant*.' One item, the reading of the *Bothnia Illustrated News* by its editor, which included such items as 'Special cable news by our special Horse-Marine Diver' on the war between Russia and Turkey, led to him being persuaded to have copies printed in England to be sent to his auditors.

Fischer and Preece found themselves sharing a table with two young men and four young ladies from New Orleans on their first visit to Europe. Preece invited all to his home and arranged a day's trip to Salisbury to show them his beloved cathedral and also take them around Stonehenge and Old Sarum. One of the men after his return home told one of the girls that it had been the most enjoyable day of his life. Preece's informant, commenting on their chatter about their holiday in Europe, added, 'You will owe your immortality not to signals or batteries but to that far more powerful electric machine – women's tongues.' The youngest of the party, Miss 'Lollipop' Carroll, aged eighteen, wrote several letters, in one of which she particularly praised Percy and in another 'Bo', confessed to weighing 134 pounds and having to figure as a bridesmaid at weddings then taking place in New Orleans. She thanked him for a copy of his textbook on telegraphy and objected, in a letter in January 1878, to a sentence in his last letter to her – 'I write this to prevent the possibility of your having any excuse to write again.' Preece felt that the gap in his life caused by the death of Agnes could never be filled and although he greatly enjoyed the company of attractive young women he was unable to contemplate seriously again forming such a close relationship as marriage.

*   *   *

A social event which involved Preece within two months of his return arose from a visit to Europe by the two daughters of General Stager of Chicago and their friends Miss Bickford and Miss Wadsworth. A copy of the menu of their dinner in the upper gallery of the Grand Salon of the Holborn Restaurant for 5th September lists a seven-course *table d'hôte* including a choice between salmon and whitebait for the fish course, and rissoles of turtle and mushrooms in the entrées: total cost three shillings and sixpence. A band under Musical Director J. Ripley played a programme of thirteen items which finished with a galop *Dover Express* by T. Browne, from six till nine o'clock. Preece and Fischer called upon two of their colleagues, Bowen and Fisher, to make up the party.

A favourite amusement of the time, at which F. E. Baines was notoriously adept, was punning, and they perpetrated a few that evening. Perhaps with the pattern of Pickwick in mind they called themselves the 'Holborn Club' and elected Bowen as secretary. He

The Holborn Restaurant
THE GRAND SALON ‡ 218, HIGH HOLBORN

THE LADIES SALON.
THE DUKES SALON.

LINCOLNS INN BUFFET. THE GRILL ROOM.

TABLE D'HÔTE FROM 6 TO 8.30. P.M. Price 3/6

Menû for Wednesday, September 5, 1877.

POTAGES.	**SOUPS.**
Purée de Tomate.	Purée of Tomato.
Printanière.	Spring.
POISSONS.	**FISH.**
Saumon, Sauce Hollandaise.	Salmon, Dutch Sauce.
Blanchaille.	Whitebait.
ENTREES.	**ENTREES.**
Rissoles de Tortue aux Champignons.	Rissoles of Turtle with Mushrooms.
Poulet à la Demidoff.	Chickens à la Demidoff.
RÔTI.	**ROAST.**
Hanche de Mouton.	Haunch of Mutton.
ENTREMETS.	**SWEETS.**
Poires à la Condé.	Pears à la Condé.
Gelée au Rhum.	Punch Jelly.
Genoise Glacé.	Genoise Glacé.
GLACES.	**ICES.**
Citron. Café.	Lemon. Coffee.
Fromage. Salade à la Française.	Cheese. French Salad.
DESSERT.	**DESSERT.**
Raisins. Melons. Poires. Prunes.	Grapes. Melons. Pears. Plums.
Amandes et Raisins. Noisettes.	Almonds and Raisins. Cobnuts.
Olives.	Olives.

Single places or separate tables for parties of three or more may be previously engaged and will be reserved until Seven o'Clock.

The dining Salons may be reached without passing the Public Buffet either by the separate entrance in the Holborn Lobby or the Lincolns Inn Entrance in Little Queen Street.

CLOAK ROOMS FOR LADIES AND GENTLEMEN.

Gentlemen are respectfully requested to examine their Bills before paying the waiter.

sent a record of the meeting on copies of the menu to the four visitors:

At a meeting of the Holborn Club held in London on September 5th 1877 the following toasts were offered: – Miss Bickford by Mr. Preece, Miss Louise Stager by Mr. Bowen, Miss Annie Stager by Mr. Fischer, Miss Wadsworth by Mr. Fisher.

In proposing this toast Mr. Preece suggested that Phidias was an ass for not going to Chicago for his model of Venus. He might then not only have picked one but Bick'd four dears. Mr. Fisher also suggested that Phidias . . . would have seen something Wadsworth all the rest of creation. Mr. Bowen maintained that Phidias would have to stride a Stager two in another direction. Mr. Fis-c-her thinks that Phidias would have been in no difficulty, for while any Stager would have done for him only Annie Stager would have done for H.C.F.

Wines, we may be sure, were as choice as, and relatively no more costly than, the *table d'hôte*.

18

THE TALKING TELEGRAPH

A TELEPHONE was first seen in the United Kingdom when Sir William Thomson obtained one, made by Graham Bell, from the Centennial Exhibition at Philadelphia in 1876 to exhibit it at a British Association meeting in Glasgow that September. He described it as 'the greatest by far of the marvels of the electric telegraph' but was quite unable to operate it: it had, unfortunately, been slightly damaged in transit. As we have seen, Preece obtained, when in America the following year, a pair of improved telephones by Bell (of the 'butter-stamp' design, similar to the receiver of the 'candlestick' telephone in general use for the first few decades of the present century) and he gave a practical demonstration of their use at a British Association meeting in Plymouth in September. 1877

*   *   *

Culley retired from the Telegraph Department in February 1878, at the age of sixty, on grounds of ill-health. Someone had to be appointed in his stead. Telegraph stores and factories were formed into a second department and W. H. Winter, Assistant Engineer-in-Chief, was appointed its Controller. Two men stood out from their fellow Divisional Engineers for consideration for Culley's post and, in the prevailing atmosphere of stringent economy, Edward Graves – 'economy was his watchword' – was preferred to Preece who was more interested in developing new services. Since Graves, whom the E.T.C. had appointed Superintendent when only twenty-two years of age, was ten days younger than Preece, manifestly if they stayed in the Post Office Preece could hope for no more than the post of Assistant to Graves, for not till fifty-five years later was an engineering officer considered for appointment to the administrative department of the Post Office. But Preece was on the best of terms with Graves; not a man to conjure up grievances, he was pleased, and more than a little proud, to be allowed to transfer the title of 'Electrician' from the Submarine Superintendent's post to add to that of his new post of Assistant Engineer-in-Chief. Events worked out quite happily for him and gave a wide scope for his interests and energies since his responsibility embraced engineering routines, testing, technical efficiency, and 'experimenting'. Whilst he had, within the confines of a limited expenditure, a free hand in those matters it was, none the less, incumbent on him when speaking in an official capacity to reflect the policy of strict economy to which the Telegraph Department had been committed.

The Treasury had unremittingly increased pressure on the Post Office, following Scudamore's inflation of capital costs, to reduce expenditure. My Lords called for staff cuts and a proportion of those officers taken over from the private companies lost their jobs. George E. Preece was one whose post was abolished: he devoted his efforts thereafter to cable designing, eventually becoming technical adviser to W. T. Glover's cable manufacturing company in Manchester.

* * *

The Secretary of the Post Office had noticed references in the press to the 'telephone' and had, early in 1877, asked Culley for a report on it. Culley submitted a description of the harmonic telegraph, on which Graham Bell had been working, in which a number of tuning forks respond to particular transmitted frequencies. He reported it as not in practical use: it had been experimented with in Sweden as well as in America. He recalled that Cromwell F. Varley had patented something of the kind. He promised that Preece and Fischer would inquire into the matter during their visit to the States.

On his return from America Preece recommended that the Post Office should secure the use of Bell's telephone together with the right to manufacture it. He added,

although in its present form the telephone is not generally applicable, there are a great many instances where wires are carried . . . where the instrument is perfectly practicable, and it will be certainly very generally demanded by our [private wire] renters. More than that it will lead to a great accession of private business.

Preece was thinking of telegraphic inter-communication, using Wheatstone ABC telegraphs, by private subscribers through a central office switchboard, first established in Newcastle in 1864 by the Universal Private Telegraph Company, which at its central office also received telegrams from other companies to transmit to its renters. He continued:

It is of course inconvenient to have an instrument that is not generally applicable, but, as you know I regard the difficulty in using it now as one that thought and experiment will remove.

Here Graves, through whom he was submitting his minute, interpolated:

Yes, but we must not take this for granted.

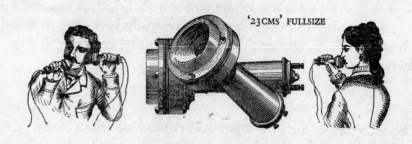

'23 CMS' FULLSIZE

THE TELEPHONE.

The Articulating or Speaking Telephone of Professor Alexander Graham Bell has now reached a point of simplicity, perfection, and reliability such as give it undoubted pre-eminence over all other means for telegraphic communication. Its employment necessitates no skilled labour, no technical education, and no special attention on the part of any one individual. Persons using it can converse miles apart, in precisely the same manner as though they were in the same room. It needs but a wire between the two points of communication, though ten or twenty miles apart, with a Telephone or a pair of Telephones—one to receive, the other to transmit, the sound of the voice—to hold communication in any language. It conveys the quality of the voice so that the person speaking can be recognised at the other end of the line. It can be used for any purpose and in any position—for mines, marine exploration, military evolutions, and numerous other purposes other than the hitherto recognised field for Telegraphy; between the manufacturer's office and his factory; between all large commercial houses and their branches; between central and branch banks; in ship-building yards, and factories of every description; in fact wherever conversation is required between the principal and

[1] P.T.O.

First Bell telephone advertisement in the United Kingdom (1877)

Preece recommended

that we enter into arrangements with Professor Bell as early as possible, paying him for its use a royalty upon each apparatus used . . . I find that in the United States – where they cannot make a sufficient number of instruments to meet the demand – that they are supplying them on hire . . . at $50 per double set, or say £5 per annum for each instrument.

He thought that Bell might be prepared to negotiate for considerably less than that sum. Graves's covering endorsement was, predictably, less than enthusiastic. He wrote:

An inventor, having started a valuable idea, finds himself limited in carrying it out . . . by various practical difficulties. He asks us to help him. If we do so . . . we must get some decided advantage for our assistance. Otherwise . . . we set a precedent which will ultimately very much embarrass us. If we do not adopt the same course to others as we now adopt to Mr. Bell, we shall make a grievance, and a Government Department cannot afford to show favouritism. We shall guard against this if Mr. Bell gives us some considerable and decided concessions that will justify our exceptional action.

2

his agents or employés, or between the superintendent and his leading men, there the Telephone will find place and employment. Ordinarily it may be regarded as a speaking-tube attended with all the advantages of telegraphic communication.

TERMS.

	Purchase.			Rental.		
	£	s.	d.	£	s.	d.
For a set of Instruments for short circuits	25	0	0 or	5	0	0 per annum.
For a set of Instruments for long circuits	35	0	0 ,,	10	0	0 ,,

Each set of Instruments consists of a pair of Telephones and a Call Bell—the equipment for one end of a communication.

Where required for Domestic purposes, Hotel, Factory, or other indoor uses, special rates will be quoted on application, stating the purposes for which the apparatus is required, with the distance between the points of communication.

A simple form of Agreement which those employing the instrument will be required to sign will be provided. In cases of rental this Agreement will be determinable at three months' notice, or, failing such notice, on the payment of such sum as the Agency may agree to accept in lieu thereof. The rental is in all cases payable in advance. The purchase-money paid for any set of instruments secures a Licence to use them only for the purposes specified within the Licence. The rental charge covers the cost of maintenance of the instruments hired. In either case the amounts specified cover all Royalty charges.

Further particulars and estimates may be obtained on application to

Lord John Manners, Postmaster-General, sought in February 1878 Treasury authority for a tentative agreement Graves had reached with Bell's agent, of 40 per cent discount on advertised charges. Manners pointed out that he would be compelled to adopt the telephone for private wire purposes under pressure from renters of ABC telegraphs. He recalled that with Mr Stearns's telegraph the principle had been recognized that a patentee should be fairly remunerated if the Crown availed itself of his invention. Bell would be treated fairly and the Post Office would make a profit in meeting the requirements of private-wire renters. Six months later the Lords of the Treasury notified their approval.

In the meantime, the Telephone Company Limited had been registered to acquire and work Bell's patent. The Edison Telephone Company was registered fourteen months later, August 1879, to work Thomas A. Edison's telephone patents. Next month Lord John Manners pointed out to the Treasury that the Law Officers of the Crown were of opinion that telegrams, as defined by the Telegraphs Acts, would include messages transmitted by means of telephones, but he considered undesirable to put a stop 'to what may, perhaps, prove to be a public convenience', and thought that either the Post Office should provide telephones for its private wire systems or should allow the companies to proceed under a licence.

The two companies intimated, in October 1879, that they did not propose to apply for licences. During that summer each company had begun to operate a central exchange in the City of London. Their gangs of workmen ran wires over its roofs, put faults on each other's lines, and scrimmaged high above the streets when running wires near each other. The Edison company applied for an injunction against the Bell company for infringement of patent rights. To bring their mutually damaging rivalry to an end, the companies amalgamated, in June 1880, as the United Telephone Company Limited.

*   *   *

The Post Office entered a plea in November 1879 against the Edison company which was heard 29 November–22 December 1880, and ended with a judgement eight days later when Mr Baron Pollock and Mr Justice Stephen ruled that the telephone was a telegraph within the meaning of the Telegraph Acts of 1869 and 1873, and that conversations held through the telephone were infringements of the Postmaster-General's exclusive privilege. The Attorney-General had pointed out that the Crown did not wish to stop improvements resulting from increased application of scientific knowledge nor to prevent the telephone companies doing anything that telegraphic communcation would be allowed to under licence, and that, since the decision which gave the Crown the right to use patents, patentees were always liberally treated: he had done no more than was necessary for the protection of the revenue.

Mr Justice Stephen, in concluding the case, expressed his opinion that

everybody would . . . wish to treat the Defendant Company as having been the proprietors of a most beautiful invention, and it has been used entirely to the public advantage to the extent that they have done . . . all one can say is, that they have simply taken a wrong view of the construction of the Act of Parliament.

Preece, in addition to assisting the Attorney-General by demonstrating the operation of a Morse sounder and other telegraphs, had submitted two affidavits which were examined in detail during the hearing. He had verified Edison's patent specifications of 1877–8, described a switching system at a central exchange, and quoted a definition by Sir William Thomson in a lecture at the Royal Institution in 1873 of what was essentially involved in every telegraph. Thomson submitted for the defence that at the time he

had not the slightest idea that an electric telegraph wire would ever be used for the transmission of speech.

Nor would he agree that a telephone invented by Phillipp Reis about 1860 could transmit articulate speech.

Preece had described the development of telegraphs from 1837 and referred to telephones, including Elisha Gray's, that he had examined in the United States. He added:

With respect to any supposed identity between the transmission of sound through the air, and the transmission of electric currents through or along a wire, I say that I do not believe that any such identity can be proved or reasonably stated to exist . . . while we know the laws governing and the nature of the process which takes place during the transmission of sound through air, we really know nothing as to the nature and mode of operation of electric currents or waves or impulses or tremors . . . it is a mistake to say that sound is transmitted along a wire between the sending and receiving stations when the telephone inventions of Professor Bell or Mr Edison are used.

For the Defence Mr Webster quoted from a textbook on telegraphy by Preece and Sivewright, in which he considered telegraphy had been well defined as

the art of conveying to distant points the first elements of written language – either letters or numerals – by certain preconcerted signals.

His colleague, Mr Benjamin, quoted the Act of 1862:

the term 'telegraph' means a wire or wires used for the purpose of telegraphic communication.

The defence later referred to 'an interesting and most eloquent account' given by Preece, in February 1878, at the Royal Institution, of Graham Bell's telephone. The Attorney-General objected to that reference on the grounds that witnesses were not to be cross-examined. Mr Benjamin said that the Attorney-General was greatly mistaken in supposing that he desired,

in the slightest degree, to throw any discredit on the evidence of Mr Preece.

His purpose was to show

that Mr Preece himself used the popular language in relation to what a telephone was at that time, just as it is used by us in our affidavits, and he described it as we described it, as a reproduction of speech at the receiving end of speech sent from the transmitting end,

and went on to read Preece's Royal Institution paper as part of his own speech.

Mr Justice Stephen commented:

that appears to me to vary very slightly in words, and not a jot in meaning, from what he [Preece] swears in his affidavit.

As for the quality of the sound emitted from those telephones, when Mr Baron Pollock asked if the voice of a speaker over the telephone could be distinguished, the Attorney-General said that he might distinguish

a rough voice from a tenor voice, but it comes out more like a voice you would hear in a Punch and Judy.

*   *   *

Henry Fawcett, who succeeded Lord John Manners as Postmaster-General in March 1880, wrote to the Treasury in December that he had good reason for his belief that the object of the telephone companies was not so much to meet a public want in a lasting and efficient manner as to establish a system which they might later compel the Government to purchase. The companies were straining every nerve to give their business an appearance of success by carrying their wires to the premises of people who had never asked for them, and offering a year's use of the system free. They were erecting those wires without regard to private rights or public safety, and in a manner which would, sooner or later, cause a public outcry. Were the Post Office to content itself with granting licences the day would come when a public agitation that the companies be bought out would be organized. That the State alone could suffice to put every community in the country on an equality would then be urged, as would the argument that the State alone could be certain of securing necessary wayleaves and connections with the general telegraph network. Further, that, as the companies had been the means of establishing and popularizing telephones, justice required that the State should purchase their undertakings. He doubted if it would be possible to resist such an agitation:

I need scarcely point out to your Lordships what would be involved in the alternative. It would not merely be a case of purchasing the plant of the companies. Regard would have to be had to their inflated capital, and an allowance would probably have to be made for prospective profits. Not only so, but the plant, so far as the wires were concerned, would have to be almost entirely replaced, for the wires of the Companies are stretched in a dangerous manner over houses and across streets, and they would nearly all have to be taken down and replaced by underground wires. I propose, then, that the Post Office should at once establish a Telephone exchange system of its own, and leave the Companies no time to set up vested rights and a practical monopoly.

The Treasury acceded to his request, with a proviso,

on the understanding that its object is, by the establishment of a Telephonic system to a limited extent, by the Post Office, to enable your Department to negotiate with the Telephone Companies in a satisfactory manner for licences.

Fawcett attached 'much importance' to that proviso, as 'limiting and controlling his policy'. Next he asked for £13000 to replace ABC instruments with telephones on private wire systems, and for authority to advertise that the Post Office was prepared to establish telephone exchanges.

TELEPHONIC INTER-COMMUNICATION.

THE POST OFFICE has for some time provided a means whereby the Renters of Wires into Postal Telegraph Offices may be placed as well in Direct Communication with each other. Such a system has been in operation in Newcastle-on-Tyne, Hull, Middlesborough, Stockton, and other Towns for several Years. The Instruments used in these cases up to the present time have been the A B C Instruments, Henceforward, in order to meet the Convenience of the Public, the Post Office will be prepared to provide for such a system either by the A B C or the Telephone Instruments. In the case of the Telephone Instruments the Annual Charge to each Renter will be £14 10s if his Premises be within Half-a-Mile of the Telegraph Office ; £18 if they be more than Half-a-Mile, but not more than a Mile distant ; and at proportionate rates for greater distances.

The Renters will not only have the facility afforded them of Communication Direct with each other, but they will also be enabled to Send Messages by Wire to the Telegraph Office, to be thence transmitted at the Ordinary Charge to other Towns. Application should be made to the Postmaster ; and, when several Persons have agreed to take Wires, immediate steps will be taken to establish a system of Inter-Communication by Telephone Instruments.

By order of

THE POSTMASTER-GENERAL.

Dec. 1880.

Those advertisements, which first appeared in the national press on 21 December 1880, evoked an immediate response from the United Telephone Company, its directors intimated through the same medium that they would take proceedings against anyone using telephones; to which the Gower-Bell Telephone Company responded by advertising that the Postmaster-General had contracted with it for large supplies of the telephone it was manufacturing (5000 within the next two years),

having found this to be the only form of telephone which has sustained the official tests for efficiency, simplicity, and permanence of operation.

Further, that it was manufacturing those telephones under agreement with the United Kingdom Telephone Company, which was directly interested in profits arising from such sales. (The Law Officers had expressed their opinion that the Postmaster-General had the power to maintain telephone systems and to lease the right of using them: and that Mr Gower was free to sell his telephones to the Post Office and that his transmitter was not an infringement of Edison's patent.)

*   *   *

The chief attraction of the early telephone was, of course, its novelty. Whilst Bell's 'butter-stamp' could be used both for transmitting and receiving it could not be described as a satisfactory transmitter. After many experiments Edison devised a much better transmitter before 1877 ended by the use of carbon to produce variations in transmitted currents.

Preece had a number of anecdotes about those early telephones. He spoke of demonstrating the telephone at a 'learned Society' meeting where he pressed a distinguished member to say 'something' into a transmitter and listen to Preece's assistant reply from another building. Apparently at a loss for some illuminating pronouncement, the member said, 'Hey diddle-diddle', and, after listening, delightedly told the audience, 'He said, "The cat and the fiddle." ' Preece thought that reply to be very much out of character and later taxed his assistant with it, only to be told, 'I asked him to repeat'.

Another was about Queen Victoria. Reports of the telephone had reached her ears and aroused her curiosity, so that when Graham Bell visited England in the autumn of 1877 she summoned him to appear at Osborne House, in the Isle of Wight, to give a demonstration. Preece arranged for telegraph circuits to be available one night in January to connect Southampton to London and also to the Isle of Wight. Preece engaged a small band to play in London, having checked that its music would be satisfactorily transmitted over the line, and leaving an assistant in charge went down to Southampton.

At the trial run that evening Bell reported that he heard the band quite clearly. The Queen was to listen in after dinner and at the pre-arranged hour Preece, thinking he had heard the Queen's voice, connected London with Osborne House whereupon the band duly played the National Anthem and followed it with another short musical score. Preece waited patiently for a report from Bell. Not so the band. By eleven o'clock the bandsmen had become so restive that Preece agreed they should be released. A few minutes after they had dispersed Bell came through to report that he had had un-expected difficulties in adjusting his instruments and would Preece start the band playing. The Queen thereupon came on the line and Preece ('prompted by the Devil', he said) hummed the National Anthem, only to hear her comment:

It is the National Anthem but it is very badly played.

19

THE TELEPHONE MONOPOLY

By the end of 1880 the Post Office administration was convinced that the United Telephone Company, which had bought out the Edison Company of Glasgow and had obtained sole rights on a carbon transmitter patented by Mr Crossley of Halifax, was aiming to obtain a monopoly. The Company had sought the Postmaster-General's agreement that in return for some concessions he would not himself set up telephone exchanges. Fifty applications for licences had been received at the Post Office but Postmaster-General Fawcett ruled that they should not be granted other than at 'those places where there appears to be some urgency in the public demand for them', to avoid exceeding Treasury authority. He sought Treasury agreement to grant a licence to the United Telephone Company for an extended maximum of thirty-one years to develop exchanges in the London area, subject to a 10 per cent royalty on gross rental charges to compensate for an inevitable reduction in telegraph receipts.

Board members of the National Telephone Company called on the Post Office Secretary to explain that they had obtained a licence from the United Telephone Company to establish telephone exchanges in certain areas of the Midlands and North and that they wanted a licence from the Post Office on terms similar to those to be granted to the United Telephone Company. The Post Office had already provided a telephone service at several of the towns in which the company was interested, but in the event demand had not increased, as could be judged from the number of subscribers (Leeds 9, Bradford 27, Huddersfield 3, Middlesbrough 21, and Leicester 6).

Fawcett thought that a measure of overlapping would have to be tolerated where companies had planned, before the 1880 judgement, to introduce telephones and the Post Office already had private wire networks where subscribers wished to change their ABC telegraphs for telephones. There was such a network at Sunderland but when a local telephone company opened an office and began to erect wires over houses and across streets the Corporation prohibited any extension of that work as dangerous to the public, and requested the Post Office to develop a telephone system, a request to which there was no alternative to compliance. No clear pattern for telephone services was, as yet, discernible, but despite Treasury qualms there was no gainsaying Fawcett's contention that,

as a matter of prudence, in view of the impossibility of foretelling what the effects of the system will be, the Department should, I think, have a share in its establishment.

Early in 1882 persistent rumours circulated about the telephone companies, culminating in *The Times* statement that the Government had decided to buy up those companies: an official contradiction had to be issued. About that time the newly formed London and Globe Telephone Company applied for a licence, which brought representations from the United Telephone Company that another company should not be allowed to open an exchange in London. The National Telephone Company also made representations on the disadvantage of granting more than one licence in a town, instancing Glasgow where three independent companies worked exchanges unrelated to each other. The Company argued that a close analogy could be drawn with gas and water, where monopoly was recognized as a public necessity. The Post Office Solicitor held that analogy to be misleading: telephonic communication was still in its infancy and needed competition, money was cheap so that the new field of enterprise would attract capital. He thought the safest course was to throw the field open to all comers,

using the veto of the Postmaster-General merely to secure royalties for the National Exchequer.

This accorded with the opinion of Fawcett but he went further in thinking that competition should also be allowed where the Post Office had already established exchanges.

Graves and Preece were asked to report on the Dolbear telephone receiver to be used by the London and Globe Company: they considered it to possess considerable merits. That company was a disappointment to Fawcett for two years later it had yet to make a move to establish an exchange in London.

The Lords of the Treasury intimated to Fawcett that they would not interfere with the exercise of his discretion in granting licences as freely as he proposed and agreed that means must always be at his command to test the comparative merits of his services and those of the companies provided that no town was thereby exposed to speculative rivalry. A little later they issued a ruling that canvassing for telephone subscribers 'can be no part of the duty of any officer of the Post Office' and also vetoed Fawcett's proposal to extend his private wire business as vigorously as possible. He was informed that

My Lords do not wish you to do more, in respect of Exchanges and private wires, than to bring your offers fairly within the knowledge of the public, and to wait for their demands upon you.

Against this background the Secretary of the Post Office asked Graves to report, in February 1884, on the telephone. Preece tactfully conceded that when he first brought the telephone to England

it was a mere scientific toy and the Department was perfectly justified in regarding it then as impracticable and interesting only.

He went on to point out the advisability of the Post Office working all trunk wires and confining companies' operations to the towns where they were already established. He urged that the wiser and bolder course would be to purchase the companies. Graves, in his covering minute, agreed that all trunk wires should be taken over but he thought it would be better to buy the companies when they asked the Department to do so rather than offer to purchase.

The Department's policy was attacked, often intemperately, in the House of Commons and by the Press from April till July that year. In the House Fawcett took full personal responsibility for that policy and proposed that all the telephone companies should meet and then put their demands to him in writing. As a result he wrote to the Treasury that he did not recommend State purchase for large sums would probably have to be paid in respect of prospective profits which may never be realised.

Patents, which the companies regarded as a large proportion of their assets, had less than seven years to run and the existing plant of the companies was almost entirely overhouse wires, which the Post Office would soon be compelled to put underground as far as possible and thus had only a scrap value although a large sum would have to be paid for them. If companies were deprived of the resource of complaining of Government interference to explain any want of success and should fail to give public satisfaction, 'which was by no means improbable', the Post Office might take over the whole telephone business on far more advantageous terms than currently possible.

The Treasury approved his proposals, a decision Fawcett announced in the House of Commons where he told Members that companies had asked to be secured against competition in towns where they had established an exchange but that such a proposal ought not to be entertained. The Post Office would reserve its right to carry on telephone business on its own account, would issue licences but no longer include as a condition of those licences an unlimited supply for itself of any patented instruments, and would abolish limits of radius from an exchange, thus allowing trunk and junction wires, and would permit the establishment of public call offices. The Post Office would be under no obligation to provide wayleaves or erect wires for the companies. No sound alternative to the existing royalty had been proposed so the public revenue would be protected as hitherto.

A Member commented that the only communication between some towns was along railway lines, to which Fawcett rejoined that the Government had to restrict wayleaves on railways to a number which would not cripple the work of his Department. Another Member asked for intercommunication telephones in the House; Fawcett reminded him that was a concern for the First Commissioner of Works.

★   ★   ★

Henry Fawcett, the blind Postmaster-General, died suddenly in November 1884 and the following year H. C. Raikes was appointed in his stead. An agitation for the State to take over all telephones was incited and sustained for the next two years. Among new licences which the Post Office issued was one, in June 1885, for the New Telephone Company. Four years later the three principal companies, the United, the Lancashire and Cheshire, and the National amalgamated under the name of the last.

The first period for company licences was to end in 1890 so the Post Office sought Treasury authority to purchase the companies at that date. If the Treasury could not agree to give such authority then the Post Office wished to engage in active competition with the companies. The Government announced, in June 1890, that it would not purchase telephone undertakings. Raikes had no course but to submit a scheme for active competition: the Government procrastinated by suggesting an inter-Departmental committee of investigation. Raikes died and his successor, Sir James Fergusson, rejected the suggestion of setting up a committee. By the end of 1891 he had obtained the Chancellor of the Exchequer's approval for what Preece had urged seven years before: the acquisition of the companies' trunk wires by the State.

A practical monopoly of such wires had by then been established by the National Telephone Company. The Telegraph Act of 1892 authorized both purchase and extension. The actual transfer began in April 1896: the State had paid half a million sterling for those trunks. Meanwhile several municipalities had applied for telephone licences, as had the States of Guernsey – whose inhabitants had cut down wires erected on their island by the National Telephone Company. A licence was granted to Guernsey, at the end of 1897, 'on political grounds'. The following year a Select Committee, on Telephones, of the House of Commons reported on the telephone services. During its deliberations the Committee had also considered published evidence heard by a similar Select Committee set up three years before: Chairman Arnold Morley had submitted a draft report at the time in which he condemned the grant of municipal licences. Some Members had disagreed with him and, as Parliament was on the eve of dissolution (July 1895), the Committee made no report. The 1898 Committee concluded that the telephone service was not of general benefit, nor likely to become so with an existing practical monopoly in the hands of a private company.

The Committee concluded that:

As it has already become of much more general benefit in other countries, affording less scope for its development than is afforded by the density of population and the greater wealth and commercial activity of the United Kingdom, so it is fitted to become in this country if worked solely or mainly with a view to the public interest, a valuable instrument in further developing the trade and social life of the nation, towards which new means of communication have always hitherto so largely contributed.

Our trunk system, which is in the hands of the Government and is worked on the toll system, is the most extensive in Europe. The exchange service, which is almost wholly in the hands of the company, and is chiefly confined to subscribers is much behind that of some continental countries. During nearly 20 years we have tried in turn, first, an unlimited competition, and afterwards, an unregulated monopoly, in the United Kingdom chiefly to England, in England to urban districts, in urban districts to the commercial classes, among the commercial classes mainly to merchants and large tradesmen, and among them to those only who find it advantageous to become subscribers.

The present subscription system, with the subscribers' right of unlimited user, means this: that persons who are rich enough to pay a fixed annual sum, and who use the telephone sufficiently often to find such a payment advantageous to themselves, whose correspondents also pay a similar sum, and use the service with similar frequency, can alone, or almost alone, avail themselves of this mode of communication. It is just as if the Post Office should decide to despatch telegrams only from persons paying an annual subscription, to despatch, without further charge, any number of telegrams, requiring at the same time that telegrams should be addressed only to persons connected with the Post Office telegraphs by private wire.

Within the London area, containing a population of over six million persons, there are only 237 call offices open to non-subscribers for the transmission of messages. In Stockholm there are over 700 for a population of only a quarter of a million.

. . . the General Manager of the National Telephone Company, admitted . . . that the system of limiting the service almost wholly to subscribers . . . had been based from the first on a wrong principle. The right system appears to us to be the one advocated strongly by Mr. Preece and which Mr. Gavey (assistant Engineer-in-Chief) . . . has shewn to be so successful in popularising and developing the service in Switzerland. Messages can be sent by non-subscribers from call offices and delivered to non-subscribers by express messengers; but, in addition to this, just as some persons in this country hire private telegraph wires to connect them with the general telegraph system and thus avoid the necessity of delivering messages at or receiving them from a telegraph office, so persons who wish to save the journey to a call office to despatch a telephone message or receive it direct instead of a written message can secure a private telephone in their house or office on payment of an annual sum of (after two years) £1. 12s. For all messages actually sent subscribers and the public alike pay the same fixed toll, smaller if the message is a local one, larger if it travels over the trunk wire. . . . Each message sent by a subscriber is numbered and an account against him is kept. It follows under this system that every telephone can be used by the general public instead of being confined to the actual subscriber, with the result that in many towns every shop or place of business which has a telephone becomes in practice a public call office.

Such a system, Mr. Preece is convinced, would be equally successful in this country, and go very far to extend the telephone service to almost every class. It would, of course, be opposed by the subscribers on the existing system, who, at present, almost monopolise the service, and pay a small sum for the large number of messages they can send. The National Telephone Company . . . had already realised the force of this opposition, but it is clearly not one to which a municipality or the Post Office starting operations in any area for the first time would be exposed.

. . . The licence of the company expires on 31st December 1911. . . . It is hardly probable that any Government will give the prescribed notice to purchase not only the plant, but the goodwill, by arbitration in 1904 – a step which was not taken under somewhat more promising conditions in 1897. . . . Unless the Government had already an alternative plant available, supplied wholly by the Post Office or partly by municipal licensees, the purchase of the company's undertaking at an inflated price might . . . be imposed upon the Government . . . your Committee cannot too strongly recommend that no delay should occur in taking adequate precautions . . . Mr. Preece informed your Committee that it would probably take five years to provide . . . alternative plant for the whole country. . . .

Competition appears to be both expedient and necessary, in order, firstly to extend and popularise the service, and next to avoid a danger which is by no means remote, if no alternative scheme is in operation, that a purchase of the company's undertaking at an inflated price may be forced upon the government of the day.

Competition by a local authority must differ in many ways from

competition by a private company, and requires special provision to meet
the special conditions of the case.

In areas where the company have already an exchange, municipal
competition, if permitted, should be conducted, so far as possible, on
equal terms. It would be plainly unfair to concede to the new licensee
a position of general advantage over that possessed by the older competitor.

. . . general, immediate, and effective competition by either the Post
Office or the local authority is necessary . . . a really efficient Post Office
service affords the best means for securing such competition.

20

LONDON SPEAKS TO PARIS

As Assistant Engineer-in-Chief and Electrician, Preece had two main objectives, to some extent mutually inhibitive, which were, improvement and standardization of equipment. His railway experience had early taught him that to standardize apparatus and techniques was essential to the effective running of a large organization. Standardization is largely a product of experience: on the grounds that municipalities had no experience of telephones Preece was to oppose a recommendation that they be granted licences when he appeared before the Select Committee on Telephones of 1895. The honesty of his evidence then was appreciated by officials of the National Telephone Company for they had expected him to be a 'hostile' witness. He replied to a Committee member's question on the efficiency of their system:

My own impression is that they [the Company] are doing all they can to make the service as good as it can be made. I have had occasion to visit several of their exchanges, and I find that they compare very favourably indeed with exchanges in the States. . . . The telephone company at the present moment are entirely renovating the whole of their system, and they can construct just as good a system, perhaps a better one, than the county council, for the simple reason that they start with experience that you [the London County Council] have not got.

With uniformity of practice in mind, Preece began to issue a numbered series of *Electrician's Circulars* for the guidance of his staffs in the field, on installing, adjusting and maintaining apparatus – often illustrated. The earliest were cyclostyled but soon they were printed. One of them – a table of the fusing temperatures of metals – is still in use. Later he inaugurated a series of *Technical Instructions* which

o

amounted to textbooks on particular sections of his department's work.

To improve apparatus which could also be manufactured in bulk to an acceptable standard of uniformity was far from simple. Bell's telephone was an excellent receiver but had proved unsatisfactory as a transmitter. Thomas Edison in developing a better transmitter had discovered that the pressure of a diaphragm on a small piece of plumbago varied its electrical resistance far more responsively than did Bell's diaphragm moving in a magnetic field. David E. Hughes showed, in 1879, that the resistance of contacts varied with pressure, however rapid or slight, by using a wire nail resting on two others (and also with the links of a gold watch-chain) to demonstrate his 'microphone'. Edison on hearing of this called it a 'straight steal' and wrote to the *Scientific American*:

After I sent one of my young men over to London especially to show Preece the carbon transmitter, and where Hughes first saw it and heard it, then within a month he comes out with the microphone without any acknowledgement whatever.

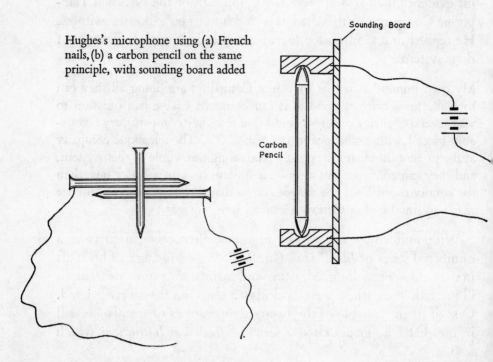

Hughes's microphone using (a) French nails, (b) a carbon pencil on the same principle, with sounding board added

Sounding Board

Carbon Pencil

When Preece's attention was called to that statement he immediately cabled the magazine editor a 'most absolute and unqualified denial' of Edison's allegation. Preece himself about that time discovered that the expansion and contraction of a very fine wire attached to the centre of a diaphragm vibrated it in response to variations in received currents as the wire expanded and contracted with the heating effect of received currents and the rapid cooling of the wire. (Campbell Swinton used Preece's telephone years later as a rectifying detector of wireless telegraph signals.)

Silvanus P. Thompson patented a 'valve' transmitter which seemed to have something of Hughes's microphone in its design: Hughes was not convinced that Thompson understood how it worked but that did not prevent the United Telephone Company from adding to the already large number of law suits on alleged patent infringements by asking for an injunction against its use by the New Telephone Company which had been formed to market Thompson's telephone patents. Thompson had been paid for his patent by shares and a directorship in that company which, as a result of the action against it, never became fully operative. (If the time and money spent in the United Kingdom and in the United States on contesting or evading patents could have been directed to the co-operative development of the telephone, inventors and investors would have had a much happier time.)

Inventions and new techniques are dependent to a much greater extent than generally recognized on improvements in the quality of materials available, on improvements in manufacturing processes, and on the development of new materials. Preece was able to give great assistance to manufacturers by drawing up *Post Office Specifications*, following tests and field trials in his department, which provided a standard that was soon generally accepted.

*　　*　　*

Professor David E. Hughes in his presidential address in 1886 to the Society of Telegraph and Electrical Engineers (the Society's title had been lengthened four years before in recognition of an expanding profession) referred to the phenomenon of inductance in electrical circuits, by which a conductor's resistance to rapidly alternating currents is considerably greater than to steady currents. Preece, during the discussion which followed, spoke of experiments in the working rate of Wheatstone automatic telegraphs – which depended on rapid reversals of current – a speed of working of 400 words a minute required 200 reversals a second: he had proved that the inductive effect of iron wire then in general use in the Post Office was a third greater than that of copper. Hughes had said that the effect could be reduced by stranding the iron wire but Preece considered such a solution not available to the Post Office as snow would accumulate much more readily on stranded wire, nor would stranded iron be as durable as solid copper.

Preece gave a talk to the members a few months later on long-distance telephony. He explained that he had not written a paper because during the past week he had been suffering from an accident to his eyes so that he could neither read nor write. He thought that improvements to telephones during recent years had not been very marked. In 1877 he had spoken with Bell's telephone through sixty miles of cable from Dartmouth to Guernsey successfully and, later, between Holyhead and Dublin when he asked Sanger, Divisional Engineer for Ireland, if he could hear his voice. Sanger replied, 'Yes, and I can smell your cigar.' At St Martin's-le-Grand they had a test circuit of four miles to their Telegraph Stores in Gloucester Road, Regent's Park, and he had yet to find a telephone with which he could speak over that short distance. The difficulty was not so much in the apparatus as in the aggravated form in that neighbourhood of induced currents from other circuits and the earth returns of electric light mains and electric tramways.

He went on to comment on a supposition that Government espionage checked improvements whereas in fact the only real improvements in telephone *working* in this country had been made by the Post Office. Policy among the companies had been to crush incipient opposition, not for the sake of furthering the business 'but to put down impudent inventors'. No inventor came to Preece's department, whoever he was or wherever he came from, whose invention was not tried and, if it showed an improvement capable of successful adoption, was accepted and well paid for.

Thompson gave members, early in 1887, an account of telephone investigations he had made at odd times during the preceding four years. He evaluated various instruments and concluded that generally transmission difficulties could be overcome with less sensitive receivers, greater resistance in the circuit, and more powerful transmitters. He had referred to 'the healthy air of criticism' but seemed none too pleased that speakers in the discussion of his paper were critical of many of his conclusions. Preece said that Thompson's objections to carbon transmitters were imaginary and that it was the environment of the line that gave more difficulty than the limitations of existing instruments; he instanced experiments over a few miles to nearly 300 where electrical interference and not distance had determined audibility.

Replying two meetings later Thompson interspersed his comments with what could be described as abuse of several who had joined the discussion; of which a specimen was,

Preece . . . went down to Hanwell and talked thence to Nevin. There is, I believe, a lunatic asylum at Hanwell; what there is at Nevin I do not know.

Unfortunately, Preece could not attend that lively meeting. There

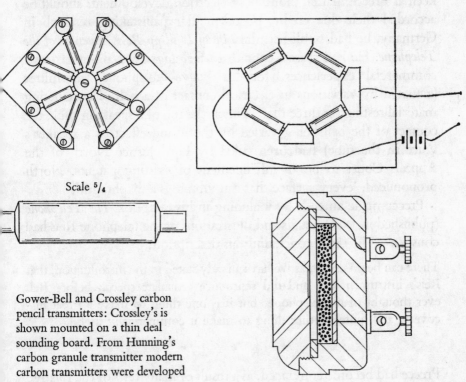

Scale ⁵/₄

Gower-Bell and Crossley carbon
pencil transmitters: Crossley's is
shown mounted on a thin deal
sounding board. From Hunning's
carbon granule transmitter modern
carbon transmitters were developed

could be no doubt about Thompson's feelings on Reis when he affirmed:

My offence seems to have been [to] name Reis . . . in the same line as Bell and Edison. Well if Bell had lived 15 years before Reis; if Bell had worked on for years, neglected and unknown, despised and rejected by the complacent telegraph engineers of his time, and if before he had been two years in his grave his great invention had been proclaimed as someone else's then I could have understood that I had been unjust to Bell. But it was Reis who lived 15 years before Bell; Reis whose invention was tossed aside as a toy; Reis who died heart-broken. Talk of injustice in naming alongside Reis those who have made a fortune out of that which he invented! . . . Nothing shall ever cause me to detract from the merit of this discovery by Bell; only he was not the first and his invention has almost ceased to be used for transmitting speech.

Nor had Thompson forgotten that Preece, when eulogizing Bell's telephone at Plymouth in 1877, had described Reis's instrument as, by comparison, 'a pretty philosophic toy'. Thompson was as equally keen as Preece that all pioneers of electrical developments should be accorded their due credit. In 1883, after painstaking research in Germany, he had published the *Life of Phillipp Reis, Inventor of the Telephone*. He had reason enough to feel aggrieved about his own commercial experiences, for his 'valve' telephone transmitter (actuated by variations in electrical contact of a ball of conducting material resting on three metal pins at the top of a speaking tube, the contact of the ball being varied by the lifting effect of a speaker's voice in the tube) had been ruled by Lord Justice North of the Appeals Court to be an infringement of existing patents. North pronounced, 'every surface that can vibrate is a diaphragm'.

Preece made amends by including in his textbook *The Telephone* (published in 1889) details and illustrations of the telephone Reis had constructed in 1860, concluding his description:

There can be no doubt, as we have already stated in the introduction, that Reis's instrument can and did reproduce articulate speech before Bell ever thought of his telephone; but it is one thing to make a great discovery, and quite another thing to make it commercially useful.

*   *   *

Preece had become convinced, as a result of many tests of the relative durability, mechanical and electrical qualities of wires, that copper was to be preferred to the iron generally in use on overhead lines: the relatively more expensive copper had been used only in short lengths where atmospheric impurities had rapidly corroded iron. His earliest experiments failed because the copper wire available was too brittle. Preece therefore approached the wire manufacturing firm of Thomas Bolton and Sons and arranged for them to prepare, from electrolytically obtained copper, samples of wire drawn to varying degrees of hardness. These he tested for tensile strength and durability with satisfactory results. He then prepared a specification for hard-drawn copper wire of particular weights in pounds per mile and the manufacturers devised new methods and machinery to produce it.

Having persuaded the Post Office administration that there were economic advantages in a 'copper standard' ('it was the biggest tussle I've ever had') Preece ran 150-pound wires overhead from London to Nevin in North Wales to join a new submarine cable to Wicklow, from whence overhead copper wires completed a circuit to Dublin. They needed more careful adjustment than iron wires so Preece had to introduce a dynanometer to regulate their sag on a span and issue new instructions to his staff. Not only did these lines allow the speed of telegraph transmission to be greatly increased but they made possible over long distances telephone speech of an acceptable quality. Working on an empirical formula used from 1854 by Sir William Thomson on submarine telegraph cables, Preece determined that speech was practicable when the value of KR – total electrical capacity in farads by total resistance in ohms (later the symbol C was preferred to K) – of a circuit did not exceed 10000 for bare overhead copper wires and 8000 for underground wires.

The Minister of Posts and Telegraphs in Paris, who had opened a telephone service from that city to Brussels and to Marseilles in 1889, expressed the desirability of telephonic communication with London: the Post Office administration concurred but Preece found it impossible over the existing telegraph lines. Experiments with an artificial line which duplicated the electrical characteristics of a possible circuit convinced Preece of its practicability. The main difficulty was in the relatively high capacity of a submarine cable link. H. R. Kempe, on Preece's staff (whose name is kept before us in

The Prince of Wales (Edward VII) speaks with President Carnot on the first telephone call between London and Paris. On his left is Postmaster-General H. C. Raikes and on his right Preece speaking with reporters. From the *Illustrated London News*, 28 March, 1891

AN AWKWARD INTERRUPTION.

Preece and H. C. Fischer suffer acoustic shock from telephone receivers. Their sets are of the 'Universal' pattern on which controlling patents expired in 1891 when the P.O. used it in preference to the Gower-Bell

Kempe's Engineers Year-book), undertook the design of a new cable, and it redounded to the credit of Siemens Brothers that in its manufacture at their Woolwich Cable Works they met his stringent specifications. Four overhead copper conductors weighing 800 pounds a mile carried two telephone circuits to St Margaret's Bay cable hut, near Dover. The circuits were made available on 1 April 1891, when, at a charge of eight shillings for three minutes, Londoners conversed with Parisians.

Within a few months the Government agreed, as we have seen, to take over private company trunk wires and Preece began to construct trunk lines to the same standard as the Paris circuits on main routes from London, with 600 and 400 pounds respectively for secondary and for shorter circuits. That system was inaugurated by the Lord Mayor of London on 12 June 1895 (less than year before the National Telephone Company began to transfer its trunk system to the State) when he spoke by telephone with his peers in Dublin, Belfast, Glasgow and Edinburgh.

21

DISTORTION

OLIVER HEAVISIDE coined the word 'inductance' to describe phenomena investigated many years before by Faraday and defined as the ratio of magnetic flux to an electric current, which surrounds as well as operates within a conductor. The mutual inductance of two circuits is the ratio of the magnetic flux, linking with one current, to the current in the other. It had little noticeable effect on telegraph transmission for it operates with each change in direction of a current, a change which it tends to oppose, and reversals of current in telegraph signalling were, compared with telephony, relatively infrequent. We can, in passing, remind ourselves that such flux is greatly increased when a magnetic material is associated with a wire (e.g. a helix of insulated wire wound around a soft iron rod), a phenomenon which has, of course, determined the design of relays, sparking coils, dynamos and similar forms of electrical apparatus. Designers had also to contend with the fact that rapid changes in current direction generate heat in the magnetic material and its response, or permeability, becomes cumulatively slower – a phenomenon known as hysteresis.

We have seen that Preece, with the co-operation of copper-wire manufacturers, had been able to reduce the electrical resistance (R) of overhead circuits to enable telegraphs with a reversal frequency of 200 per second to be operated without distortion by inductance; indeed he had by careful measurements determined KR (capacity in farads by resistance in ohms) limiting values for circuits over which conversations could reasonably be held. Speech frequencies as late as in the 1920s were being regarded for purposes of circuit measurement and design as 800 per second but in fact complex waves made up of frequencies from 100 to 1500 were being transmitted: the higher frequencies were, therefore, much more quickly attenuated and distorted by inductance. We learnt that, when the telephone was first introduced, what one heard through it was to a remarkable extent subjective, thus to determine how far distortion could go or what higher frequencies could be cut off altogether before speech became unintelligible was difficult. The higher performance of wireless loudspeakers in the late 1920s gave the public a standard for comparison which made it incumbent to design circuits where the 'cut-off' of higher frequencies was raised, when the individuality of voices could be more easily recognized. In Preece's time the miracle was that a distant speaker could be heard at all, much less identified. Said Preece:

In England it is not possible in the numerous shops employed as post offices to secure that privacy which the telephone requires, nor have we got over our early prejudices, resulting from the errors made through the inability of the instrument in the earlier form to repeat the sibilant sounds.

Oliver Heaviside, of the Great Northern Telegraph Company, concentrated on the problem of telephone transmission and was driven to invent an operational calculus to enable him to attack its mathematical complexities. The *Philosophical Magazine* and the *Electrician* published articles by him, to the great credit of their editors, for few readers could have followed his mathematics. He produced a theory of the distortionless telephone circuit which, in its most simplified form, could be written:

$$LG = RC$$

(L being inductance in henries and G leakance in ohms) when currents of all frequencies are equally attenuated and travel with equal velocity. Since R and C (or K) determine the attentuation of a current it seemed reasonable to keep those as low as possible; as indeed was Preece's practice and the *raison d'être* for his well-insulated heavy copper overhead circuits. Oliver suggested increasing inductance in underground lines to counteract their greater capacity (C or K). To such an end conductors might be lapped with soft iron wire, or bundles of such wire introduced into the circuits. Manufacturers would have great difficulty at that time to produce iron wire of uniform high permeability but, nevertheless, Preece did get a quantity of copper wire lapped with iron which he had Arthur W. Heaviside (P.O. Divisional Engineer for the North East, and Oliver's younger brother) test in telephone transmission. Arthur reported that it gave no noticeable improvement. Preece also tried introducing induction coils into the London–Paris telephone circuit before it was brought into service, but with no appreciable effect.

M. Vaschy of France had begun to study the same problem about two years earlier than Oliver: on his instigation the American 'Long Distance' telephone company tried 'loading' a telephone circuit by inserting at intervals induction coils of insulated wire wound around soft iron: it failed to improve transmission. Credit for a practical solution is generally given to Michael I. Pupin, a Serbian immigrant to the States, who successfully calculated spacings for 'loading-coils' and then demonstrated that a telephone circuit thus loaded behaved as if the inductance thereby introduced was uniformly distributed throughout its length. Pupin wrote that his solution, in 1899, was obvious in the light of Thomson's 'KR Law' of 1854 for the Atlantic cable and the mathematical work of Gustave R. Kirchhoff of Berlin four years later in developing that formula to apply to land-lines, twenty years before Vaschy and Oliver Heaviside worked on the problem. He conceded that

these two celebrated mathematicians, however, deserve much credit for their enthusiastic backing of inductance among the sceptical engineers who, at the time, knew little of . . . the general principles of the transmission of vibratory motions.

Preece gave a paper on Pupin and Telephone Transmission in 1907 to the British Association at Leicester, to bring members up to date on improvements made.

*   *   *

Silvanus P. Thompson later wrote that Preece had been unable to appreciate Oliver Heaviside's work on transmission but he might equally well have written that Oliver had neglected opportunities to persuade Preece that Thomson's KR was not enough. Instead of interjecting an occasional sarcastic remark into his erudite articles, to the alarm at times of editors to whom libel suits were not unknown, if he had emphasized his arguments by reiterating their gist in relatively simple terms his purpose might have been better served. His prose did not possess the persuasive quality found in the writings of Clerk Maxwell, originator of the electro-magnetic theory of light, who wrote, in 1856, on Faraday's 'Lines of force',

It is by the use of analogies . . . that I have attempted to bring before the mind, in a convenient and manageable form, those mathematical ideas which are necessary to the study of electricity . . . suggested by the processes of reasoning which are found in the researches of Faraday, and which, though they have been interpreted mathematically by Professor Thomson and others, are very generally supposed to be of an indefinite and unmathematical character, when compared with those employed by the professed mathematicians.

Pupin, as it happens, has recorded that by just such a process of reasoning from physical analogies to advanced mathematics had he managed to produce a practical solution to the problem of introducing extra inductance into a circuit.

Clerk Maxwell's tactful phrasing is seen in his reference to inductance:

When a conductor moves in the neighbourhood of a current of electricity, or of a magnet, or when a current or magnet near the conductor is moved, or altered in intensity, then a force acts on the conductor and produces electric tension, or a continuous current, according as the circuit is open or closed. This current is produced only by *changes* of the electric or magnetic phenomena surrounding the conductor, and as long as these are constant there is no observed effect on the conductor. . . .

Considerations of this kind led Professor Faraday to connect with his discovery of the induction of electric currents the conception of a state into which all bodies are thrown by the presence of magnets and currents. . . .

Faraday, however, has not contented himself with simply stating the numerical results of his experiments and leaving the law to be discovered by calculation. Where he has perceived a law he has at once stated it, in terms as unambiguous as those of pure mathematicians; and if the mathematician, receiving this as a physical truth, deduces from it other laws capable of being tested by experiment, he had merely assisted the physicist in arranging his own ideas, which is confessedly a necessary step in scientific induction.

Oliver Heaviside's articles were also read by others of greater mathematical attainment than Preece but, with rare exceptions, their

understanding of Oliver's import was no clearer than his. Professor
G. F. FitzGerald, a great admirer of Heaviside's work, had written
that Heaviside

has the faults of extreme condensation of thought and a peculiar facility
for coining technical terms and expressions that are extremely puzzling
to a reader of his papers. . . . In his most deliberate attempts at being
elementary he jumps double fences and introduces short-cut expressions
that are woeful stumbling blocks. . . .

The Institution of Electrical Engineers commemorated the centenary of Heaviside's birth in May 1950. Sir Stanley Angwin,
Engineer-in-Chief of the Post Office throughout the war years,
proposed a vote of thanks to those contributing to the proceedings:
he added, with his customary frankness,

I still feel rather like Mr Preece, even with the illumination Mr Josephs
[H. J. Josephs, a mathematician, had given an explanation of his paper
on 'some unpublished notes of Oliver Heaviside'] has brought to the
subject.

Oliver had become dissatisfied with his work as telegraphist in the
Great Northern Telegraph Company when he resigned in 1874; it
had given him too few opportunities for research. His brother
Arthur, who felt responsible for him, could take Oliver on his own
staff and Preece agreed he could be employed on research of his own
choosing in the North East Division: he would, of course, be required to send reports of such work to the Engineer-in-Chief's
office. Preece made an attempt to get on friendly terms with Oliver,
whose response was ungracious. Taking no offence, Preece asked
Arthur to try to persuade his brother to join the Chief's experimental
staff in G.P.O. West – his mother, who lived in London, wished to
have him at home – but Arthur reluctantly concluded that Oliver,
who unfortunately suffered from spells of deafness, was becoming
increasingly introspective and too suspicious of his fellows to be a
useful member of a team. Oliver came to London with a heavy cold
which developed into a serious illness. On recovery he stayed at home
to occupy himself with mathematical problems: in an important
study of his, published in the *Philosophical Magazine*, August 1876, he
concluded that electrical energy became excessive in long circuits

and, therefore, inductance must be added to increase magnetic energy.

The Institution of Electrical Engineer's Council, of which Preece was a member, was disappointed when Oliver did not attend any of the Institution's ordinary fortnightly meetings, and when he failed to pay his subscription during 1880 Preece made inquiries, only to learn that Oliver was short of money; he tactfully offered him, *via* his brother Arthur, a post in the Western Union Telegraph Company for which Preece had the nomination. To Preece's regret, and bafflement, Oliver would have none of it. Eight years later Oliver moved with his parents to South Devon. He kept in touch with the outside world by corresponding with a number of other mathematicians, particularly G. F. FitzGerald who died before the age of fifty, a few years after he had congratulated Oliver, in 1896, on being awarded a Civil Pension.

*   *   *

On the basis of Oliver Heaviside's conclusions, Silvanus P. Thompson took out a patent, in December 1891, for ocean telephone cables, in which he proposed that inductance coils, in the form of bobbins, be inserted at intervals as 'shunts' between two conductors in a cable: his conviction was that it would introduce sufficient inductance to smooth out frequency distortion but it seemed clear that it would increase the rate of attenuation. He was one of two Englishmen – the other was Preece – invited to present papers at the International Electrical Congress in Chicago in 1893. Preece was to speak on electrical signalling without wires and Thompson chose ocean telephony as his subject.

On the eve of that Congress a rumour burgeoned in the American press that H.M. Treasury was to vote half a million pounds to finance a telephone cable across the Atlantic. On Preece's arrival in the States reporters button-holed him: he answered that experiments to that end had not taken place and, with truth, told them he had not even contemplated asking for money for that purpose. He forbore from explaining what would be involved, even with the backing of his personal prestige, to get £100 granted by the Treasury for particular experiments, for anyone to suppose for a moment that £500 000 was even remotely possible. That a trans-Atlantic telephone service by cable would one day be given he did not doubt, but he thought that an American of the calibre of Cyrus W. Field was necessary to finance such a project.

Preece on his return to Wimbledon from Chicago found a parcel of ferns for his greenhouse had been sent from Waterville, County Kerry, by F. J. Wilmot, superintendent of the Irish terminal of the Commercial Cable Company's two Atlantic telegraph cables. Wilmot acknowledged his prompt note of thanks and wrote that if Preece was not so busy he would have liked to know what he had thought of Thompson's paper, adding:

My own conclusion is that it [Thompson's proposed Atlantic telephone cable] is wholly impracticable . . . you have seen Oliver Heaviside's recent chapters in the Electrician. He seems to be indicating the right direction in which we want to work. I should like to see a cable with three equidistant 10,000 ohms leaks, bringing down the apparent resistance to about 2,000 ohms. Of course, it would be much better if the same end could be reached by a uniform leakage. Of course an Atlantic cable is too costly a thing to try radical experiments upon. Still we know that a leakage in a cable does considerably increase the working speed. As Heaviside says, we have been working in the wrong direction in increasing instead of diminishing the insulation resistance and the result is that signals are choked to death. That is what we '*practicians*' have been doing!

Preece sent a note to M. Cooper, one of his assistants, asking:

Do leaks bring down KR by reducing R?

Cooper replied:

I think not, because leaks have not been found to improve speaking [signalling] and we have often tried them. They were tried in connection with inductance also but did nothing except reduce the current.

Thompson had written home from Chicago to report that his paper, and the discussion it occasioned, had been one of the features of the Congress. He added that a banquet for the official delegates was given one evening, at which Elisha Gray presided. Professor Mascart, of the Sorbonne University, Paris, had been very amusing 'and so was Preece' in after-dinner speeches. It had been the only affair at the Congress where Edison had put in an appearance and Graham Bell had not turned up at any.

Six years later, when Pupin's success had become known, Professor J. A. Fleming wrote to Thompson:

If you had received more encouragement from the practical monopolists, GPO and Telephone Camps, you would no doubt have been able to anticipate Pupin . . . the mathematics is, however, very complicated and I should be sorry to dogmatise. Owing to the expensive nature of the work, experiments are difficult.

★   ★   ★

Preece reviewed the whole field of electrical development over the past fifty years when he gave an eloquent Presidential address to the Institution of Electrical Engineers in January 1893. But though he held his audience in rapt attention, all was not well with him for he confessed that he was beginning to feel the evidences of age growing upon him. He certainly did not show any physical signs, but, despite the lift to his ego given by his colleagues in electing him their president for a second time, there was a note of frustration in his condemnation of the effects of limited liability legislation whereby

the rapacious financial promoter – whose plunder in one year of our period far exceeds in amount the sum of the thefts of all highwaymen . . . that were ever hanged. He has ruined the prospects of private enterprise and has rendered necessary the [Electricity Supply] Acts of 1882–88 which have thrown the industry into the hands of local authority.

He spoke, too, of public disillusionment caused by damage following the bungling of unskilled men wiring private houses with inferior materials. (That was a problem which the I.E.E. was to attack with resolution; Preece, recovered from his malaise, in the van.) He complained of

visionary mathematicians who monopolize the columns of our technical literature, scorning the practical man and scoffing at his experience.

He felt that had Clerk Maxwell lived (he died in 1879 at the age of forty-eight) he would probably have combined all physical phenomena in one great science of 'energetics', and regretted that the public at large did not know about Maxwell's electro-magnetic theory of light. He prophesied that in another fifty years' time, when a similar review of progress over that period was made, his address that evening might well be quoted

P

as an illustration of the ignorance of the great Victorian period.

Early in 1894 the American consultant electrician Dr A. E. Kennelly wrote to Preece from Edison's laboratory enclosing an advance copy of an article on the theory of telephone transmission

as a tribute and not as a challenge to your KR law. . . .

Hitherto, as you are aware no reasonably simple theory or formulas have been advanced for the determination of even the elementary case discussed . . . by confining our attention to overhead copper wires, we can find a limiting current strength for the receiving end of the line which shall not only render these equations [in his article] directly applicable, with proper reservations, to determining the distance limits of actual telephony, but will also shew how very close an approximation to nature and truth the simple KR law has been. In fact when the complexity of the actual problem is considered, I should not be surprised to learn that the KR law was practically the better guide, except that it does not make allowance for lines of large inductance and small capacity.

Preece replied,

I fear . . . you are attempting an insoluble problem. I have discussed the question pretty freely with Lord Rayleigh and Lord Kelvin at different times and they both regard the mathematical treatment of these telephonic questions as impossible. . . .

I have submitted my KR law as an empirical law. . . .

Kennelly responded promptly,

I quite agree with you as to the great difficulty of the general problem and it is remarkable that the results I have obtained bear out your KR law to the degree, that up to a certain length of any uniform line, the received current strength diminishes approximately as the square of the length, but my results are at variance with your formula in the fact that inductance enters into them and is not considered directly in your formula. I therefore, may fairly claim to be the strongest advocate of your empirical formula on a mathematical and theoretical basis to be found on this side of the Atlantic, and in the points where I do differ from you, you have the advantage of me, in that you say your empirical formula is practically borne out, while I have as yet no practical evidence to sustain my views.

I feel sure that in assuming this relative attitude we shall never be far separated.

*　　　*　　　*

Despite his administrative duties and widespread commitments Preece still found time to consider, *inter alia*, transmission problems and, in September 1896, gave an account of what he had learnt to the British Association at Liverpool. He spoke of the three cables still working between East Anglia and Germany when a fourth was laid, in 1891 with four conductors, each with earth return, on which Hughes's type-printer telegraphs were to be employed. (The Hughes's telegraph is worked by short, sharp, intermittent currents, separated from each other by varying intervals of time. These time intervals determine the letter to be printed.) Although made of improved materials the new cable was subject to far more electrical disturbances than the older cables, one of which had been laid twenty years earlier. To duplex a Hughes's telegraph satisfactorily was impossible because of inductive interference from its neighbouring circuit.

Preece decided that the older cables worked better because the hemp yarn packed around and between each gutta-percha-insulated conductor had become saturated and that had a shielding effect. Preece had used tinfoil lapping for a similar purpose over insulated conductors in London underground telegraph cables as early as 1878. He had not bothered to patent his invention (which was a few years later used by continental cable manufacturers).

He laid another cable to Germany in 1896 but this time each insulated conductor was lapped with brass tape to reduce electrostatic disturbances to telegraph signals to a negligible factor. He went on to consider telephone cables: the four gutta-percha-insulated conductors of the Dover–Calais cable link on the two London–Paris telephone circuits

would not do for a greater distance than, say, 30 nautical miles. . . . With paper as the dielectric, having half the specific inductive capacity of gutta-percha, and with our later experience of air spaces, cannot we devise a new form of cable . . . [to] bridge . . . greater distances? We must eliminate all disturbance, and . . . reduce capacity and resistance to their lowest limits. The former is simple, for well insulated, symmetrically-twisted metallic circuits are free from all external disturbances. The latter is more complicated, and is surrounded by great practical difficulties.

If there were no time constant [the time that the current takes to rise to the necessary strength to work a relay in normal adjustment] current waves would rise instantly to their working maximum, and as rapidly fall to zero. If we could materially diminish the causes of retardation in such cables, speech by telephone would be possible to great distances. This can be done theoretically by neutralizing the effect of static capacity by the opposite effect of electro-magnetic induction . . .

. . . consider the case of a concentric cable; for in this case the number of lines of electric force does not increase in the same ratio as the number of lines of magnetic force, while the outer conductor approaches the inner. The maximum induction from each source must take place when the two conductors are infinitely near each other, and this maximum must equal the primary current, for it cannot exceed it unless there were fresh creation of energy. Thus, as the separating dielectric becomes smaller and smaller, the two effects approach each other closer and closer, until, at absolute contact, they annul each other. The result must be that if these be the only conditions present, the time constant must diminish as the two conductors approach each other, and in the limit must disappear. Twenty miles of concentric cable insulated with paper, were made and laid in the streets of London to test this reasoning, and comparisons were made with ordinary parallel cylindrical conductors, insulated both with gutta-percha and with paper and air. The result was very encouraging; but an unexpected difficulty arose from the want of symmetry of the capacity of each conductor and the earth. The insulation resistance of each conductor was also different, and the result was that when the concentric cable was joined with overhead wires, serious disturbances were experienced in the working circuits, which, however, were remedied by crossing the conductors of the concentric cable at several points, so that each side of the circuit was sometimes the inner and sometimes the outer conductor. This however, is a cure that could not easily be applied to a submarine cable. It is clear that in such a cable symmetry of capacity with earth and insulation is essential.

Sixty years later, with the continued improvement in manufacturing techniques, the invention of new materials, the remarkable development of electronics after the Second World War, and a new transmission system of 'carrier' telephony – in which a frequency spectrum is split into adjacent bands each yielding a defined bandwidth of some 3000 cycles per second for each distinctive telephone circuit – the concentric cable came into its own. ('Loading' is a serious disadvantage for 'carrier' working.) Preece's and Thompson's dream came true when, in 1956, two concentric cables – one for each direction of transmission – with submerged repeaters inserted at intervals along their length provided twenty-four telephone circuits across the Atlantic.

Preece's problem was: what is the best form to give a cable with the experience and materials available? The solution he proposed was a cable with apparently four conductors but each conductor 'split' – that is, of a semi-circular cross-section – the two wires thus formed being insulated from each other by a wrapping of paper. He reported that the manufacture of such a cable to be laid to the Isle of Wight was under consideration. The editor of the *Electrician* commented that Preece's cable might reduce inductance to a minimum but would enormously increase permittance (inductive capacity):

Here we have two sets of eminent authorities in sharp disagreement ... as to the correct method of embodying in a concrete cable certain mathematical abstractions or, as some would say, fictions. . . . It would seem both fair and expedient that the mathematicians whose views are at last finding acceptance at the hands of practical telegraph engineers, should have some voice in the construction of the cable which is to embody their ideas, and in the experiments which are to put them to the only test capable of allaying the healthy scepticism of the true 'natural philosopher'.

There was little response to his invitation. Kennelly opined that Preece's arrangement would not have the desired effect. The editor asked Oliver Heaviside for his opinion, to get:

I have explained my own views so fully already that I am reluctant to do it again. . . . Mr. Preece . . . thinks it right and proper to bring the two members of a pair of conducting leads as close together as possible. . . . Now, it is a long way to America, and one may never get there; but it is as well to go in the right direction.

G. F. FitzGerald wrote from Dublin University that Preece would have to supply far more information on his experiments before a decision could be made between Preece's and Heaviside's contentions. In the event a design for the projected Isle of Wight telephone cable, by Messrs Willoughby S. Smith and W. P. Granville of the Telegraph Construction and Maintenance Co., was preferred. Laid in 1897, it was an early air-spaced cable: four gutta-percha-insulated conductors, evenly spaced, were attached to the inside of a gutta-percha tube with air separating them from each other (except, of course, at their separate attachments). Its performance encouraged Preece to lay a similar cable to Ireland the following year but on that being brought into service serious 'overhearing' was experienced between the two telephone circuits. A series of experiments attempting to overcome the defect proved unsuccessful so the cable was relegated to telegraph use in 1902, the year when a second telephone cable was laid to the Continent (between Dover and La Panne, forty-three nautical miles). Of a design similar to that of the London–Paris cable of eleven years before, it allowed satisfactory speech between London and Brussels. Eight years later the first (Pupin coil) loaded cable was laid across the Channel from Abbot's Cliff to Cape Grisnez.

*   *   *

The biologist also had to be called to the aid of submarine cable engineers. Preece, in May 1879, sent to Thomas H. Huxley of the Science Schools, South Kensington, some marine organisms recovered from the jute serving around the gutta-percha-insulated conductors cut from a damaged cable during repairs. Huxley replied:

I have examined the specimens you have sent to me. They are almost all Annelids of two kinds, neither of which I believe can be fairly charged with burglarious intentions or practices, though they have sharp enough jaws for simple murder. So I was rather perplexed with the case, until looking narrowly, I found a single example (which I send you put up in Canada balsam) of what I believe to be the real offender. It is the *Limnoria*, a 'gribble' – a little crustacean not very far removed from the woodlice and well known as one of the most destructive attackers of submerged wood.

Some years ago I remember receiving a piece of cable, the sheath of which had been attacked by these creatures, and I have no doubt if a bit of jute packing were carefully examined you would find them in thousands. If you will examine the *Limnoria* with a microscope you will see that he has jaws strong enough for any mischief.

I should suggest soaking the jute in coal tar or creosote if a cable had to be laid in a locality infested by these troublesome pests.

These minute animals, found in the English Channel and the Irish Sea, had been damaging the gutta-percha insulation by scoring grooves in it. Huxley's suggested remedy lost its effect with a few years of submergence and, from 1893, Preece specified brass tape lapping outside the jute serving of all new Post Office cables.

22

LE JARDINIER DE M. PREECE

AT the Society of Telegraph Engineers' meeting on 10 March 1887 members listened to a paper on the use of lead batteries for electric lighting; the speaker believed such a system to be cheaper than gas but thought that no private individual would be willing to incur the cost and trouble of a small steam or gas engine and a dynamo machine for charging those batteries despite the example of that capable individual 'celebrated among our Parisian confrères as *le jardinier de M. Preece*'. Preece, with the assistance of his coachman-gardener, had been lighting Gothic Lodge for the past three years with a battery of secondary cells, had checked its performance by hydrometer readings during charge and discharge, and had made freely available to all interested, copies of his daily records. (Such a system was eminently satisfactory since batteries charged during daylight supply lighting current at night: it might well be in general use today but that it is incapable of producing large quantities for power for which industry has steadily built up such a massive demand.) But a lot had happened before Preece had been able so satisfactorily to light his home.

When the Society was formed in 1871 the only practical applications of electricity, apart from telegraphs, were two or three lighthouses with carbon arc lamps and a few small electro-plating plants. Despite improved forms of carbon rods, notably those of a Russian, Pavel Jablochkoff, in 1876, carbons needed daily renewal. The Société Générale d'Electricité of Paris made an offer in 1878 to the Metropolitan Board of Works, which was accepted, to light the Victoria Embankment between Waterloo and Westminster Bridges by installing an experimental system of arc lighting with lamps forty-five yards apart. The Société supplied the twenty lamps, with their Jablochkoff 'candles', that were needed and all the necessary electrical machinery, while the Board supplied an engine to drive the dynamos. A few days before the Embankment lights were switched on Billingsgate Fish Market was lit inside and out (29 November 1878) with arc lamps. We may note, in passing, that during 1878 a football match was played in Sheffield, before 30000 spectators, under arc lamps. Next year Silvanus P. Thompson (a lecturer in physics at the recently formed Bristol University), who was to become a warm friend of Preece's, persuaded W. D. and H. O. Wills to light their factory by electricity.

British Museum officials (who had much earlier sought Michael Faraday's advice on protecting the Elgin Marbles from damage by London's smoke-laden atmosphere) asked Preece (14 February 1879) if there would be a fire risk were electric light installed in the Reading Room. Preece assured them that with proper wiring there was no risk. They sent him a report two years later on the carbon arc lamps they had installed: the dynamo was driven by a steam engine, the complete equipment being hired from Siemens Brothers with a resultant light cost of $3\frac{1}{2}$d. an hour. Readers approved of the new lighting with one dissentient who wrote to the *Illustrated London News*: 'a quivering light and a cold light; it makes by eyeballs throb and I cannot read by it with comfort'. At Billingsgate there was no general approval; the Market Committee thought well of the light but the salesmen complained that it did not show fish to advantage, and during that cold winter the porters certainly missed the warmth from a thousand gas jets. That innovation was short-lived.

Joseph Wilson Swan of Newcastle had experimented, about 1860, with cellulose threads in a vacuum (to prevent oxidation): such a thread heated to incandescence when a current passed through it but quickly burnt away because of the imperfect vacuum in its containing glass bulb. Vacuum pumps were improved sufficiently for Swan to return to his experiments after fifteen years and he was able to demonstrate a successful lamp to the Chemical Society in 1878.* That year Thomas A. Edison turned his attention to the same problem: news from America that he had solved it occasioned heavy selling of gas companies' shares on the London Stock Exchange.

---

* During the next two years he availed himself of the resources of P.O. engineers in Newcastle to test specimens of his lamp.

1. Detail of portrait of Preece by Beatrice Bright, 1899. Science Museum, London

2. Bryn Helen, Carnarvon, where Preece was born in 1834

3. Caricature of Preece and Lodge. From cover of *Electric Plant*, December 1888

4. Gower–Bell telephone. Standard P.O. instrument until 1891: carbon pencil transmitter; two flexible tubes with ear pieces lead from a Bell receiver. By courtesy of the Post Office

5. Wheatstone's ABC telegraph. Movements of the hand-operated pointer of the transmitter are reproduced in the distant receiver. By courtesy of the Post Office

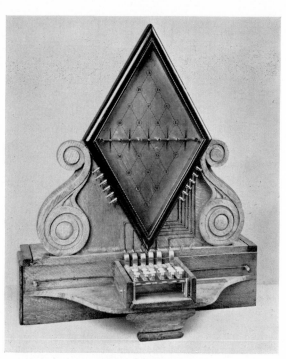

6. Wheatstone's five-needle telegraph, 1837 – a Science Museum facsimile. Science Museum, London

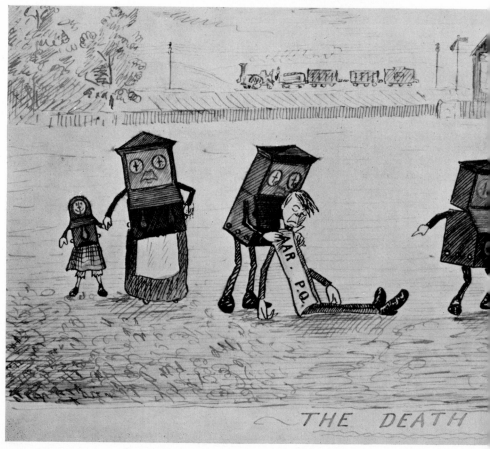

THE DEATH

7. *Below:* PQ was the E.T. Co. code for 'message ends' which the P.O. replaced, c. 1875, with NN 'end of communications'. A single- and double-needle 'drop-handle' telegraphs are with the victim. Charles Wheatstone with his automatic telegraph is caricatured in the centre, and the group of principal Telegraph Department officers depicts (from left to right): F. I. Scudamore, W. H. Preece, W. E. Baines, R. S. Culley, H. C. Fischer and A. V. Tubb. The caricaturist (F. Preston) was on Fischer's staff

POOR. P. Q.

8. Preece at Gothic Lodge, Wimbledon. From *The Sketch*, 6 July 1904

9. Preece in his office in G.P.O. West, 1892. A Wheatstone's four-needle telegraph is on his right. From the *Electrical Times*

10. Preece opening the Electrical Exhibition, Olympia, 1911

11. Main entrance of Penrhos, showing wind-direction indicator

12. Penrhos, Carnarvon, where Preece died in 1913

Swan obtained a preliminary Court Order against infringement of his patent, but wishing to avoid another of the all too frequent legal disputes over patent priority, with expense and delay, that were bedevilling technological improvements, Edison and he agreed to amalgamate their interest in 'glow lamps'.

The British Museum sought Preece's advice in June 1886 on the introduction of secondary batteries which

might lead to a great saving in steam

and,

very much greater satisfaction to students in the North Library and in the Manuscript and Prints Department, as they could get the light without sending someone to set the engines in motion.

Preece approved that suggestion, added a number of recommendations for improving lighting, and advocated purchase rather than hire of plant. This led to the Treasuary agreeing that Preece should act as adviser to the Museum Trustees at a fee of £30 a year.

Preece thereupon took his opportunity to urge that the Museum itself should be lit by electricity to enable it to be opened of an evening so that those who had to work during the day could visit its galleries. His proposal was raised in the House of Commons during the Estimates Debate in the following August and agreement reached to make a start at the Natural History Museum in Cromwell Road, regarded as 'the most attractive for the working classes', subject to safeguarding the premises. The previous three years had been marred by a number of strikes in the course of which mobs damaged shops and other buildings in the West End and 1887 had seen 'Bloody Sunday' with a particularly violent demonstration in Trafalgar Square during which the police had arrested Members of Parliament John Burns and R. B. Cunninghame Graham. The Assistant Commissioner of Police therefore thought

that under existing circumstances the present time is not suitable for introducing the proposed change

but his opinion was not shared by the Commissioner who was confident that such an institution as the British Museum would not become a target for attack.

As an example of the extra staff costs involved, the Museum Trustees had informed the Treasury, in January 1880, that if the galleries (but not the Reading Room) of the Bloomsbury building were opened Sundays during the year for 183 hours one Assistant Keeper would have to be paid 5s. an hour, thirty-two attendants 18d., four ladies' attendants 9d., and five labourers 12d. an hour; and seven constables, say £91.

In the meantime Preece had produced detailed specifications and obtained estimates for plant and installation at the Bloomsbury building. By the end of January 1889, with no further progress, Preece was suggesting that part of the museum be opened experimentally in the evening. He also reiterated that to rent plant was extravagant.

We have paid Messrs. Siemens over and over again for the value of the plant. There is no company within reach of the museum that can supply the current, nor could it furnish it with such economy, safety, and convenience as you can do on the premises.

The Chief Librarian wrote Preece in April,

Preliminaries are settled and the Treasury places us under your wing. We must set to work at once. I shall have to consult you on the purchase of Siemens's gear on the premises.

Next month Siemens's tender to extend wiring throughout the building was accepted, and an order placed with Marshall, Son and Company of Faringdon Road for a 198 h.p. steam engine and boiler at a cost of £1050. Experiments favoured glow lamps, with a great increase in the number of lighting points; the Reading Room had hitherto been lit by five 30 amp arc lamps. November came and Marshall had not yet supplied an engine. Chief Librarian E. M. Thompson, who was known to his colleagues as a querulous character, grumbled to Preece that

it is evident to me that they have put us on one side in order to execute for sharper people than the fools at Bloomsbury.

A few days later he wrote Preece, 'your credit is at stake as much as ours' – Siemens was also behind schedule –

swearing has gone out of fashion but I have heard of strange progress sometimes made under the influence of strong language – and a few amperes of that material may be necessary.

Thompson seemed at least to be picking up something of technical language in letting off steam: he should have known that Preece was the last man to swear at or bully anyone. Next day Thompson wrote again having received a letter from Preece explaining delays at Marshall's were because of difficulties at the Britannia Ironworks, Gainsborough.

These Yorkshiremen imagine, apparently, that because they are proverbially supposed to know all about horses, they may be accounted equally good judges of the less noble but still useful quadruped. Really James Marshall seems to think us very simple people and his letter to you is not only unsatisfactory but impertinent.

Preece insisted with Marshall that everything should be ready for the evening of New Year's Day when the formal opening had been planned.

In the event the Trustees invited 1200 guests to inspect the new installation, 'now the largest in London', on Tuesday, 28th January. Current was generated by four Siemens's dynamo machines in pairs, each giving 450 amps at 130 volts to supply 147 arc lamps and 850 glow lamps of 12 to 16 candle-power. Total cost was under £7000. East and west halves of the building were to be opened on alternate weekday evenings.

The *Evening News* reported:

No money has ever been better spent than that which the House (both sides of it agreeing) voted last year for the electric lighting of the British Museum. Some eight or nine years ago the electric light was introduced into the beautiful reading room and its approaches, as also into the courtyard . . . occasional flickerings and changes of colour are very ordinary faults in arc lighting. Last night the arc lights were as steady as any glow lamp. [The galleries would be] open in the evening at hours which will allow the working and the shop keeping classes to visit it. From 7 to 10 in the evening is likely to be henceforth the most crowded time.

'Very bad' weather kept a fair number of the invitees away but among those present were Professor Crookes, J. A. Froude, Richard Garnett, the Greek Minister, the Italian Ambassador, Professor Ray

Lankester, and Norman Lockyer, the Astronomer Royal. Preece assured a *Pall Mall Gazette* reporter that on the Elgin Marbles

not even the sun of Greece brought these statues out more beautifully than does the electric light.

* * *

The proposal to light the Thames Embankment by electricity in 1878 had caused a controversy in the columns of London newspapers: that a frontage of over a thousand yards could be lit from one central source was held to be preposterous. Some (said to be gas engineers) published a pamphlet seeking to prove that to light the streets of London alone would need at least 1700 power stations, and as many 2 h.p. gas engines, each with its driver. Others predicted that all the current would be lost if an attempt were made to divide it among several lights. That they had only to go to Paris to see such lighting in operation at the Avenue and Place de l'Opéra, and in the Théâtre Français, seemed beside the point. Twenty arc lamps were soon lighting the Embankment between Westminster and Waterloo Bridges (13th December); ten more lamps were added in May on Waterloo Bridge itself, and, in October, ten lamps between Waterloo and Blackfriars Bridge completed the lighting of the Embankment. The price charged by the Jablochkoff Company for each lamp was then reduced from 6d. to 3d. an hour. The single power station was on the opposite side of the river, under an arch of Charing Cross Bridge.

A Select Committee on Lighting by Electricity was appointed, with Dr Lyon Playfair as Chairman, to consider whether it was desirable to authorize municipal corporations or other local authorities to adopt schemes for lighting by electricity. The committee held ten meetings during April–June 1879 to conclude that the time had not arrived to give general powers to private electricity companies to break up streets to lay underground mains without permission of local authorities who should themselves be given full powers to use electric light for public illumination, that gas companies had no special claims to be considered as future distributors of electric light, and that the House should show willingness, when the demand arose, to give all reasonable powers for the full development of electricity as a source of power and light. They also reported that electric light had not progressed sufficiently to enter into general competition with gas for ordinary purposes of domestic supply: there was no system of central origin and distribution suitable for houses of moderate size.

Among the technical witnesses called before the committee was Preece, who described himself as 'Electrician to the Post Office', which he said was interested in electric lighting on grounds of economy and hygiene. There could be as many as a thousand staff in a large telegraph gallery at night, dealing mainly with press telegrams. That staff vitiated a million cubic feet of air each hour and the gas it used as an illuminant four million cubic feet. He had examined all the systems in London and Paris. He had not yet found equipment which met with such a gallery's requirements of six 1000 c.p. arc lights, steady and with carbons lasting all night, which was eighteen hours in winter. He referred to a paper of his, recently published in the *Philosophical Magazine*, on the positioning of lighting points; and to experiments he had made in Aldersgate Street to demonstrate that electric light currents (3000 times greater than telegraph currents) needed to be screened by iron pipes or kept at least six feet from telegraphs where the wires of each ran parallel for a quarter of a mile or more, otherwise currents would be induced on the telegraphs to interfere with transmitted signals. While telegraph wires might be put underground the cost of doing so was three to four times overhead costs. The Post Office used only batteries to power telegraphs, all of which worked on single wires with earthed returns and to use return wires would cost a very large sum indeed for the 117000 miles involved. Electricity companies could have return wires.

* * *

The Society of Telegraph Engineers recognized that by 1878 an appropriate time had arrived to stage a public exhibition of electric light and chose the Albert Hall to house it. The Society agreed that an inaugural lecture should be presented at the opening on 7th May and each member was sure that Preece was the man to give it. In the event his masterly performance was referred to, by electrical engineers who heard him, for many years afterwards. The hall was lit by numerous bat-wing gas jets as normally but as Preece proceeded with his lecture groups of arc lights of particular systems (seven, including that in use at *The Times* printing office, were being demonstrated, together with ship's lights, and a forerunner of the searchlight by the War Office) 'burst forth to his word of command'. The *Standard* leader-writer assured his readers next day that:

The brilliant display of the Electric Light in and about the Albert Hall last evening affords an indication of the earnestness with which men of science and ability are endeavouring to make this powerful form of illumination available for practical purposes. The Council of the Royal Albert Hall have shewn a wise discernment in placing before the public the various achievements which have thus far been accomplished in reference to the Electric Light, and the imposing assembly which came together last evening under the presidency of the Prince of WALES to witness the inaugural proceedings proves that the subject is one of very general interest. A scientific 'feast of lanterns' is now being held in South Kensington, and will last until the end of the week. The new lamps which are in some degree to supersede the old, are now brought together into one spot, and it will be seen how vast is the diversity, where it might have been thought there was little scope for variation. In the presence of the Prince of WALES, accompanied by his brother the Duke of EDIN-BURGH, and other Royal and distinguished personages, an admirable lecture was given last evening on the science and art of electric lighting, by Mr. W. H. PREECE, the electrician to Her MAJESTY'S Post Office. The audience numbered several thousands and the arena of the Hall was occupied by a splendid array of apparatus connected with the subject of the lecture. As Mr. PREECE proceeded with his remarks lights came flashing up as if by magic to illustrate the several passages of his address. Not only on the floor of the hall, but away up to the topmost gallery, and higher still, in the centre of the lofty ceiling, various forms of the Electric Light presented themselves.

The value of the Electric Light for preventing collisions at sea was adverted to last evening by the Duke of EDINBURGH, who also alluded to its utility in the Royal Navy as a protection against torpedoes. One scene of peril, which happened to escape notice last evening, is that afforded by the deep underground workings of our collieries. The Electric Light, being independent of air for the maintenance of its flame, would seem to offer a mode of illumination exactly suited to the necessities of the miner.

The Admiralty are also alive to the value of the light for naval warfare. If we cannot, by means of the electric beam, actually put out the eyes of our enemies, we can at least deprive them of the opportunity of carrying on their designs unobserved in the dark. Apprehensive of torpedo attack, the ironclad may surround herself with an artificial sunshine, and the commander of a fortress may, in like manner protect himself against nocturnal surprise.

After that divergence to naval warfare, occasioned presumably by the Royal Visitor's remarks, the writer returned to Preece.

Inherently, therefore, the Electric Light is cheaper than gas, but its production on a small scale is disadvantageous. Even on the large scale it has some drawbacks, and it will be seen that Mr. PREECE recognises certain virtues in gas, together with sundry defects in its powerful competitor. So the case stands at present, and it is satisfactory to find that the world is likely to afford room for both descriptions of light, while there is at the same time the prospects that each will undergo improvements, though the greater scope for that purpose is on the side of the Electric Light.

Nor did he then know that Swan and Edison were already taking advantage of that greater scope with the glow lamps they had developed, even though they were not yet ready to show those at a public exhibition.

23

ELECTRIC LIGHTING COMPANIES

PREECE was elected President of the Society of Telegraph Engineers for 1880 and in the traditional presidential address he reviewed historically theories of heat, light and electricity, the disturbances to telegraph lines occasioned by sun-spot activity, culminating in 'Mr Crooke's recent beautiful experiments in molecular physics in high vacua . . .' He noted that matter was constructed from sixty-four known elements:

there may be others that have not yet been discovered . . . the scientific man, while rather too fond of decrying the exercise of faith in others, is himself the humblest slave of the imagination. A physical theory may be complete. The various facts and laws which it embraces may be related mathematically with one another. Yet one single incompatible phenomenon may dissolve it, 'and like this insubstantial pageant faded, leave not a rack behind'. Hence, while apparently dogmatic in my description of the present theory of matter and force, I wish it to be distinctly understood that it rests, and must continue to rest, on the imaginative power of the mind.

He reported that although the increase in mileage of wire of State telegraphs since 1871 had been small, traffic had doubled and the average weekly number of messages was now 600000, made possible by improvements in Wheatstone's automatic apparatus, the introduction of duplex working and, recently, quadruplex (two signals simultaneously in each direction), and the insertion of intermediate relay stations on long lines.

But, he continued, 'we have reached a limit; our system is actually gorged with messages, failures of wires cause considerable trouble, inconvenience, and complaint, the public – our watchful but not lenient masters – are beginning to growl, and the erection of additional wires has become essential. It is hoped that a new trunk line to the North and many additional wires will be erected during the ensuing summer. . . . The cry that invention has been checked by the monopoly of the Government is made by those who are ignorant of contemporaneous history, who are too callous to enquire for themselves into the truth of the accusation, and with whom most probably the wish is father to the thought.

He referred to the telephone, 'the great excitement of the previous session', and on electric light he pronounced that

the lamp of the future has not yet been produced though steadiness and duration have very much advanced during the past twelve months. One of its most notable and useful applications has been on board ship, to further the operations during the night in laying and repairing cables. I was present on board the S.S. *Dacia*, in the Mediterranean, when this was done, and the success was unequivocal. Gas is not going to be affected by electric light. The proper function of gas is to generate heat. Ninety-four per cent of the ingredients of gas are consumed in generating heat and only six per cent in producing light.

Latimer Clark proposed a vote of thanks to their new President for a very able and 'of course, very eloquent' address.

*   *   *

An Electric Lighting Act came into operation on 18 August 1882. It empowered the Board of Trade to grant licences authorizing any local authority or company to supply electricity in any area, but limited licence periods to seven years when it might be renewed for a similar period, but at each renewal, were a private contractor concerned, the local authority would have the option of purchasing the undertaking.

The Gas Light and Coke Company was collecting an annual rental of £370000 for lighting the City of London streets. Colonel Haywood, engineer to the Commissioners of Sewers, the City authorities responsible, reported to them on the success of public arc lighting in Paris in 1878 and suggested an experiment whereby Holborn Viaduct, from Holborn Circus to the Old Bailey, should be lit by electric arc lamps for three months that winter: when the experiment was discontinued sixteen arc lamps of 16 c.p. each had proved four

Q

times as costly to run as eighty-six 14 c.p. gas jets. Nevertheless, the Commissioners decided to renew experiments in 1880 and selected the main streets in the zone bounded by the Thames from London Bridge to Blackfriars Bridge and the Bank to Ludgate Circus. The Anglo-American Brush Company was given a contract for the Blackfriars area, a company using the Lontin system the Southwark area, and Siemens's company the London Bridge area which was later taken over by the Brush Company whose central station was in Belvedere Road, Bankside, the mains being carried over Blackfriars Bridge. The experiment was sufficiently successful to encourage the Commissioners to consider adding more districts but following the Electric Lighting Act came a flood of applications for provisional orders and licences including three for areas of the City.

The Commissioners had to consider, therefore, the position in which the Act had placed them. They decided to approach Preece to inform him that they proposed themselves to apply for powers to light the City. He agreed to act as consultant and, in recommending a circumspect approach to their project, wrote

I know no branch of engineering where more forethought is necessary to calculate all the contingencies likely to be met with than a system designed to illuminate a large city like that of London.

Later experience certainly fully justified his caution. He experimented with the installations then in operation in the City and as a result reported:

While the arc lamp is admirably adapted for the illumination of large spaces, the glow lamp is eminently adapted for our streets and narrow thoroughfares . . . the lamp which in my judgement best lends itself to street lighting is the glow lamp, I prefer the 50 c.p. lamp for the main thoroughfare.

Major-General C. E. Webber, speaking at the S.T.E. twelve years later, described what Preece had written as 'certainly the standard report on the subject of public lighting'.

The Edison Company, in 1882, had experimented with glow lamps in Holborn Viaduct which, despite twelve months' run, were not considered a success; nevertheless, Preece recommended further trials with glow lamps in a small area of the City, in which a means of distribution for private lighting could be combined. Such trials were not carried out because of a stagnation in large-scale electrical enterprise in England, largely as a result of the short period of seven years before a local purchase option became available. In consequence an amending Act was passed to increase that period to twenty-one years. Meanwhile, Preece had, at the Commissioners' request, reported in detail on lighting at Sheffield, Taunton, and St Pancras Station.

The Bristol Corporation had given a trial, in 1881, to arc lamp lighting at High Cross, where four main streets meet, but without much success. None the less, they decided to apply for permission, under the Act, to light the City streets: they were actuated also by the wish to prevent applications by private companies. They obtained the services of Preece as consultant and he recommended a waiting policy, until power generating and distribution technique had been further improved. In 1893, on his advice, a power station was built at Temple Back; arc lamps lit the streets and private consumers were supplied with current: speaking that November on the latest views on electric lighting he said,

Why at Bristol though the place is not yet officially opened there are 11000 lights booked and the engineer-in-charge is beginning to talk of the necessary immediate extensions.

Preece also acted as consultant to the Great Eastern Railway on the lighting of its London terminus. Not everyone approved of his advocacy of electric lighting. He was invited to address the Great Yarmouth Town Council after which its members agreed to apply for a provisional order and to retain his services as a consultant. Later a member who had opposed that agreement referred to Preece's address as

the dogmatic utterance of a self-complacent monopoly defender.

The Vestry of St Pancras began to supply electricity on 9 November 1891 and advertised it with an exhibition at the Town Hall from that day till the end of the month. Thomas E. Gibbs introduced

the inauguration of what may be called the municipalization of electricity in London . . . 6d. a Board of Trade unit. . . . Hitherto local bodies have looked to capitalists to inaugurate such all-important matters as their water supply, the supply of gas, tramways, and even markets . . . the

1882 Act originally intended to limit monopoly rights to seven years, was extended by the House of Lords to 21 years and later increased to 42 years. The Corporation of the City of London which ought to have set an example has surrendered its powers to the City of London Electric Light Company.

During the run of the exhibition four public lectures were arranged, the second of which – on the relative cost of lighting by gas and by electricity – was given by Preece. He informed his audience that he was a gas shareholder but his sole object was to get at the truth. In Manchester the quality of gas supplied was above average for the country: there a pound of coal produced 17·2 candle-power of illumination by gas for an hour that would have been sufficient to light a 48 c.p. glow lamp. The Manchester Corporation had applied for a provisional order to establish an electric light station. The Post Office had been able to produce a Board of Trade unit (kilowatt-hour) of electricity for 4d. and were lighting St Martin's-le-Grand (G.P.O. East and Central Telegraph Office) with 10000 lamps. They were laying a similar plant at Coldbath Fields (Mount Pleasant Postal Sorting Office).

In my own house, where I generate my own electricity and have done so for the last eight years . . . I find, although I have a gas engine and accumulators, and have over 70 lamps, I am not paying more than when I had gas burners.

He commented on the electricity companies by then operating in London (Metropolitan, Chelsea, Kensington and Knightsbridge, St James and Pall Mall, and the House-to-House). In the Savings Bank Department in Queen Victoria Street electric light had diminished sickness by two days per head a year (1200 staff), which at 10d. an hour overtime represented a saving of £680 to set against an electricity cost of £700 a year. At St Martin's-le-Grand, where the light had been put in just before Christmas, the Controller told him that it had speeded up work to the equivalent of an extra 200 staff.

The price of gas is going up from labour disputes and strikes; the price of electricity is coming down because we know so very much more about it.

A difficulty with electricity at the time was that the load was variable, a constant load would be cheaper to provide for.

There is one reason why gas is still ahead of electricity . . . there is such a market in this country for residuals, the price obtained for coke and ammoniacal liquor and the other productions of gas works, practically reduces the price of coal to the gas manufacturers in London to 6/4d a ton . . . Welsh coal in London is 23s. per ton . . . that is why we pay more for electric light than for gas . . . in Gibraltar and Malta, where I recently went to see whether it is possible to introduce electric light there is no market for residuals and it required no difficulty on my part to show that it was possible to produce electricity cheaper than gas. . . . The electric light is the light of the future, and not the light of luxury merely, but the poor man's lamp as well.

*　　*　　*

Interest in electricity was also burgeoning in northern Europe and an International Electrical Exhibition was arranged in Vienna in 1883. The British Post Office did not intend to participate but a direct invitation came from the Austrian Administration. For the British Isles three Commissioners were appointed (Thomson, Siemens and another) under Lord Sudeley. Preece arranged for H. R. Kempe to deal with the Post Office exhibit, the Treasury having granted £200 for expenses. Lord Sudeley wrote to Postmaster-General Fawcett complaining of the Post Office exhibit, and Kempe informed Preece that it compared unfavourably with that of the French Post Office. Preece thereupon dispatched a collection of historical telegraph instruments. Kempe returned on 25th August, before it had arrived, and Preece left for Vienna that night at his own expense. Less than a week later he reported that the British pavilion was very nice and that on arrival he, and two members of the local staff, had unpacked twenty-one boxes and had put their contents in position. He had been

a great object of attraction all day for superior officers are not often seen here in their shirts with their sleeves tucked up to their shoulders and perspiring at every pore.

Part of his consignment did not arrive till Wednesday, 12th September, when Preece wrote that its contents would be in place on the following day, and that he had arranged for two Austrian telegraphists to give descriptions of the equipment, for which he had promised them a gratuity of £5 each.

I will leave on Sunday and you will see me on Wednesday morning. I lecture tomorrow on telegraphs in England compared with those on the Continent, and on Friday on the principal novelties and the scientific instruments shown by the S.T.E.

He mentioned several who had helped him arrange the exhibition, including a Lieutenant Anstruther of the Army. The Emperor was giving a reception to the King of Spain on his arrival on Friday evening. There would be a press reception on Saturday, 'so what with lectures and royalty I shall have enough of it'.

Fawcett saw all the correspondence, said there was no need to reply to Sudeley yet, and regarded Preece's report as most satisfactory. He wished his appreciation of Preece's success to be conveyed to him and letters of thanks written to the gentlemen mentioned by Preece. 'If there is money to spare should not Mr Preece's expenses be paid?' (the British Commissioners had caused the difficulty by apportioning four counters at the exhibition to the Post Office instead of one as planned). Edward Graves passed on Fawcett's appreciation to Preece, concluding:

A very pleasant ending to what threatened to be a troublesome and unpleasant matter.

* * *

A paper was given, at a Society of Telegraph Engineers and Electricians meeting in February 1884, on an experiment the year before when Staat Forbes, Chairman of the Metropolitan District Railway, had a train equipped with electric light, a small engine with dynamo being coupled to the locomotive to take steam from the boiler, a London Chatham and Dover Railway parcels van being borrowed for the purpose. The lecturer recalled that there had never been a serious attempt in this country to light trains efficiently with oil lamps, although various systems of gas lighting had been tried.

In the discussion which followed Preece expressed himself strongly:

If in this civilized age there is anything more disgraceful than another, it is the abominable darkness in which we are compelled to be confined during those long railway journeys some of us have to make to the north of Scotland and to different parts of this country.

The difficulty he saw was that most trains were not run as on the District Railway but divided *en route* so that each portion would have to be supplied with its own engine and dynamo, and youth in attendance. The train would have to remain in darkness whenever the engine was disconnected, often up to three-quarters of an hour at Crewe. Although objections to steam as a prime mover were considerable, all objections, more or less, by experience, were got over. The London Brighton and South Coast Railway had tried secondary batteries. These had been successful on the Victoria–Brighton trains, the company supplying them being responsible for maintenance. Primary batteries had been tried in the past on the Midland, Great Northern, South Eastern, and South Western railways. Experiments had been tried on the London and South Western Railway whereby the energy dissipated in a train's movement was collected and stored but the air engine available was very inefficient.

A lively discussion followed during which it was pointed out that a train had for the past eighteen months been running between London Bridge and Victoria equipped with secondary battery lighting. One speaker had no doubt that the public would be very glad to be able to read on a long journey in a comfortable manner without having recourse to the railway reading-lamp, of which railway companies would like to see the last, for they often damaged a compartment's upholstery with their grease and sometimes even tore the cloth.

The lecturer concluded his reply by thanking

Mr Preece for having administered what I hope will prove a death-blow to the wretched dog-in-the-manger game which has been played so long with such disastrous results.

*   *   *

Colonel R. E. Crompton in April 1888 gave a paper on 'Central Station lighting: transformers versus accumulators', at a meeting of the Society of Telegraph Engineers and Electricians (the title had been expanded in 1881: it was changed to the Institution of Electrical Engineers in 1889). During the following discussion Preece said that there were thirty or forty corporations and communities that day waiting for electric light: some had consulting engineers who were not yet able to advise them which system to install.

I am in that position and have held back during the past two or three years some very large installations because it has been impossible to decide whether the best system to adopt is that of secondary generators or secondary batteries. . . . I do not suppose there is any man present in this room who has not had more practical experience of secondary batteries than I have myself . . . there are few forms of them which I have not burst up. I went over to Paris when M. Faure first brought out his battery before it was made public, and I formed, as I have often formed before, a wrong opinion about it. Shortly afterwards I found others who were rather more far-sighted than myself, and now it is one of the most beautiful of instruments that an electrician has at his disposal.

Preece had used secondary batteries in his own house since early in 1884 and during the past two and a half years, since he put in a battery of twenty-five E.P.S. cells, his lamps had never had a flicker 'as we see every night we come here in this hall lighted by gas'. He forecast that in future electric motors would be used to a large extent for small trades, and for household purposes such as sewing machines. Something that was also to come was a motor to work with alternating currents. Transformers, on the other hand, which enabled the use of a very high difference of potential and high e.m.f., led to cheap conductors for current could be transmitted over great distances with small loss of energy. When the twenty-one years, or as they hoped forty-two years, were up there would be no local authority which could possibly buy up a system that distributed over a very large area. The Grosvenor Gallery Company were pioneers in distributing high-voltage alternating current. He suggested that several engines and dynamos were more economical than one very large one. He thought the Society should take a stand on the voltage of lamps: they now had nine voltages in operation between 20 and 110. Another member pointed out that in early days a lamp of higher voltage than 40 could not be made but he hoped they would 'get by-and-by to 200'. Three years later Preece, when discussing specifications, noted that

a very curious practice has recently developed itself among our wiring contractors. They have asked the manufacturers to reduce the over-all diameter of their insulated conductors . . . to enable them to utilize the grooved boards which they happen to have in stock . . . the interests of the users of the light are to be sacrificed to the interests of the wood-carvers!

On systems of supply, he affirmed his conviction that

engineering works must necessarily be considered a species of compromise . . . what is good for one place need not necessarily be good for another. The independent engineer . . . must give every plan his consideration . . . despite the tyranny of Patent Laws and the susceptibilities of inventors. He must, however, be just and see that merit is rewarded and claims respected.

*   *   *

Preece gave evidence before a Joint Committee of Lords and Commons on Electric Power Protective Clauses, in the summer of 1893. He reported a gradual increase in the disturbance to Post Office telephones through induced currents from tramways and electric lighting mains which could be remedied by using metallic circuits. Earth returns were universally used on telegraphs: duplex and quadruplex could not be worked on metallic circuits which in any case would double costs and thus be financially impossible, but otherwise telegraphs had yet to be affected. The Post Office was using metallic circuits for telephones but, except for main lines, telephone companies used earth returns for their circuits, as did railways for block signalling. Electric light companies were now prohibited under a provisional order from using earth returns.

Although the City and South London (Electric) Railway did not designedly use earth returns it had disturbed electrical observing instruments at Greenwich, for there was a leakage from the (uninsulated) railway lines used as a return. That leakage led to a decomposition of lead pipes: at a house in Clapham Road 0·3 volts had been measured between gas and water pipes due to leakage when electric trams passed the house.

The Committee recommended metallic circuits for telephones, insulated metallic return circuits on railways, and the enforcement of Board of Trade standards in the generation and distribution of electricity.

The Board of Trade appointed, on 27 November 1895, a committee to consider whether the limit of low pressure defined by the Board of Trade Electric Lighting Regulations for the protection of public safety should be altered. Its members were Lord Kelvin (whom Preece had first met as William Thomson forty years before),

Major Cardew and Preece himself. The question had been discussed at a conference on electricity supply at Westminster Town Hall the week before when, among proposals carried at the meeting, was a weekly testing of the whole of a distribution system. Preece had referred at that conference to the daily test of telegraph circuits carried out by the Post Office which, Major-General C. E. Webber pointed out in a letter to the technical press, was scarcely parallel to having each consumer's installation tested together with the mains system which would have to be done on the earlier, straggling, pioneer electric lighting systems in operation.

The regulations defined low pressure as not exceeding 300 volts d.c. or 150 volts a.c.; high pressure being up to 3000 volts and extra high pressure over that value. The Committee amended the low pressure figures to 500 and 300 respectively and specified 250 volts as the pressure to be supplied to the consumer (instead of 150) and ruled that no earth connection should be higher than 300 volts. They handed in their report on 3rd December and were officially thanked for their celerity.

24

JUBILEES

THE year 1887, which saw the jubilee celebrations of Queen Victoria's accession to the throne, was also the jubilee of the electric telegraph. In the Post Office there was a sufficient number interested in marking that occasion even though it would make little impact amidst the national junketings. They agreed on a dinner at the Holborn Restaurant, on 27th July, and sent invitations to more than two hundred notable members of the telegraphic profession. Postmaster-General H. C. Raikes presided. Other speakers were G. B. Bruce, President of the I.C.E., Latimer Clark, G. Shaw Lefevre, M.P., the Earl of Onslow, John Pender, Sir Lyon Playfair, the President of the Royal Society G. G. Stokes, and Sir William Thomson.

Preece's contribution to the proceedings was to read letters from invitees unable to be present and congratulatory telegrams from Australia, India, New Zealand ('May Macaulay's prophecy never be realized!'), Peru, and (addressed to Preece by Eckert of the Western Union) the United States. A letter from New South Wales reported that its Telegraph Department, which included telephony, had 425 stations, with a staff of 1200, and 735 telephone subscribers, adding:

Our railway telegraphs include 203 stations and 2,500 miles of line. ... On double lines where the traffic is very heavy Preece's block system is operated with a success which cannot fail to gratify the eminent and genial inventor. Whilst our material progress has thus been advancing by rapid strides, there has sprung up amongst us and grown into vivacious maturity that brotherhood of feeling towards our fellow-workers throughout the world which seems characteristic of telegraph men; but the line of least resistance, and therefore that which carries the greatest share of the current of our sympathy, is that which connects us with the land whence so many of us have come, and which, although separated by great spaces of time and distance, is yet thought of and spoken of by us as the dear old home where telegraphy now holds its first Jubilee.

A memorable occasion for all those present, which included Preece's elder two sons then newly embarked on careers as electricians. Llewellyn had the year before been given a post on the Midland Railway under Preece's old Southampton colleague W. E. Langdon. Preece had not forgotten his expressed wish for those two boys written at Dresden twelve years before. He had sent Arthur, after his attendance at King's College School, to Germany to study before enrolment at King's College. Llewellyn's indifferent health regrettably precluded as strenuous a course of training and he had completed his studies at an Electrical College in Hanover Square.

The Postmaster-General three years later again presided over jubilee celebrations of concern to the whole of the Post Office, that of Uniform Penny Postage, associated with the name at Rowland Hill. These also began with a dinner at the Holborn Restaurant on 17th January, but did not end there. The Lord Mayor of London held a 'conversazione' at the Guildhall on 16th May: it included a Post Office exhibition, with telegraphs, which stayed open for two more days. Post Office officials really spread themselves on a comparable occasion on 2nd July at South Kensington Museum when they staged a most comprehensive exhibition.

A colleague of his described Preece's contribution to those celebrations:

To judge by Mr. Preece's report, telegraphy as practised on this occasion [the Guildhall 'converzatione'] was instructive rather than amusing, the whole technical staff being assiduously and zealously engaged in explaining the history and working of the various telegraph systems. Mr. Preece assures us that it was very popular and interesting; but joining up appears for the time being to have choked the joking down, for the only funny thing on view was a stuffed woodpecker who had made a hole nearly through a telegraph post, probably under the impression that there were some bees inside. No one, however, who knows Mr. Preece will accuse him of a want of humour, and we can only suppose that he was then ruminating the great jest which was to enliven the South Kensington proceedings, and that, meanwhile, he scorned all meaner things in that line.

The great joke of the evening [at South Kensington museum] . . . is thus described in the official programme: –

'In the Textile Gallery there may possibly be met with a telegraph 'office of 1990, where special facilities for the transaction of new develop-'ments of Post Office business will be provided, and where, by means 'of contrivances which are certainly not as yet publicly known, the 'expectation will be held out of instantaneous communications passing 'between London and all parts of the world by sight and speech, and not 'by the old-world contrivances of the nineteenth century, and its 'so-called electric telegraph. Moreover, the greatest invention of the 'age, the electrophonoscope, will be shewn there for the first time.'

By this invention, a person standing at a telephone and conversing with another through it, sees the features of the person with whom he is conversing. Every great invention from the time of Tubal Cain to the present day has been the subject of depreciation and we are hardly surprised, therefore, to hear it confidently asserted that vision was effected not by electricity as claimed, but by an ingenious arrangement of mirrors, and that this can be effected only when the interlocutors are not more than a few yards distant from one another.

*   *   *

A semi-jubilee (the 25th anniversary of the establishment of sub-marine telegraphy to the Far East) was celebrated on 20 July 1894 when the Eastern, Australasia, and China Telegraph Companies gave a banquet in the Great Hall of the Imperial Institute: their chairman Sir John Pender, M.P., welcomed 450 guests, among whom were J. C. Lamb P.O. Third Secretary, Fischer, and Preece with others from the Post Office. The meal was followed by a reception of 5000 visitors, including the Prince of Wales who pre-viewed an exhibition of cable instruments and equipment in the upper galleries and tele-graphed special messages throughout a system of 50000 miles of cables, receiving replies from the Viceroy of India and from as far as New Zealand within a few minutes.

A second 25th anniversary followed, on 28th January the next year, of the transfer of telegraphs to the State, with a dinner at the Hotel Metropole and Postmaster-General Arnold Morley in the chair. Among the two hundred guests were several distinguished electri-cians: although not referred to in reports of the occasion, Preece and other P.O. engineers were undoubtedly present. In speaking of the increasing rapidity of communications Morley instanced that in February 1836 Charles Greville, then in Paris, wrote (in his *Journal*) that the King's speech had been received there at nine o'clock in the morning within twenty-nine hours of its delivery in London, a degree of rapidity which to him was almost incredible. When, however, it was remembered that the news of the Great Fire of London took five days to reach the Duke of Buckingham in his country house in Bognor, within sixty miles of London, they ought not to be surprised at Greville's incredulity.

The May issue of the *Gentleman's Magazine* that year carried an article under the title *The Semi-Jubilee of State Telegraphy* which described in detail the Central Telegraph Office, the systems in use there, and the effect of the telegraph service on the economies of comparatively isolated communities in the United Kingdom, concluding with:

At the moment in which these pages receive their final touch, there comes the announcement that the Prince of Wales has just sent an autograph telegram from the Royal United Service Institution to the Duke of Connaught at Aldershot. This was accomplished by means of the 'Telautograph' of Mr. Elisha Gray, an apparatus requiring as many as four wires, and representing in its present condition, rather the luxury than the liberty of telegraphing. But who can tell what it may have accomplished when the Jubilee, or, still more, the Centenary of State Telegraphy comes to be celebrated, and when Mr. Preece's dream of telegraphing *without wires* shall have been realised?

25

AMERICA REVISITED

PREECE's second visit to the New World was not on official business: he went on holiday in September 1884, sailing on the S.S. *Parisian* from Liverpool, with two hundred other members of the British Association, for Montreal, there to attend its first meeting outside the United Kingdom. Preece later reported that the only novelty he could recall was a paper on the voltaic cell by Oliver Lodge, 'introduced in an original, an efficient, and a chirpy manner'. Preece while there had advocated the kilowatt as the standard unit of work, which incurred the displeasure of leader-writers of most scientific journals. His comment on that reaction was:

One will always find ridicule and ignorance running side by side: and it is almost an invariable fact that when a new proposition is brought forward it is laughed at. I am always glad to see that, because it always succeeds in drawing attention to the matter.

Leaving Montreal Preece travelled south to Philadelphia to attend a convention of the American Institute of Electrical Engineers being staged there. The discussion which followed a paper on secondary batteries gave him an opportunity 'to bring the matter up to date' by giving an account of recent work he had done on them. He recalled with relish that

a young reporter who was below me amused himself while I was speaking in cutting and paring his nails and when I had finished he came to me and said, 'I guess I'd like them notes of yours.' I asked, 'What notes?' 'Notes of your address' he said. 'They are in my head' I said. He went away in scorn and I read in the local paper next day that 'an Englishman here made some incoherent remarks and evidently was quite ignorant of his subject'.

After Philadelphia Preece visited exhibitions in Chicago, St Louis, and Boston. He found telegraphs not noticeably improved since 1877, except for Delaney's invention whereby six Morse messages could be sent simultaneously in each direction over a circuit. He noted that telephone companies were taxed by the towns in which they operated 'for every pole they erected and every wire they extended'. One flourishing company was thus mulcted of three-quarters of its receipts.

Here we ask the companies to pay the poor, impoverished, British Government ten per cent.

Where you exist in a Turkish bath at from 90° to 100° you want to be saved every possible reason for leaving your office to conduct your business; and the telephone comes in as a means whereby you can do so, and can loll back in your armchair, with your legs up in the air, with a cigar in your mouth, with a punkah waving over your head and a bottle of iced water by your side. By the telephone under such circumstances, business transactions can be carried out with comfort . . . here we are always glad of an excuse to get out of our offices. In America, too, servants and messengers are the exception; a boy is not to be had, whereas in England we can get an errand boy for half a crown a week. That which costs 2/6d here costs 12–15s. in America.

He noted too that Americans were keen to adopt electrical contrivances for domestic purposes and that in each house he had visited he had seen in its hall a small dial on which an indicator could be turned to a selected contact and pressed, to communicate to a central office which in turn summoned the service thus requested of cab, doctor, fire-engine, policeman, and so on. Domestic telegraphs were rare in Europe, nor did Preece suppose that anyone in London would have a telephone if he thought he could conveniently do without it, although its annual cost was £20 compared with New York £35–£44, Chicago £26, Boston and Philadelphia £25. He had learnt that thirty-two separate companies were supplying New York with electricity and had six distinct lines of poles carrying wires down Broadway. Philadelphia's local government was going to force wires underground by chopping down poles. He had seen seven fires caused by high-tension wires falling on telegraph and telephone wires below, on the same poles.

He visited Edison who 'took me all over his place and showed me everything'. Edison, he found, had solved the problem of supplying electric light to houses in New York. That electric light might be distributed to households from common mains as with water and gas had not been thought possible by many electricians. Preece spoke with confidence on its possibility though that was yet to be demonstrated (early in 1880); he held that the sub-division of light had a bright future and paraphrased Wordsworth's 'She was a phantom of delight'. C. W. Siemens, in the chair at that meeting, listened not to the voice of the charmer, and flatly disagreed: centralized light (that is, in rooms of 6000 square feet or more) would hold the field, he was sure, for 'the eye could not bear the intensity of such light brought near it'. When a report had first reached England two years before that Edison had applied for a patent to distribute sub-divided light (using carbon thread in small vacuum glass bulbs) Preece had noted that Edison had 269 current American patents at that time, and he recalled a saying that an American infant would think of a way to improve his cradle, clamber out to patent his idea, and then get back into the cradle again.

Preece returned from that visit on the S.S. *Aurania* which left New York on 22nd October to take nine days under steam and sail to reach Liverpool.

★   ★   ★

Among the events planned under the aegis of Chicago's 'World's Fair' in 1893 was an International Electrical Congress, particularly to discuss electrical units, to which leading electricians in Europe each received an invitation. Preece as President of the Institution of Electrical Engineers was invited and the Secretary of the Post Office facilitated his acceptance by requesting him to report on telegraphs, telephones and electrical engineering generally in the United States.

Preece sailed from Southampton on 5th August aboard the United States liner *Paris*. On that visit he had to give interviews to journalists and had their products been as admirable as in the *New York Sun* which filled three columns on Sunday, 20th August – the day before the Chicago congress opened – he should have been well pleased:

. . . leading electricians of this country and Europe have been personally

R

invited . . . never before has there been such a gathering of the genius and talent devoted to the new and growing profession of electrical engineering.

. . . In Mr. W. H. Preece, the President of the English Institution of Electrical Engineers and the chief electrician of the Government telegraphs and telephones in England, is found the leading exponent of all the best thought and practice of England. At the same time he is a man who fully realizes the necessity of watching closely the development of electrical practice in this country, where electricity had made more rapid strides than anywhere else in the world. It had been said of Mr. Preece that he is himself the great argument for Government telegraphs: that the English telegraph system is the only one in all Europe that can compare with our own for efficiency and promptness, and that the success of the experiment of handing over the telegraphs to the Government in England has been largely due to the wonderful enthusiasm and ability with which he has developed and perfected the technical branches of his department . . . with an ease and facility which mark him as being one of the great English administrators of the age.

The opportunity was seized, while Mr. Preece was passing through New York this week to Chicago, to interview him at the Windsor Hotel, and to elicit some of his views and opinions on the comparative merits of English and American telegraphs.

'Do you consider' he was asked, 'Government telegraphs a success in England?'

'Yes, they are undoubtedly a success in England. I regard the telegraphs in England as even more republican than those in the States. In England the telegraphs belong to the people: they are maintained by the people: they are supervised by the people, for every Englishman has the right to complain of any delay or anything wrong, not only through the press, but in the Houses of Parliament, and every complaint of every kind received directly from any member of the public receives as much attention as though it came through the Houses of Parliament. The result is that telegraphs in England are magnificently worked. We can send a message to any part of the United Kingdom and get a reply in an hour. The facilities in England are greater than they are here for we go to every town and every village, irrespective of the fact that they pay or do not pay: while in the States the places that pay appear to me to be the only ones that receive the attention of the telegraph companies.

. . . The distinguishing feature of our English system is the facility given to the press. . . . There is not a single town in the United Kingdom where a daily paper is published that is not in direct communication with the Post Office in London, and where verbatim reports of proceedings of Parliament are not reported. The provincial press of England is almost entirely supplied with news from this telegraph system. The rates paid are ridiculously small: In fact it was owing to a mistake in drafting the original bill transferring the telegraphs to the State that the rates amount now to about twopence, or four cents, per hundred words. The result, however, while satisfying the newspapers . . . is serious to the Postal Telegraph Department, for this press service costs the country $2,000,000 a year. It is, however, questionable whether the benefit which the public derive from the dissemination of accurate news is not worth this additional charge on the taxes.'

'What is the relation of telegraphs to politics in England?'

'The telegraph is, of course, a branch of the civil service of England, and most of those who are employed in this service were bodily transferred from the service of the telegraph companies. I have failed to perceive any difference whatever between the zeal and energy displayed in private service as compared with the same characteristics shown in the Government service. A change in the Government of the day makes not the least difference. Not a single officer is dismissed, and the political chief of the department is not only selected for his eminence in Parliament but for his business qualities. He comes there as a political chief: but I have never known an instance of a political chief interfering . . . with the executive. Hence the service is absolutely uninfluenced by politics. I don't think the Postmaster-General has the least knowledge of the political leanings of those in his department. I can speak for myself, that I do not know the politics of a single man on my staff, and I am quite sure that not one of my men know mine.'

'Are there many women in the telegraph service in England?'

'A large proportion of the operating branch is female. They are very well paid. They advance and are appointed to positions of great trust, and the incentive of reward is always held before them by their appointment to these vacancies when they occur. An annual vacation is allowed to all. They receive medical assistance, and the department supplies cooking and other conveniences, such as would be found in clubs. They are entitled to a pension on the same scale as that in the civil service generally. . . . The proportion of women in the telegraph service is probably about one third, the difference being due to the fact that we never employ them for night service.'

'How do female operators compare with the male in England?'

'As operators there is very little distinction to be drawn between the two in the matter of dexterity: but occasionally the women are wanting in the physical strength required to maintain hard service on special occasions: they are apt to break down.'

'How do the English and American operators compare in the matter of skill?'

'I have failed to observe any difference between them.'

'Is there anything that we can learn from England in general telegraph work, or that it can learn from us?'

'I think it right to say that this is now my third visit to this country, and on each of my previous visits I took great pains to examine the workings of the telegraph system here. I have taken over to the other side nearly all that was good in it, so that at the present moment it is most difficult to say which of the two is the better. If I see anything new during my present trip I shall certainly take it back with me. I have also had the benefits of visits in London from friends on this side, and the result is that the two services have welded themselves very much on the same lines. The Western Union are employing very largely the main features of our Wheatstone automatic system, and I have seen results here which fairly astonished me. I was surprised to find that on one day 4,200 messages had been sent on a single wire from New York to Chicago.'

'What is the connection in England between the Government and the telephone?'

'The telephone service in England has hitherto been conducted almost entirely by private companies: but the Post Office has established exchanges. The telephone companies have gradually been absorbed by the National Telephone Company, and there is now but one company. Its operations are going to be confined to town circuits pure and simple, while the trunk service of the country, that is, the long distance telephone, will be conducted by the Post Office. There seems to be an opinion that divided responsibilities will not work: but I find that the long-distance work in this country is conducted by an organization separate from the town service and I cannot find that any difficulty has arisen from this division of service. I do not expect any difficulty in England, except it arise on the side of the company, who do not look with particular favour on the new regime. I am ashamed to say that in England the conduct of the telephone business compares most unfavourably with that in this country. One object of my visit here is to endeavour to trace the reason why. One reason has already proved itself to me to be very evident: it is that the business of telephony is conducted just as much by those who use it as by those who maintain it. In England, there is constant friction between the users and suppliers. The service has not been well done, and the public growls, loses its temper, and makes it worse.'

'I understand that the Government has begun to acquire the submarine cables landing on its shores?'

'Yes, in a measure. The Government has acquired all the submarine telegraph cables of the United Kingdom connecting with the continental administrations. The whole service to Europe now passes through the General Post Office. They have not touched the ocean submarine service, and I do not think that they will. In fact, the consideration of the question has not even reached the inquiry stage.'

'Is the telephone line between London and Paris a success?'

'The success of the Paris telephone cable has been so great that I have no doubt whatever the extension of the telephone cables to other countries will soon become a matter of investigation. In fact, long distance telephony has become such a simple matter that there is no difficulty whatever in establishing telephonic communications to every European Capital. I do not despair of telephoning even across the Atlantic: indeed it is quite possible to do so but its practicability is dependent on the success of experiments which have not yet been undertaken. I have seen it reported in several papers that the British Government has allotted £500,000 towards the cost of these experiments but there is no foundation whatever for this report. I have not even contemplated asking for any money for this purpose. Experiment in this direction appears to me to be rather a function of private enterprise. It really wants another Cyrus Field: such men do not grow in England.'

When asked to give some specific points of difference between American and English practice in electrical engineering, Mr. Preece said: 'I have only just arrived in this country and my visits to various electrical departments have so far been visits of courtesy; so that, really, I am not in a position to say more on this subject at present.'

Mr Preece was very much impressed with the development of electric railroading in this country since he was here in 1884, when there was only one electric road, and expressed much pleasure at the extent and efficiency of the Brooklyn lines.

Preece was also reported in detail by the columnist Kate Field, Boston bluestocking, lecturer on Women's Rights, and friend of Anthony Trollope:

'Delighted to welcome you again to the United States Mr. Preece . . . as a British Commissioner to the World's Fair, and especially as a delegate to the Electrical Congress you are just the person to tell . . . about a Congress of which little is known by the general public. Was it one of the one hundred World's Fair Congresses?'

'No, but it was projected in connection with the World's Fair. American electricians thought it a favourable opportunity to consider the question of electrical units, the assistance of the Government was invoked, it responded promptly and all European Governments were invited to send delegates with most gratifying results.'

'How many electricians met?'

'About three hundred and fifty. We discussed important questions which will for months make technical journals of all countries very interesting reading.'

'How was your Congress divided?'

'Into three sections: pure theory, practice and theory, and pure practice, presided over by Professors Rowland of Baltimore, Cross of Boston and Houston of Philadelphia. We met in the Art Institute, a most inconvenient place, situated far away from the Fair Grounds where we wanted to be, and practically placed in a railway yard where the puffs and yells of the engines rendered day hideous and speech inaudible. The General Congress included a smaller body called 'the Chamber of Delegates', numbering twenty-seven delegates who were officially designated by the United States and various other Governments. . . .'

'What was the special purpose of your Congress?'

'To consider the various modes to be adopted in various countries to measure electrical quantities so as to establish a uniform system of units all over the world. This was done and there is no doubt that we shall now in electricity have but one universal system of measurement, and but one language to express and indicate the different magnitudes we use. The unit selected will be made legal by every government. The arrangements for holding our meetings were very unsatisfactory. The public had to be temporarily cleared out of the art galleries. There were no table, pen, ink or paper. We then adjourned to the Grand Pacific Hotel where we were more comfortable; still, for an official gathering we were queerly cared for. Our proceedings were not reported or printed. We ought to have met in Washington where there is no doubt we should have been well and properly looked after.'

'Who presided?'

'Our Honorary President was Dr. Von Helmholtz, the most distinguished German scientist of this or any age in the variety of his fields of work. Whatever he has touched, he has adorned. He speaks English remarkably well. The Chairman of our proceedings was Professor H. A. Rowland of Johns Hopkins University, Baltimore, unquestionably as a mathematician and physicist, the most eminent man in the States. The most prominent man in our deliberations was Professor T. C. Mendenhall of Washington, who, with a perfect mastery of the subject, a cool, judicial mind and a charming manner, kept us well together and perfectly straight. Another foremost man was Monsieur Mascart of Paris, who has been a member of all previous electrical congresses, and is a most admirable and delightful Frenchman. He is now the most eminent scientist in France. The Chairman of the local committee was the eminent electrician, Dr. Elisha Gray of Highland Park, Illinois.'

'Electricity seems to have become part and parcel of our daily lives.'

'Decidedly. It is a universal agent for transmitting bodies and thought, for illumination and heat, and for innumerable useful purposes. It is manufactured, supplied and paid for. It is supplied in the form of a current which is measured in *amperes*, and it is driven through conductors of copper by electrical pressure, which is measured in *volts*. Seven amperes flowing under a pressure of one hundred volts will consume about one horse power, and will maintain alight about fourteen electrical glow lamps, giving two hundred and twenty-four candles. Volts multiplied by amperes are called *watts* and one thousand watts supplied continuously for one hour is called a *kilowatt-hour*, and that is the basis on which charges are made for the supply of electricity. The electric dimensions of conductors are given in *ohms*, so that when we are told that a copper conductor has a resistance of ten ohms, we know exactly what it is. The ohm, volt, ampere, farad and watt are the principal electrical units adopted. The names are selected from eminent scientists of the past, Ohm, Volta, Ampere, Faraday and Watt. Another unit was honoured with the name of Henry – America's most eminent electrician. Our meeting was extremely pleasant, and all the foreign delegates will carry away with them the liveliest recollections of the hospitality and geniality of their hosts. One of our most charming entertainments was given by Dr. Von Helmholtz, in the large hall of the German Village at the Fair. . . .'

*　　*　　*

In his report to the Secretary of the Post Office, after his arrival at Liverpool on S.S. *Etruria* on 30th September, Preece wrote of the Chicago exhibition:

Nothing grander in design or more beautiful in execution has ever been seen in this world than the group of buildings situated in Jackson Park, Chicago, and called the World's Fair. . . .

Of the exhibition itself he was less enthusiastic:

having taken part in nearly every exhibition for the past 15 years I am sick of exhibitions.

(Among those exhibitions were Paris 1881 – the year that Preece was elected a Fellow of the Royal Society – and Paris 1889 for each of which he had been a British Commissioner and had been awarded for his services the decoration of *Chevalier* and, later, *Officier* of the *Légion d'honneur*.)

He reported, nevertheless, on several novelties in the electricity building, including Elisha Gray's Telautograph which reproduced the sender's handwriting, as he was actually writing, at a receiving instrument: since it had not reached its final stage of development Preece did not encourage Gray to send it to England yet. He noted,

but I find that financial troubles in the States have driven them to try and sell the patent in London.

The remainder of Preece's report consisted of summaries of telegraph companies' finances, plant, organization and traffic, together with some technical details, which he had obtained in New York, Chicago, Buffalo, Boston and Philadelphia.

He noted improvements in

The type printing telegraph that we tested between London and Liverpool – namely the Van Hoevenburgh – has been very considerably improved by a Mr. Sheehy. I saw this instrument in operation and the defects . . . have been apparently entirely removed. This instrument had been at work between New York and Boston on a metallic telephone circuit, fitted on the Van Rysselberghe system, which we tried between London and Paris. The use of a metallic circuit as a separate and distinct earthed telegraph circuit is making great headway in the States. The telephone companies lease these circuits to subscribers between New York and Boston, and between other centres. There is litigation on the matter. . . .

The use, however, of telephone wires in the States in this particular way renders it necessary that we should certainly look into the matter more carefully at home. If these circuits can be made profitable in the States, they can be made so in the United Kingdom.

. . . It may be that our renters who take from us a metallic circuit for their telephone will find this circuit of much greater value if we can also add typewriting telegraph instruments . . .

. . . the management of the telegraphs in the States in the hands of private enterprise does not compare favourably. . . . It must not be assumed that because the Government have advantageously taken the telegraphs in hand at home that such a process would be possible in the States. . . . The principal appointments are four years' appointments only and are filled politically. The principal postmasters come and go with each new President. We in England scarcely consider that a postmaster is fit to be a postmaster until he has had many years' experience. . . .

In the business of telephony, however, he noticed 'gigantic strides': it was a 'gigantic monopoly' in the hands of the American Bell Telephone Company which owned more than one-half the stock in every telephone company in the United States and the whole of the stock of the long-distance company. Every town had but one system and under the monopoly the Bell Company had ensured a uniformity of working and practice which Preece regarded as extremely beneficial.

In those parts of the country where metallic circuits have not yet been adopted there may be defects in working but those would soon be changed to metallic circuits. Wires in towns had largely been forced to run underground to meet requirements of municipal authorities.

Preece had nothing but praise for the operating staff:

The operators are chiefly girls, but for trunk work . . . males are employed. The discipline and order are most marked. Perhaps the best office that I visited in this respect is the Central or main Exchange at Chicago. Here all the girls dressed in black stuff with a view to the prevention of fluff flying about, getting among the switches and impairing the working. Every girl wears a headgear telephone. . . . The transmitter invariably used is the 'solid back', the best produced in the United States. A whisper only is required in using it, and in a large exchange, like the one under notice, not a sound is heard. All the conversation being done in whispers, silence may be said practically to reign.

. . . I saw a change of duty effected, with military precision, without fuss or noise of any kind.

. . . The chief element of delay is the lag in the customer himself. . . . There are special inspectors who go round and educate customers in the use of the telephone. The customer invariably assists the operator. There is none of that obstruction or difficulty that we meet with in England.

. . . The operators are supplied with admirable chairs constructed on the music stool principle, to screw up and down, and fitted with strong back and arms. This enables the operators to sit in comfort at their work, and to adjust the height to suit their form or fancy.

He observed remarkable development in electrical lighting but found that accumulators had been a failure:

strong prejudice exists against their use. It has led to much litigation, and the best forms seem little known there.

The town work [of electricity supply companies] . . . is as solid and substantial as anything we can show in England, but when we inspect the outlying works in country towns we can only express our thanks that we have the control of the Board of Trade and the protection of an Act of Parliament. It is the fashion to decry grandmotherly government, and to wince at Departmental espionage; but the protection of life on our railways, the absence of accident in our electric light undertakings, and the character of the work done everywhere as compared with the same conditions in the States, can lead to but one conclusion, viz., that we do these things better in England. . . . The accidents in the States are terrible in their number and fatality.

Electric Railways . . . progress . . . is the most wonderful instance of growth of electric industry observable in the States. In 1884 I found only one railway so worked, and that experimentally, at Cleveland. Now every town has its electric railway.

. . . I cannot too gratefully speak of the attention and kindness I received from everyone, and I certainly feel that I have personally profited from my visit very much indeed from a departmental point of view.

Preece also gave an informal report at the Institution of Electrical Engineers when he related that at the Lexington Hotel in Chicago he found both the Western Union and the Postal Telegraph Companies had offices in the hall, each operator clattering on his sounder. When he asked the Postal operator – whose sounder was the louder – why he allowed his instrument to make such a row he got the reply, 'We must beat the Western Union Company anyhow.' Long-distance telephone call charges were a cent a mile for five minutes' talk, the longest, Portland–Milwaukee, costing $11. Labour, though plentiful, was expensive and an office boy cost more than a telephone subscription. The use of a small electric motor to open a door when the doormat was stepped on caught his attention, as did

a kind of baby cloakroom where mothers could book their babies for the day, and who were carefully tended, nursed, amused, and fed for a very small charge. Each mother received a small brass check, which was her guarantee for the safe custody of her little beauty.

Interviewing is a feature of American journalism that, thank goodness, has not taken root here. I was surprised to read of interviews with myself extending over two or three columns, that resulted from the passage of a few compliments; but I was more surprised to find that statements supposed to have been made by me to an interviewer were taken *en serieux*. One irate functionary compared an official statement of a past Postmaster-General with a mythical statement made by me, and triumphantly pointed out such a glaring contradiction as a complete refutation of my fallacies. I even read that I had stated that we electricians in England had *nothing* to learn from America . . . an absurdity . . . if I had done so it would have been *everything*.

A visit to the United States is something like charging an accumulator. It stores the visitor with energy.

26

ELECTRIC SIGNALLING WITHOUT WIRES

PREECE was called upon to travel to Dundee, with Sivewright in a supporting role, to unveil in September 1901 a monument to James Bowman Lindsay. They had both met Lindsay forty-seven years earlier. The English proprietor of the *Dundee Herald* had raised public subscriptions to pay for this honour to a local man, who died in 1862, held responsible for taking the 'first step' in signalling without wires.

Preece's imagination had been freshly stimulated by the sight of an advertisement in the *Dundee Advertiser* of 11 April 1834:

J. B. Lindsay resumes classes for cultivating the intellectual and historical portions of knowledge and instruction on April 14th, 1834, in South Tay Street, Dundee. In a few weeks hence a course of lectures will be formed on frictional, galvanic, and voltaic electricity, magnetism and electromagnetism. The battery, already powerful, is undergoing daily augmentation. The light obtained from it is intensely bright, and the number of lights may be increased without limit. A great number of wheels may be turned [by electricity] and small weights raised over pulleys. Houses and towns will in a short time be lighted by electricity instead of gas, and heated by it instead of coal: and machinery will be worked by it instead of steam – all at a trifling expense. A miniature view of all these effects will be exhibited, besides a number of subordinate experiments, including the discoveries of Sir Humphry Davy.

Preece in his oration, with an almost Judaic respect for prophets shared by most Britons of his time, held that there was nothing in Scipture so marvellous, so close and well defined as that prophecy uttered by Lindsay 'sixty years before the development of electricity'. Professor Steinheil of Munich had by accident discovered in 1838 that the earth itself could be used to replace the 'return wire' of an electric circuit. Lindsay arranged fifteen years later for two such circuits on opposite banks of a river not to be 'earthed' but to have their terminals submerged in the river: he found that the water would conduct current so that signals transmitted on one circuit would be reproduced in the circuit on the opposite bank. He came to London next year to sell his invention to the Electric Telegraph Company and the Company deputed Preece to investigate Lindsay's claims: they experimented successfully at Percy Wharf on the Thames and then at Portsmouth. Lindsay's claims were substantiated but there was no practical use in prospect for his system: he had to be told, too, that it had been anticipated thirteen years before by Samuel Morse, who, when a cable had been damaged by a ship's anchor between Governor's Island and Manhattan, had found that he could still signal because of current 'leakage' and had later demonstrated the phenomenon at Washington D.C. across an eighty-foot wide canal. Lindsay continued his experiments with varied success for a few years and gave an account of them in 1859 to the British Association when it met in Aberdeen.

A number of experiments using the phenomenon of conduction, or leakage, were made by others on each side of the Atlantic but Preece was the first to put it to commercial use when, in March 1882, a telegraph cable across the Solent broke down. He immersed a six-foot square copper plate in the sea at Ryde Pier, to which he joined an overhead wire to the Newport post office and thence to another copper plate in the sea at Sconce Point. At Hurst Castle, one and three-quarter miles across the Solent, was another copper plate from which a line led to the Southampton post office and on to Portsmouth to terminate in a fourth plate at the head of Southsea Pier six miles distant from Ryde Pier. Telegrams in Morse code were transmitted by buzzers operated by telegraph keys, with batteries of thirty Leclanché cells at Southampton and Newport, to be read on telephone receivers.

Preece reported to the British Association when it met at Southampton in 1882 that the telephone

has made us acquainted with many strange phenomena. It has enabled us, amongst other things, to establish beyond a doubt that fact that electric currents actually traverse the earth's crust. The theory that the

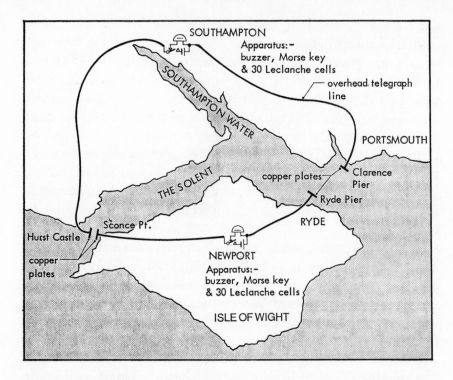

earth acts as a great reservoir for electricity may be placed in the physicist's waste-basket.

Telephones have been fixed upon a wire passing from the ground floor to the top of a large building (the gas pipes being used in place of a return wire) and Morse signals sent from a telegraph office 250 yards distant, have been distinctly read. There are several cases on record of telephone circuits miles away from any telegraph wires, but in line with the earth terminals, picking up telegraphic signals; and when an electric light system uses the earth, it is stoppage to all telephonic communication in its neighbourhood. Thus, communication on the Manchester telephones was not long ago broken down from this cause; while in London the effect was at one time so strong as not only to destroy all correspondence, but to ring the telephone call-bells. A telephone system using the earth in place of return wires, acts, in fact, as a shunt to the earth, picking up the currents that are passing in proportion to the relative resistances of the earth and the wire.

In the course of his official work Preece had received many such reports of disturbances to telephones from telegraphs on parallel routes: in Gray's Inn Road in 1884 telegraph signals were picked up on telephone circuits even though the telephone lines ran over roofs eighty feet above telegraph cables in iron pipes below the roadway. Preece arranged therefore for Divisional Engineer A. W. Heaviside (brother of Oliver) to carry out a series of experiments in the Newcastle area in an attempt to determine at what distance parallel wires no longer had an appreciable electromagnetic inductive effect on each other. Heaviside, in the course of those experiments, spoke by telephone with an assistant in a mine shaft 360 feet below him, and observed similar interference on circuits forty miles apart. His conclusion was that induced currents were negligible when wires were separated by a greater distance than that during which they ran parallel.

Preece minuted Graves, in February 1892, about a press report that Edison had sent telegraphic messages without wires, which had recalled to mind his own experiments. Now that communication between light-ship, lighthouse, and the mainland had acquired so much interest he thought his experiments to be worth continuing. He asked for funds to carry them on: the papers passed in due course 'through the usual channels' and Treasury agreed £100 might be spent to that end. In November he set up a line of 20-foot poles for three-quarters of a mile along 70-foot cliffs at Lavernock, Penarth, and suspended two 400-pound copper wires on them, earthing the wires at each end instead of constructing wire rectangles as in earlier experiments, thus the earth replaced the fourth side of a rectangle. He succeeded in communicating with Flat Holm Island, 3·1 miles distant, where he had run a parallel insulated copper wire for 600 yards. He also transmitted perceptible signals to Steep Holm Island 5·35 miles distant. The Royal Engineers, who had a fort on Flat Holm, made available a steam yacht to extend the scope of Preece's experiments but attempts to communicate with it were unsatisfactory. Gavey remained to continue the experiments when Preece had to return to London to attend to his more routine duties. Within a day or two Gavey wrote to Preece that he was on Flat Holm when he heard on the telephone there that a message had been sent to him at Penarth by Preece:

then followed the announcement of the sad and sudden death of Mr. Graves which cast a gloom over the success of the experiment. It seemed extraordinary fact that the first readable messages transmitted from such a distance by such means should announce the death of the Head of the Technical Department.

The Lavernock–Flat Holm system was handed over to the Royal Engineers as a permanent telegraphic installation.

Preece wrote an obituary of Graves for the Post Office's house magazine:

his financial acumen, his wonderful memory, his quick perception and his intimacy with both railway and telegraph work led Mr. Scudamore to entrust him with the defence of the interests of the Post Office during the arbitrations of 1874–78 between the Department and the various Railway Companies who were entitled to compensation under the Telegraph Acts of 1868–69. His ability in this severe occupation was most marked, and his eminent services were suitably recognised. His cross-examination by one of the most eminent lawyers of his day, John Horatio Lloyd, was almost an intellectual treat. He was never at a loss, and his command of figures always left him master of the position. 'You have not always thought so,' said Lloyd on one occasion when he announced some legal heresy. 'No; my opinions change with my experience' replied Graves. In this electrical age we cannot be conservative.

The arrangements of the engineering department were not altogether fortunate. Several round men were put into square holes. Matters were rather getting into disorder when Mr. Graves and I in 1877 were appointed a kind of roving commission to examine and report on the organisation of the department, and to suggest modifications. This we did pretty effectually. The matter was taken up by Parliament also. A committee of the House of Commons enquired into the whole matter, and the result was that in 1878 a shuffle of the cards took place. Several retirements followed, and the engineering department has worked on its present footing very satisfactorily ever since. Mr. Graves became engineer-in-chief, and no department of the State has ever been served by a more faithful and zealous officer. He never had one thought but of his duty. He would not even take a holiday. He died in harness, and became almost unconscious in his official chair.

Thus by blind chance Preece found himself appointed head of his department. He was now Engineer-in-Chief but that did not entirely reconcile him to losing a title he valued above all else; he was, therefore, allowed to retain 'and Electrician'.

27

LIGHTHOUSES AND LIGHT-SHIPS

AROUND our coasts lighthouses usually and light-ships perforce were in isolated positions and coastguard stations were out of communication with each other so that in an emergency a single unit could be thrown on its own resources with no means of getting in touch with life-boat or life-saving stations. When the American mail steamship *Schiller* was wrecked off the Scillies in May 1875, with a loss of over three hundred lives and half a million sterling of specie, J. G. Uren, the Penzance postmaster, wrote to *The Times* to point out that had the Bishop Rock Lighthouse been connected by telegraph to St Mary's many of those lives might well have been saved. He persisted, thereafter, in writing to the Board of Trade during Joseph Chamberlain's Presidency, 1880–85, to urge that lighthouses and light-ships should be connected with the shore and coastguard stations connected with each other by telephone circuits, only to receive replies that it could not be done:

cables would chafe against the rocks, or snap as the light-ships swung with the tide: the lighthouse keepers had too much to do, it would distract their attention from the ordinary work, and so on.

Another Post Office employee, F. H. Maberley, published in January 1888 a pamphlet on the subject. The editor of the *Standard* in 1892, on receiving such a letter from Uren, supported it with a leader. Other newspapers were publishing similar representations and the Associated Chamber of Commerce supported the cause. Sir Edward Birkbeck raised the matter, 26th April, in the House of Commons, which led in June to a Royal Commission being appointed of nine members (including J. C. Lamb and Edward Graves) under the Earl of Mount Edgcumbe,

s

to inquire and report what lighthouses and light vessels it is desirable to connect with the telegraphic system of the United Kingdom by electrical communication, for the purpose of giving information of vessels in distress or casualties at sea, and of transmitting storm warnings, having due regard to the practicability of establishing and maintaining such communication without impairing the efficiency of the Light Service, and at a cost bearing a reasonable proportion to the advantages that might be expected to result; and to suggest the manner in which such communication should be established, wherever it might be recommended.

Post Office engineers were meanwhile busy installing apparatus and running circuits to link coastguard stations, Parliament having voted for the current financial year £20000 to such work.

Next month the Commissioners as passengers on the Admiralty yacht H.M.S. *Enchantress*, then the Commissioners of Irish Lights yacht *Princess Alexandra*, and the Trinity House yacht *Vestal*, sailed along the south-west coast to the Scillies, then to Ireland, Wales and later to Dover, Great Yarmouth and the Firth of Forth.

Preece was appointed to the Commission on 26th November 'in the room of Edward Graves deceased'. Next July the Commissioners assembled at Glengariff, Bantry Bay, to board the Irish Lights steamer *Moya* to visit Bull Rock and the Fastnet. They landed at Baltimore,

the place where Lady Burdett Coutts has rendered so much help in furnishing the fishermen with boats and nets, and in the establishment of a fishery school. The school has more than 120 poor boys, who are lodged and fed, and taught to make fishing nets, to mend their own clothes, to play musical instruments, and to manage boats. They are also given instruction in the habits of the fish. At the request of Lord Mount Edgcumbe they were given a day's holiday, and their delight was expressed in a very hearty and noisy manner.

The Commissioners proceeded by train to Cork, thence to Kingstown where they boarded H.M.S. *Enchantress* to visit Chicken Rock Lighthouse south of the Calf of Man, then to the north-east coast of Ireland, on to Ailsa Craig, Rathlin, and Instrahull,

a rocky little islet off the north coast of Donegal. . . . The island contains about 60 persons all told. When the Commissioners visited it they found there was no resident priest or minister of religion of any kind. A school had only been established in the previous year. Every Sunday the people were in the habit of gathering on a green, and kneeling down and saying their prayers. A priest from the mainland visited the island once a year, and his visit was duly recorded in the log book of the lighthouse. The men possessed a few fairly good boats, and caught a considerable quantity of fish. They had goats and fowls, and grew a few oats and potatoes. They relied for a large portion of their food on supplies from the mainland, and sold their fish to enable them to effect the necessary purchases. In the recent succession of gales they were unable to engage in fishing, or cross to the mainland, (being reduced to the point of starvation). . . . The weather was extremely rough on the occasion of the visit of the Commissioners. . . .

They had arrived at the island before breakfast and only Lamb, Preece, and two others of their number landed. Thereafter the *Enchantress* coaled at Oban before proceeding through the Sound of Mull when after several calls and passing Cape Wrath they reached the Orkneys. The voyage had lasted sixteen days when they disembarked at Scrabster to go south by rail to Seahouses, where the Trinity House steamer *Argus* took them to the Farne Islands, the last visit of their second tour.

★   ★   ★

The Danish Government was willing for the Royal Commission to visit its coasts where electric communication with lighthouses had been established for many years, and at the end of July 1895 H.M. Telegraph Ship *Monarch* (built on the Clyde in 1883 for cable laying and maintenance) left her depot at Woolwich with members of the Commission aboard to take them to Copenhagen where arrangements had been made for a tour of Danish lighthouses. Preece realized that gave him an excellent opportunity, during more than a fortnight's visit, to look at the telephone systems of Scandinavia in the light of discussions in the House of Commons where some members sought to prove that the marked success of the telephone in Scandinavia (Sweden in particular being regarded as the best telephoned country in the world) was due to the activity of private enterprise. Uncertainty existed on the real cause of their telephone success so Preece urged the desirability of an official investigation on the spot and the Postmaster-General agreed that

J. C. Lamb and Preece should visit Christiana and Stockholm while in the Baltic.

The Commissioners found that four strategically placed lighthouses had associated signal stations from which were sent weather reports and information on passing vessels, whose captains made considerable use of facilities to communicate with owners and others. The lighthouse service had a long waiting list of applicants. We can see Preece's influence in one paragraph of the Commissioners' report:

The multiplicity of duties which the staff at some of the principal Danish lighthouses have to perform does not appear to affect the efficiency or popularity of the lighthouse service.

★　　　★　　　★

The Norwegian Government, Preece learnt, had not undertaken local telephone work but had decided on developing the trunk service, 'as we are doing in Great Britain'. All the private telephone companies had formed an association with the chief aim, it seemed to Preece, of getting the State to buy them out. In Sweden the Government had acquired a monopoly of trunk circuits but was in competition with the General Telephone Company of Stockholm in that city and in a number of towns.

Stockholm possesses the largest telephone manufactory on the Continent, viz., that of Ericsson, a self-made mechanical genius, who, by magnificent organisation, the application of cheap labour, automatic machinery, and personal supervision, has developed a factory that is a sight to see, and a business gigantic in its extent. Packages were visible ready for transport addressed to all parts of the world. Switches and apparatus were being made for England and its colonies, for Russia, for Denmark and for Norway. The very latest developments from America were being improved upon. Nothing seems to escape the eye of this enterprising telephone manufacturer. Stockholm derives great benefit from the existence of such an active centre in its midst. It is very remarkable that this particular manufacturing business in England has never flourished. It was checked by the terrible tyranny and exclusive policy of the holders of the Bell patents, and the labour troubles involving high wages and working restrictions having prevented the possibility of its securing a position against the untrammelled rivalry of Antwerp and Stockholm, the two principal manufacturing centres in Europe. Berlin, has, however, made an excellent start, but the industry is not yet in the same flourishing development there as in Stockholm.

Preece's reference to Berlin arose from his having returned not with the other Commissioners, who were picked by up H.M.T.S. *Monarch* at Frederikshaven to be disembarked at Harwich, but overland, stopping in Berlin *en route*.

In Berlin Preece discovered that the German telephone service was a well-organized State monopoly and although it had not yet developed to the same extent as in Sweden all country districts had been provided with facilities for emergency calls. He noticed that

in Germany, the uniform, as a symbol of authority, and as a sign of discipline, is so general, that all officers in telegraph and telephone offices are in uniform. The women operators wear a faced blouse and skirt of authorised material and colour.

He related what he had seen to the position in the United Kingdom to conclude that:

The British public does not care for the telephone. It is unpopular becase it has been badly managed in the past. Given a perfect service, and a moderate and equitable tariff, it would become as popular, as remunerative, and as successful as in Berlin or Stockholm.

Why has it been so successful in those two places? It is not the mere cheapness of the service, for the facts show that the difference in the actual charges made is not marked. It is rather an apparent cheapness that has tempted numbers to join, and numbers give the service its real advantage.

Again the service is more effectively conducted, and it owes its popularity to its real efficiency more than to any financial reason.

It has certainly supplied a want in Sweden, and it has become a necessity in Berlin, but in each place it has become the fashion, and fashion rules the world with a force that is not easily measured or fathomed. We see that in the rage for bicycles, as much as in the change of dress.

In Sweden another exciting force has been competition, but there has been no competition in Germany, and therefore, however potent competition by private enterprise may be in developing new industries it has no influence in Germany in developing the telephone industry.

Preece had, the year before, compared United States telephone development with that in the United Kingdom at the end of 1892, on a basis of the average number of inhabitants of a city or town for each exchange subscriber: New York with a population of 1 515 301 had 9066 subscribers, that is, one for every 167 inhabitants; London had 4 263 294, 6700, 636. Subscribers and ratio to total population were for:

Chicago	9684	114	Glasgow	3200	209
Philadelphia	3260	289	Liverpool	4500	114
Brooklyn	4439	182	Manchester	2300	222
St Louis	3561	127	Birmingham	1200	403
Boston	5668	79	Leeds	1300	289
Baltimore	2116	205	Edinburgh	900	294
Cincinnati	4015	83	Hull	400	512
San Francisco	4528	66	Newcastle	1300	148
Cleveland	3182	82	Plymouth	300	285
Buffalo	2240	114			

Alfred R. Bennett, general manager and chief engineer of the Mutual Telephone Company of Manchester, at the British Association meeting at Ipswich, September 1895, admitted that telephone development in the United Kingdom was inferior to many other European countries. He claimed as the criterion of excellent service the inclusion of smaller towns and villages and that on such a basis the Scandinavian countries, Finland, Luxemburg, and Switzerland were superior to France, Portugal, and Russia – ignoring, for the purpose of his argument, differences in area, although he urged very cheap trunk calls as the best means to popularize telephones in the United Kingdom.

* * *

The Commission's fifth, and last, report was published in September 1897: although the telephone circuits which had been brought into service to link up all coastguard stations had manifestly been completely justified by events, the Commissioners could come to no definite conclusion on the part played by electrical communications from lighthouses, compared with rockets and maroons, when assistance had been sent to ships in distress although a Royal National Lifeboat Institution schedule indicates that the facilities had already proved valuable. At light-ships the snarling of electric cables had in some instances been due to inexperienced crews and only two such cables had been broken by ships' anchors. Their report included a suggestion that a member of each crew should be trained in cable repairing by the Post Office.

Installations had been put in hand without delay after each report of the Commission and when the fifth report was published six hundred coastguard and lifeboat stations (including more than a hundred in Ireland) had been put in communication; fifty light-houses had been connected with telegraph or telephone circuits and half of them were displaying storm-warning signals as recommended in the third report. Only five light-ships had been joined by cable, and Preece suggested, in the light of the considerable expense, that no more light-ships be connected till 'the aetherial system of wireless telegraphy' had been fully tested.

28

MARCONI

A SLIM young Italian, unduly serious for his age, English-speaking (his mother was Irish), called at the G.P.O. West building one morning in July 1896 to send in a letter of recommendation to Preece from A. A. Campbell Swinton, consulting electrician. Preece had the youth brought into his office. P. R. Mullis, then a boy assistant on telegraph maintenance, has given us a description of what followed. Mullis was carrying in items from Preece's brougham: he noticed the young 'dark-looking foreigner' waiting in the corridor along one side of which was a quarter-scale model of a railway mailcoach with bag-catching apparatus on a short length of track and he was pushing the coach along to see how the travelling post office dropped and picked up mail. (That model was destroyed when the building was bombed on 29 December 1940.)

He had two large bags. After handshakes and while the Chief cleaned his gold-rimmed spectacles Marconi placed on a table the contents of the bags: they included a number of brass knobs, a large sparking coil, and a small glass tube from each end of which extruded a rod joined to a disc fitted in the tube. The gap between the two discs was filled with metal filings. The Chief seemed particularly interested in that piece of apparatus. I obtained a Morse key, batteries, and wire. We joined up two circuits, fitting rods ending in knobs to the coil. We put the second circuit, containing the glass tube, on another table. When this had been completed the Chief – who was the kindest man I have ever met – pulled out his gold hunter. He said very quietly, 'It has gone twelve now. Take this young man over to the refreshment bar [in the G.P.O. East building on the opposite side of St Martin's-le-Grand: it was demolished in 1913] and see that he gets a good dinner on my account, and come back here again by two o'clock.'

After a good dinner and over our basins of tea – no cups in those days – Marconi talked to me about Italy. Afterwards since we had plenty of time, we walked in Farringdon Road where he was interested in the street trader's barrows with their loads of junk, books, and fruit.

Back in Mr. Preece's office Marconi depressed the key in the sparking coil circuit whereupon an electric bell in the coherer circuit rang. Marconi tapped the coherer tube and the bell stopped ringing. He had to repeat that action each time he caused the bell to ring. I knew by the Chief's quiet manner and smile that something unusual had been effected. The rest of the afternoon passed very quickly and with the appearance of the old coachman to take the Chief back in his brougham to Wimbledon. . . . For the rest of the week there was further experimenting . . . Marconi would say, 'We will try this', 'We will try that'. . . . The Chief arranged for Marconi's apparatus to be greatly improved in the Mechanics' shop for demonstration to the Admiralty.

Preece arranged a demonstration on 27th July before members of the P.O. administration. Marconi's transmitter was a Hertzian oscillator with its spark gap placed in the focal line of a parabolic mirror of sheet copper made in the Mechanics' Shop, and his receiver a Branly coherer, with a Morse inker in circuit, was placed in a similarly curved sheet of copper. With the transmitter on the roof of G.P.O. West and the receiver on the roof of G.P.O. South in Carter Lane 300 yards distant, signals from the transmitter were satisfactorily recorded on the paper tape of the inker. Another improvement which had been added in the Mechanics' Shop consisted of an electric bell wired in parallel with the inker, the coherer taking the place of the gong so that it was 'de-cohered' (its metal dust tapped loose) by the bell hammer after each incoming signal.

Preece had been committed to give a public lecture at Toynbee Hall, East London, that December and thereupon decided to use the opportunity to demonstrate Marconi's invention. With transmitter and receiver in metal boxes, painted black, he created considerable excitement when on his pressing a telegraph key wired to the transmitter box on the platform table a bell rang in the box Marconi was carrying in the body of the lecture hall. Preece further indulged his sense of the dramatic by telling his audience that he had the greatest pleasure that day in telling Mr Marconi that the Post Office had decided to spare no expense in experimenting with the apparatus.

'Spare no expense' was rhetorical. No Treasury authority had been sought for any such expenditure. Preece, at that time fully engaged on replanning telephone trunk lines transferred from the National Telephone Company, could give little personal attention to experiments. His total headquarters staff was less than thirty but it did include such engineers as John Gavey, H. R. Kempe, and J. E. Taylor, men whom Preece had selected for qualities which included an ability to analyse and improve apparatus new to them. Further, his expressed opinions carried authority and were widely reported. To Marconi at that moment those factors were of great value.

H. R. Kempe took Marconi down to Salisbury Plain, after Preece had been in touch with the Army authorities. Captain Henry B. Jackson, R.N., and Professor A. Slaby of Berlin (who through arrangements made by the German Embassy had witnessed some of Preece's own experiments in wireless) also went to see Marconi's system in action. (Slaby, with Professor Braun and Count Arco, later developed the Telefunken wireless system.)

That visit to the Plain had been preceded by Marconi being asked to attend at the War Office on 1st September to show his apparatus and explain its purpose; Captain Jackson was ordered to be present. He wrote to Gavey over a year later describing that meeting, where he first saw Marconi. Before the apparatus was unpacked Jackson told Marconi that, from the description Marconi had given, he Jackson had been working since December 1895 on what was

evidently the same thing which rather upset him, till I told him that I had no idea of patenting it, and after seeing his, that he was further advanced in the details than I was, though he could do no more than mine did except as regards distance, but he was using an 8″ coil, I only a 2″.

The idea of wireless telegraphy as a much required secret signalling system between ships and torpedo boats had occurred to Jackson when first he read of Hertz's experiments and in August 1896 after months of experiment with various forms of coherer he had successfully transmitted Morse signals the length of his ship H.M.S. *Defiance*, 'Through the various wooden bulkheads' using a metal-filings coherer associated with an electrically operated tapper.

I can positively assert that I got Morse signals . . . with my apparatus before I saw Marconi or knew what his system was, the date [Jackson went to the War Office] I well remember . . . as I lost a day's partridge shooting through having to be in town that day.

1 Sept 96

Kempe sent Preece reports of experiments carried out that September (as did Marconi) on the second method covered by Marconi's patent where transmitter and receiver were each in circuit with an earthed wire. Each wire had its free terminal connected with a metal cylinder raised on a pole to increase its capacity. After a while the experimenters realized that the Hertzian oscillator was redundant since an effective oscillator was formed by the aerial capacity and the earth itself: the Hertzian oscillator used only a small part of the available energy to oscillate, at a much higher frequency than the main transmitter, much shorter waves which soon became too diffused to be detectable. They therefore replaced Hertz's oscillator with a simple spark gap. They increased the aerial capacity simply by raising just the wire itself to 100–150 feet above the ground.

Salisbury Plain

With that improved apparatus Kempe and Marconi arranged more experiments in November to signal successfully across the Bristol Channel between Penarth, near Cardiff, and Brean Down, a distance of nine miles.

Nov 96

Preece added to the long line of memorable Friday evening lectures at the Royal Institution next June when in a crowded lecture hall he spoke of signalling without wires. Beginning with a review of Clerk Maxwell's association of light and electro-magnetic phenomena, he operated a mechanical model Silvanus Thompson had lent him to demonstrate electrical oscillations. He referred to low-frequency oscillations which had interfered with telephone circuits and to the limitations of a wireless system he had devised therefrom. He gave the distances already covered during Marconi's experiments and assured his audience that by no means had a limit been reached.

4 June '97

It has been said that Mr Marconi has done nothing new. He has not discovered any new rays; his transmitter is comparatively old; his receiver is based on Branly's coherer. Columbus did not invent the egg, but he showed how to make it stand on its end, and Marconi has produced from known means a new electric eye more delicate than any known electrical instrument, and a new system of telegraphy that will reach places hitherto inaccessible. There are a great many practical points connected with this system that require to be threshed out in a practical manner before it can be placed on the market, but enough has been done to prove its value and to show that for shipping and lighthouse purposes it will be a great and valuable acquisition.

Reports of those lectures reached Italy whose government had repelled Marconi's approach, to drive him to England where he expected more attention to be paid to his invention: he was summoned to return. That July he left for Rome accompanied by J. E. Taylor, to arrange demonstrations of wireless signalling between Italian warships. Marconi was back on Salisbury Plain in September to continue his experiments but meanwhile the Secretary to the Post Office had asked Preece to report on the practicability of using Marconi's system to communicate with light-ships, and on how matters stood between him and Marconi. Preece was confident that the system was valuable to off-shore signal stations; and to the Admiralty and War Office to whom Preece had, with Marconi's agreement, submitted details.

He referred to Marconi's British patent of December 1896:

His patent is a very strong one but its validity is sure to be contested. Professor Lodge claims priority of invention. I have, however, carefully examined Professor Lodge's claims . . . and I find them baseless. They will, however, have to be submitted to the Attorney-General for his opinion.

My own view is that . . . the Government would be justified in acquiring the patent rights for £10,000. . . . Marconi is a very young man (22). He is a foreigner. He has proved himself to be open and candid and he has resisted many tempting offers.

Preece's recommendation was filed away and a request that the Treasury authorize an expenditure of £150, the Post Office share of experiment costs, was not submitted by its administration.

Marconi had returned to Salisbury Plain with H. R. Kempe by mid-March 1897, sometimes using kites in preference to balloons to raise transmitting and receiving aerials from 50 to 150 feet above the ground and to get signals at distances of four miles. Captain Jackson witnessed their experiments one day: 'He was very pleased of the results,' wrote Marconi to Preece, 'and has made a report to the Admiralty.'

Marconi confessed, on 10th April, to being in a difficulty.

Those gentlemen . . . which desire to form a company for acquiring the

Copies 67 Talbot Road
Westbourne Park
W.

1st April 1897

My dear Sir.

I enclose a copy of the description of what I did and noticed during the last experiments at Salisbury.

Pardon me if I have not written in good english

With the system I have lately experimented with, the energy is radiated or conducted (by the earth) in all directions, whilst with the system in which reflectors are used the radiation is transmitted in one direction only.

I have not yet been able to find a satisfactory explanation as to how the signals get to the other side of hills.

I once wondered that this was owing to conduction through the earth, but I have since obtained results through, or over a hill without any connection to earth.

Thanking you again for the assistance you have so kindly afforded me I remain dear Sir

Yours very truly

G. Marconi

W. H. Preece Esq. C.B. F.R.S.
General Post Office

Letter from Marconi to Preece, 1 April, 1897

rights of my invention, and to which I had notified that I could not deal with them, or give them any definite answer until the experiments I am carrying out with your assistance are concluded, have notified me through my solicitors that they want to know without much delay whether I intend to accept their offer or not. . . .

For me to receive £15,000 in cash and half the shares of the company. The company would also have a working capital of £25,000 which would be used in experimenting and in developing the system.

What makes me consider the offer is not so much the £15,000 which I would receive (which I would accept more as a guarantee than anything else) but the £25,000 working capital which would enable me to largely experiment and well protect the patents. . . .

The Company would make money through constructing apparatus for use on board ships for the purpose of enabling the ships to be warned in fogs, when in the proximity of rocks or dangerous shallows, or for preventing collisions.

I beg to state, however, that I have never sought these offers, or given encouragement to the promoters.

Soon after his return from Italy Marconi called at G.P.O. West only to learn that Preece was in Carnarvon. He wrote to Preece with descriptions of experiments and improvements in apparatus he had made and asked, since 'our Company is not yet quite organized' if Preece would allow J. E. Taylor or G. S. Kemp (a P.O. mechanic, ex-R.N. petty officer, who had been exceptionally interested in Marconi's apparatus) and one of two of the R.E. Sappers on postal telegraph duties to help him on Salisbury Plain, the Company paying all expenses. He also asked if Preece could recommend two young electricians for employment in the Company. Preece telegraphed: 'Kemp and Royal Engineers at your service as long as needful.'

Upon learning from Marconi that his company had been registered Preece wrote to him under instruction from the Post Office Secretary that collaboration in experiments had to stop until they knew the 'conditions that were to obtain between the Wireless Telegraph and Signal Company [that title was changed to Marconi's Wireless Telegraph Company in 1900] and the Government Departments who have encouraged you and helped you so much'. The Company's directors at their meeting later in August recorded their appreciation of Mr. Preece's friendly assistance in experimenting with the Marconi system and their desire to continue in such friendly relationship with Her Majesty's Government.

Preece was on sick leave in Carnarvon when he learnt that in collaboration with the War Office, which was making Fort Burgoyne available for the purpose, members of his staff were to attempt to send signals to the French coast. He suggested to Marconi that he should go along. Marconi replied (9 September 1897):

In consequence to your letter, my experiments arranged to take place last week at Salisbury were postponed, you having suggested that I had better go to Dover. I now understand that the Post Office people have gone to Dover without me, Mr. Gavey having told me in confidence that my presence cannot be permitted.

At a board Meeting of my Company yesterday, much regret was expressed that the experiments at Dover are to be conducted in my absence with apparatus which may or may not be satisfactory.

Three days later he wrote informally to Preece from Hill Crest Bungalow, Three Mile Hill, to record that he had engaged an assistant, W. W. Bradfield (recommended by J. W. Curra of Preece's staff), and was proposing to interview others: G. S. Kemp had gone on to his payroll. He was starting experiments on the Plain and Army Captains Baden-Powell and Kennedy were going to watch them.

If as I fear the department does not intend continuing in the friendly bona fide relations as you and I believed it would I shall be obliged, immediately after settling experimentally certain little theoretical points at Salisbury, to proceed to Russia, Austria and other countries which are very anxious to have extensive experiments carried out at their expense. . . .

I wrote to you at the request of the Board of Directors of my Company, expressing their views. I shall inform you of the results of my experiments at Salisbury. I hope I have not said anything that may displease you, but I wished to let you know openly what I thought. . . .

I am convinced that if any hitch should arise with the Department it would be in consequence of the attitude of others. . . .

Preece, who was keenly disappointed at not being fit enough to travel with the British Association to Toronto that August, tried to console Marconi with an assurance that the Dover experiments were not to be regarded as a final test of Marconi's system and, when he met Marconi on his return from Carnarvon to London a few days later, he invited Marconi to stay at his Wimbledon home. Marconi replied on 3rd October:

1897

When I had the pleasure of meeting you the other day I quite forgot that I had undertaken to carry out some important experiments for Lloyds before the 24th of this month. I fear that in consequence of this I shall be unable to be at your house at the time stated which I greatly regret as I was looking forward with pleasure to pass a few days in your company. Anyhow I will try my best to arrange matters. I am going to Dover with new apparatus on Tuesday . . . [where Marconi was to carry out experiments for the War Office].

Preece was again on sick leave when Marconi wrote a month later to give details of further Salisbury experiments and of improvements in his apparatus.

We wrote to the Secretary of the P.O. asking under what lines he would be prepared to deal with the Company, and received a reply signed by Lamb [Third Secretary] stating that although the P.M.G. would be prepared to consider any proposition we should make yet he might point out that so far as the P.O. is concerned the practicability of the system has not yet been sufficiently demonstrated. . . .

The Company has however practically decided that before trying [to establish communication between] Guernsey and Sark or Lloyds' stations, to have two permanent stations where the system can be worked and its practicability demonstrated for a sufficiently long period. The place we seem to prefer would be to have one station (transmitter and receiver) somewhere near Bournemouth and the other on the Isle of Wight, a distance of about 15 miles. . . .

1897

In mid-November he wrote:

Very many thanks for your letter. I am very sorry to hear you are still so poorly but trust the journey you are now undertaking will restore you completely. . . . Lodge is going to make a union or league with all other holders of Patents connected with Wireless Telegraphy in order to fight me and my Company.

Preece had not been responding to treatment for bronchitis so he left for Egypt and did not return till the New Year. He wrote Marconi a personal letter the following September when he learnt

1898   1898

of an accident while Marconi was fitting a permanent installation for Lloyd's on Rathlin Island to connect the lighthouse with the mainland. Marconi replied from the Antrim Arms Hotel, Ballycastle:

thank you very much . . . for your expressions of sympathy. . . . Mr. Granville was a very good and skilled fellow and his untimely end grieves us all exceedingly. He apparently went for a walk on Sunday (21st) when in Rathlin Island, but having ventured on a very dangerous path used only by sheep he must have lost his footing or slipped, and fell a height of fully 300 feet. His remains were found next morning . . . by a search party.

He then gave some details of the success of his experiments in signalling between Osborne House and the Royal Yacht.

Preece heard from him again the following year:

I have been intending to write to you this long time but my recent demonstrations for the French Navy have procured me such a lot of work that I have had to put off doing so. . . .

and he went on to refer to his installation between South Foreland and Boulogne (distance 30 miles). His last letter to Preece was a formal communication:

In reply to your letter of May 6th, I shall be happy to show the Dover-Boulogne installation of Wireless Telegraphy to the Postmaster-General, Mr. Murray, Sir Francis Mowatt, and the other gentlemen you mention with you on the 3rd June or 13th. if you will let me know before-hand the date of your visit.

*   *   *

The Wireless Telegraph Company objected to a paragraph in the Postmaster-General's published report for the year ending 31 March 1898:

A series of trials was undertaken with the Marconi apparatus with special reference to its adaptability for lighthouse, lightship, and other communications: but although signals were successfully transmitted a certain distance, no practical results have yet been achieved.

On being asked his opinion Preece agreed that the accuracy of the report could be defended although it would have been better if it had read 'commercially practical results'.

T

1892—

The Company had applied for a ship–shore licence the previous December to link East Goodwin light-ship and South Foreland light-house with its stations, undertaking that messages received would, at the request of senders, be handed over to the Inland Telegraph system. The Post Office administration asked the Admiralty, War Office and Board of Trade if they had any objection with only the Board of Trade making any reservation (about the use of the fore-shore). Directors of the Company called at the Post Office to be told that the Postmaster-General wished to facilitate the Company's scheme consistent with the protection of his monopoly. The following month the matter was transmitted to the Treasury with the Postmaster-General's opinion that a licence should be granted to the Company subject to 'a royalty of a very moderate amount'. The Treasury wanted to know if Preece's parallel wire system offered any prospect of competition and was advised that Preece's system was much more limited in its application.

*   *   *

The first wireless signal to be sent across the Channel, 28 March, 1899

1899 Preece age 65

By this time Preece, having reached the age limit of sixty-five, had retired from the post of Engineer-in-Chief. In the next Birthday Honours list he was awarded the honour of Knight Commander of the Bath (he had been made a Companion of the Order five years before). His brother Richard appeared in the same list: J. R. Preece Her Majesty's Consul at Ispahan to be Companion of the Order of St Michael and St George (unfortunately *The Times* printed his name as 'Mr. W. H. Preece').

Preece did not sever his connection with the Post Office; he managed to arrange under a special Treasury dispensation to be retained for a further five years as Consulting Engineer to the Post Office on a salary of £400 a year. Preece thought that amount might have been increased and the Postmaster-General, the Duke of Norfolk, was prepared to make a case but the Post Office Secretary, J. H. Murray, told Preece,

it would be hopeless, as I understand from the Treasury that the provision of the Superannuation Acts absolutely debar a man from receiving more (either in meal or in malt) than he would have been getting previous to his retirement.

That is, including his Civil Service pension.

[The Duke] hopes that you will see your way clear to accept it in spite of the apparent incongruity between the title and the emoluments . . . he presumes that during that period you would consider yourself precluded from taking work or giving advice which would in any way conflict with the interests of the Post Office. As regards your local habitation, while not wishing to be inhospitable he feels bound to say that in his opinion it would not be desirable . . . that you should have quarters in the Post Office buildings. It is only fair to your successors that their actual position should be marked by some clear break in the continuity of your own authority and labours. . . . I need scarcely say that we hope always to see as much of you as your other engagements will allow; and we will do our best to give you any temporary accommodation that you may require.

★   ★   ★

The Royal Academy's summer exhibition that year included a three-quarter-length portrait of Preece. Not a good painting, apart from an easily recognizable head which appears to have been worked from

1899?

a few colour notes at a sitting and a photograph, its chief interest is
that the artist was the daughter, Beatrice, of Sir Charles Bright.
(After seventy years on a wall of the I.C.E. Lecture Hall it lies in a
Science Museum store.)

In August 1899 the chairman and a director of the Wireless Telegraph Company discussed the Post Office's position as a user of
Marconi's apparatus with J. C. Lamb, who pointed out that the
Post Office only wished to acquire the right to use the system. The
Board offered, a fortnight later, to allow such a use for £30000 a year,
or £50000 if that use was to extend from the United Kingdom to
British Possessions. The Treasury agreed such charges were excessive
and that the Post Office should discontinue negotiations: meanwhile
the Admiralty proposed to use the apparatus under powers granted
by the 1883 Patents Act.

Preece was then asked to report on the validity of Marconi's patent.
He provided his characteristic historical review on wireless conduc-
tivity systems beginning with Samuel Morse's in 1842. Then the
electro-magnetic induction system which he had helped to develop
(emphasizing that it was the only system by which speech could be
transmitted):

recent experiments at Carnarvon have shewn the possibility of extending
this means of communication to much greater distances

than the one and a quarter miles across Loch Ness successfully demonstrated in 1893. He pointed out that the system was unhampered by
any patents. His electro-magnetic induction installation had been
left *in situ* at Flat Holm fort; to repair the cable to Lavernock was not
thought worth while because of constant damage from ships'
anchors, and 'unskilled' soldiers there had continued to operate it.

He reviewed the electro-static induction system demonstrated by
Hertz, Popoff, Lodge, Muirhead, and Captain Jackson, which
Marconi was using. He noted that during the latter half of 1897
Lodge had applied for four patents which

rapidly following each other show how excited and energetic Professor
Oliver Lodge was to secure the *kudos* that he had been deprived of by
Marconi's success in attracting so much attention. . . . [Lodge's patents]
have prevented the Wireless Telegraph Company from strengthening
their position. . . .

The proper use and function of vertical wires was not fully realised by Mr. Marconi. He had been experimenting with flat surfaces of metal and with hat-shaped cylinders raised on poles. The Post Office made them [vertical aerials] for him and it was at Lavernock by such means we signalled to Brean Down, a distance of nine miles. . . . Marconi applied for a vertical wire to be included in the original patent but was successfully opposed by Lodge and Muirhead.

Preece pointed out that the Company had no commercial circuit at work anywhere and concluded there was no case yet for granting the Company a licence

to make money, not to fill a public want . . . public appreciation of Wireless Telegraphy is only sensational following the wonder of a solution of an apparently impossible problem.

A licence granted now would cause the Syndicates to play upon this ignorant excitement. A new company would be formed with a large capital, the public would wildly subscribe to an undertaking endorsed by the imprimatur of the Postmaster-General and the Government would encourage another South Sea Bubble.

Llewellyn Preece on 5 September 1899, two months before his father signed that report, sent Herr Schäfer, another wireless inventor, who had called at the Preece & Cardew offices, 8 Queen Anne's Gate, to Gavey with a covering letter:

. . . as my father is away I am giving him [Schäfer] this note thinking you might be interested . . . he says he has sent messages 86 kilometers . . . he is genuine . . . he uses a strip of looking glass with a slit down the back instead of a coherer.

Gavey arranged for trials but their results were inconclusive: since the stations he selected were G.P.O. West and Mount Pleasant there were certainly good chances of interference from other electric currents. Later tests at Lavernock showed that though the detector was remarkably sensitive it was capricious and unstable in operation.

Murray asked the Treasury at the end of the year for authority to call for reports from Oliver Lodge and Silvanus P. Thompson on the validity of Marconi's patent. They were willing to oblige for a fee of a hundred guineas each. Their conclusions did not entirely coincide but they agreed that Marconi's devices had been anticipated in nearly every particular except application to telegraphy. Lodge pointed out that the system was not syntonic (tunable) and concluded that Marconi's position was not invalidated but that he was not likely to be anxious for a contest, a result of which might demonstrate to the world that his method did not constitute a novel and mysterious discovery. Neither of them saw much future in Schäfer's 'anti-coherer'.

Preece was asked to comment on those reports. There was little doubt, he wrote, that Marconi was the first to demonstrate the use of Hertzian waves in telegraphy. Oliver Lodge never considered such a use till he (Preece) reported to the British Association on what had been done on Salisbury Plain. He thought that Lodge was more generous in his appreciation of Marconi's work than was Thompson, 'but both waste much energy in disposing of immaterial details'. (They were intent on giving money's worth for their fees.) Preece recommended that the Company should be allowed to enjoy 'their imaginary strength' and in the meantime the Post Office should concentrate on developing the electro-magnetic system or a new electro-static system.

The Post Office supplied the Law Office Department with all the relevant information and asked for an opinion. Edward Carson and R. B. Finlay signed a statement on 14 August 1901:

Marconi's claim for the combination appears to be good. If Schafer's apparatus were substituted we do not think that its substitution would prevent the combination being an infringement of Marconi's patent.

29

WIMBLEDON

DESPITE calls on his time Preece joined in Wimbledon's social activities as when, in November 1891, he formed with a number of other residents the Wimbledon Literary and Scientific Society. Elected President at its inaugural meeting he remained in that office till his death when his vacancy was filled by a noted botanist, William Bateson, F.R.S. In December Preece gave the Society's first paper, 'Science as a relaxation', to be followed in January with 'Telegraphy without wires'. By then the rapidly increasing membership had reached eighty. At 'delightful parties' which he gave at Gothic Lodge he usually had some scientific novelty to exhibit and explain. A neighbour recalled seeing one of his earliest demonstrations of Marconi's wireless telegraph and Preece saying that he 'had just seen the amazingly clever Italian engineer' and predicting that 'if Marconi could be kept from the financiers he would be a great scientific genius': that may have been on a Saturday afternoon in April 1897 when he gave the Wimbledon Society members a demonstration of Marconi's system, rigging an aerial to his swamp cypress tree.

Preece had said, jokingly, three years before,

I have established some claim to the 300,000 francs which are now lying somewhere in Paris, having been offered as a premium to the man who first showed how to communicate with the inhabitants of Mars,

and went on:

one cannot help speculating as to what may occur through planetary space. Strange, mysterious sounds are heard on all long telephone lines when the earth is used as a return, especially in the calm stillness of the night. Earth-currents are found in the telegraph circuits, and the aurora borealis lights up our northern sky when the sun's photosphere is disturbed by spots. The sun's surface must at times be violently disturbed by electrical storms, and as oscillations are set up and radiated through space, in sympathy with those required to affect telephones, it is not a wild dream to say that we may hear on this earth a 'thunderstorm' in the sun. . . .

If any of the planets be populated with beings like ourselves, having the gift of language and the knowledge to adapt the great forces of Nature to their wants, then, if they could oscillate immense stores of electrical energy to and fro, in telegraphic order, it would be possible for us to hold commune by telephone. . . .

Here were attractive subjects for light-hearted speculation at some of his Gothic Lodge parties; indeed one of his friends has recorded how 'with twinkling eyes' he assured parting guests that,

when the moon and the planetary system are in thorough communication with the earth, you shall be the first to be told.

★   ★   ★

The National Rifle Association had held, since 1859, an annual camp, with a fortnight's competition in marksmanship, on Wimbledon Common that in the course of time had become a fashionable social occasion. The camp was enclosed by palings, members of the public charged admission fees and refreshments sold to them. Admittedly the site was not ideal for rifle ranges and, in 1888, a proposal was put forward that it be transferred to Richmond Park. Preece wrote to The Times specifying the greater unsuitability of that nearby park; he thought the camp could well stay on the Common without the expense of costly hoardings; that the 'social flummery and coffee-shop business' could be dispensed with and ranges sought further afield in the interest of

real shooting and the real promotion of volunteer efficiency . . . we want a permanent shooting ground and place of training.

In the event the competition was not transferred to Richmond Park and within a few years permanent ranges were established on Bisley Common, Surrey.

★   ★   ★

A reporter who visited Gothic Lodge in May 1890 described a collection of Persian antiques disposed about the house; suits of armour, weapons, sculpture and glazed plaques. Preece's brother Richard, then living in Shiraz, put the collection which he had formed during his years in Persia on public exhibition in the Vincent Robinson galleries, Wigmore Street, during June 1913 when Her Majesty Queen Mary was among those who saw it. That Gothic Lodge was lit throughout by electricity impressed the reporter who admired an adjustable, centrally pendant, lamp in the dining-room and a doll's house and model ship each fitted with electric lights. Had he been invited to delve into cupboards he would have discovered the remarkable novelties of electric kettle, flat-iron, and curling-tongs heater. He noted that Preece had fitted up a private laboratory. He duly admired a bedside lamp – Preece described it to him as 'my best friend' explaining that when he awoke after a few hours' sleep he switched on the lamp, donned a bedjacket and scribbled notes in pencil.

Our reporter had observed that romance and general literature had a place on Preece's bookshelves. His library included long runs of bound volumes of the Journals and Proceedings of the many professional societies of which he was a member – volumes which eventually became part of the furnishings of Messrs Preece and Cardew's offices. In addition to an appreciable collection on physics were Oliver Heaviside's *Electrical Papers*; runs of journals on archaeology, anthropology, Hellenic and Roman studies; several atlases, a collection of Baedeker's guides, and books on countries and explorers. Books from the Everyman, Home University, and Loeb libraries accounted for more than a hundred volumes. The sixty-six-volume *Dictionary of National Biography* filled several of his shelves. He was a fully-paid-up subscriber to the *New English Dictionary* which the Oxford University Press began to publish in 1884: and alongside such volumes as had appeared were the *Encyclopaedia of Islam* and *Dictionary of the Bible* (three volumes each). Shakespeare was represented by two series of separate volumes of the plays and poems and Howard Staunton's three-volume (1858) edition. Was it for ideas on education or the plain style of sixteenth-century Roger Ascham that prompted Preece to acquire a complete collection of his works? Clearly the pioneer work on magnetism of Ascham's contemporary

William Gilbert of Colchester was of direct interest to him. Charles Darwin, Faraday, Benjamin Franklin, and Laplace were also represented. Among several hundred volumes of current fiction were novels by Guy Boothby, Conan Doyle, Anthony Hope, Rudyard Kipling, and Ian Maclaren. There were complete sets of the works of S. R. Crockett, Charles Dickens, Rider Haggard, Captain Marryat, H. M. Thackeray and Walter Scott. And if no volume of Wisden's *Cricketers' Almanack* could be seen, at least there was *Bennett on Billiards*.

Preece, rarely able to sleep as long as six hours, was almost invariably awake at five o'clock (unlike Anthony Trollope who had to pay his groom to wake him at that hour to give him three hours in which to write before breakfast). Preece spent those pre-breakfast hours drafting and polishing lectures and making notes on official work. It was with a sense of gaining a rare luxury that he had fitted a bedside 'glow lamp', for working many hours in poor light had weakened his eyesight. A sketch made in 1875 shows him with full beard and moustache, and luxuriant side-whiskers merging into a beard cut to chin level, wearing a monocle in his right eye but he soon found it necessary to wear spectacles at all times. He seems to have worn a bowler, or derby, in preference to the ubiquitous top hat of those days. He was often seen with a cigar in his mouth until a doctor treating him for bronchitis told him smoking aggravated the trouble, whereupon he never smoked again. He had successfully habituated himself to making full use of his waking hours, though an uncertain digestion, and a tendency to bronchitis for which he sought relief by winter holidaying in Egypt when possible, became increasing handicaps as he aged.

No lecturer ever gained a reputation for eloquence by reading his paper to his audience: many of those early-morning hours were spent committing his lectures to memory to permit a minimum reference to notes in a lecture hall. With the natural advantage of a superb voice, clear enunciation – a chairman at one of his talks described his performance as 'quiet, unassuming, lucid' – a recognizable enthusiasm for his subject which manifestly he wished to share on equal terms with members of his audience, and an ability to fire their imaginations, made him, in the words of a contemporary, the Demosthenes of Electricity. He developed, too, considerable skill at extempore speaking when his sense of humour and facility in calling to mind appropriate allusions and quotations served him well.

He is never more thoroughly at home than when he rises at some festive gathering. . . . One gets that movement of animated expectancy on the part of the guests which betokens that they know their man, nor does he disappoint. The appropriate anecdote . . . the humourous and always good humoured paraphrase of the remarks of the previous speakers makes the lot of a dinner a pleasant one while Mr. Preece is on his feet.

A chairman of one of his lectures spoke afterwards of three types of speakers:

those who don't understand. Those who do but can't explain. Preece understands what he is talking about and can describe his subject to those who don't know to make them almost equally understand it and send his audience away in the happy consciousness of having been instructed in such a manner as to make them capable of taking their knowledge home and retaining it.

He drew crowded audiences.

Much the same picture of Gothic Lodge as was described in 1890 is sketched by a reporter fourteen years later: it adds references to the *1904* garden and shows Preece in his small conservatory handling a potted fern – 'one of my hobbies'. Preece may have been indulging a daydream to occasion the comment that had his desires found full sway he would have been a musician but certainly he had not encouraged the well-meaning waffle which followed:

it may be remarked in passing that the relationship between music and mathematics is by no means infrequently noted.

Nor did he instigate an editorial on the turn of the century:

Sir William H. Preece is the ablest and most practical engineer of the day. *1900* Lord Kelvin, of course, is the *doyen* . . . in point of theoretical knowledge he stands unrivalled . . . Preece is by no means deficient in theory . . . he knows a good deal more . . . than some of the young professors at the universities who gird at him for the sake of displaying their book knowledge or drawing attention to themselves, but he only rates himself as a practical man and in this regard he is easily first, not only as a telegraphic but as an electric light and power engineer. . . .

Marconi figures in the eye of the public as the inventor of the wireless telegraph but in reality Marconi has not invented anything of importance. He has only adapted and improved what Hughes, Righi, Lodge and others did before him . . . Preece introduced . . . wireless telegraphy based on inductions [*sic*] ten years in advance of Marconi and his method is now in daily use in the Post Office . . . the only system for transmitting speech through ether . . . it is likely to remain so. . . .

He is a broad, kindly, human sort of man, without any stuffiness or affectation, and with whom all, even the most difficult or youthful, can feel at home . . . a born administrator whether he knows it or not . . . the gift of reading men, choosing them and setting them to work for him, without any trouble . . . so easily and naturally that he may not be fully aware of his ability . . . but others have seen it. He rules with so much good humour and tact that his subordinates like him . . . one never hears the faintest murmur against his governance.

His colleagues would have agreed with that valuation of his personal qualities. Professor Ayrton, on retiring from the Presidency of the I.E.E., said,   *Pres 1892 —*

I am cheered by the recollection that my successor Mr. Preece, is undoubtedly the most popular man in the whole engineering profession.

Sir David Salomons, who could be obstreperous at meetings, spoke at the I.E.E. on the occasion of Preece's award of a C.B.:

He is a gentleman – one of the very few to be found in the world – with whom no one could quarrel. I do not mean he is one of the weak, good natured men. . . . He is a man of strong character. He presides in the Council room as a chairman should do. . . . No one ever desires to dispute his authority, even when a difference of opinion arises . . . goodwill he has shewn to every member down to the youngest recruit.

Professor Forbes at another I.E.E. meeting said,

If I comply with this specification [for rubber] I know I have got the right thing: Mr. Preece has told us so . . . the opinion of the Electrician to the Post Office, whether it be on the subject of electricity or any other subject you care to mention, is very deservedly treated with great veneration.

Preece's talent for bringing out the best in his assistants by encouraging originality and assumption of responsibility was later recalled by John Gavey:

He was generally happy in his choice of the right man and broad-minded enough to leave the rest to him. The resulting *esprit de corps* . . . was a great asset at the time and something to remember with pride and delight.

Against administrative prejudice, he pressed for the technical instruction of engineering and telegraph operating staffs and was instrumental in the award of 'technical increments' to those who passed examinations (under the aegis of the Society of Arts and, later, the City and Guilds Institute).

His was a remarkably attractive personality, level-headed and cheerful; definite in his views and kindly in his expression of them; meeting objections with a quiet courtesy and seeming almost to enjoy criticism; loving a good story either in the telling or the hearing but able tactfully to prevent a general conversation from becoming frivolously anecdotal; a first class conversationalist with a broad outlook that extended far beyond the profession to which he was so devoted, his society was always a source of pleasure.

★   ★   ★

In the House of Commons, 20 May 1892, Henry Labouchere (editor of *Truth*), keen to nose out a scandal, asked Postmaster-General Sir James Fergusson if he was aware that the chief electrician engineer of his Department was in the habit of taking private practice in electrical work. Postal reformer John Henniker-Heaton interposed:

Before the question of my genial but misinformed hon. friend is answered I beg to ask the Postmaster-General whether he is aware that Mr Preece has a high European reputation and that he could command double the salary he now receives from the Government if he would devote himself exclusively to private practice . . . that in the work he now does in his spare moments he is rendering substantial service to the community.

He need not have been so anxious to defend Preece for Fergusson replied:

The case of Mr Preece is exceptional. Before he entered Her Majesty's service 22 years ago, he held certain employments beside Engineer of the Electric Telegraph Company. These he relinquished as being incompatible with his appointment at the Post Office but with the knowledge of the Department he continued to advise on the great electrical questions outside his regular duty, he being an expert of the highest standing. Such advice had generally been afforded to public bodies, for example, lighting the House of Commons, the British Museum, the Dublin Museum, and the principal cities . . . his action has been quite public and his reports have been published. As an electrician of European eminence he takes part in the development of electrical science. He never turns to any work other than departmental during office hours without special permission but his official work is by no means confined to those hours. It is performed unsparingly early and late, and even on Sundays. His case is altogether exceptional and cannot form a precedent.

(That reply was given with no prior approach to Preece himself.)

*　　*　　*

'Welshmen who have made notable contributions to science' was the title of a paper which I. C. Jones of the National Physical Laboratory presented at a meeting of the Society of Cymmrodorion in London, March 1933. Among the ninety-two he listed was Preece who became, he recorded, the Post Office's Engineer-in-Chief in 1892, adding 'an office of much more importance then than now': he appeared to be echoing an interjection, twenty years before, by S. P. Thompson in his obituary of Preece, in *Nature*. It had been based on a misunderstanding of Post Office organization before and after the transfer of telephones to the State in 1912. The relative standing of engineers vis-à-vis administrators in the Civil Service, despite conservative reactions, improved with the development of a technological society. The year before Jones gave his paper it had been agreed that engineers in the Post Office would be considered for administrative posts, something which would not have been entertained for a moment during Preece's service.

Preece presided at the annual dinner of Old Boys of King's College School at the Criterion in 1899. John Henniker-Heaton – a major part of whose scheme for Imperial Penny Post had been brought into operation the preceding Christmas Day – proposed a toast to Preece and recalled gratefully the encouragement and assistance he had from Preece during his fourteen years of struggle to get his reforms introduced. He described Preece as a mastermind and prophesied that his remains would be given a last resting place in Westminster Abbey. Preece responded in similar euphoric mood, claiming that in the Civil Service one's progress was entirely dependent on merit –

forgetting for that moment the words of the Preacher, 'time and chance happeneth to them all' – and he may well have been accurate when he told them he had never suffered vexation or annoyance in dealings with those above him. A good dinner, as much as an innate modesty, can be his excuse, for

I look forward to the day when my bones will be laid in a beautiful little cemetery in Wales within sound of the roar of the sea

(not a particularly recognizable description of Llanbeblig churchyard), but he sufficiently recollected himself to express his 'every wish that that day is some distance off'.

We will go back to Wimbledon and, with breakfast over, watch his old coachman harness the horse in a brougham to drive Preece down to his office in St Martin's-le-Grand for yet another day's work as the Post Office's Engineer-in-Chief and Electrician.

* * *

The editor of the *Wimbledon News*, a weekly paper first issued 6 October 1894, commented in his opening editorial on bad street lighting: 'we hope that the District Council . . . will introduce a thoroughly efficient scheme for lighting the town with electric light'. Council members turned their thoughts to the possibility of replacing the oil-lamps they were using for street lighting, having seen a successful demonstration by Preece of lamps suspended from the mid-points of transverse wires on their High Street, a system of lighting he was advocating for the City of London. As a preliminary their Roads and Drainage Committee invited Arthur Preece, who had set up as a consulting electrician, to attend their meeting on 1 May 1895 to tell them just what would be involved. They then instructed him to make a detailed report. He proposed that the Council should also supply electricity to the public and within four days of issuing explanatory circulars 2100 lights had been applied for. The Council convened a public meeting at the Drill Hall, where the audience was told that the price of oil was rising and that electric lamps would be two and a half times brighter than oil-lamps. At rather less than £2 10s. an oil-lamp street lighting had cost £1800 a year. Gas would cost nearly double. Preece had co-operated by lighting a 32 c.p. electric lamp near Gothic Lodge to enable it to be compared with the 'Ipswich' oil-burner already *in situ*. The general feeling of the meeting, usual with an increase in rates in prospect (for Arthur's scheme would need a capital of £32000 – though there would be profits on supplies to private houses within a short time) was not altogether in favour. The meeting adjourned 'pending further inquiry'.

Subsequent letters to the local paper were revealing. One writer recommended the 'Welsbach' gas light by which he had 'saved £50 on his gas bill last year'. Another recalled that the Council had postponed consideration of an electric lighting scheme five years before; the informant was of opinion that the Council would be wise to do so again. Another writer, living near the edge of the Common, held that the '4 c.p. oil lamps' had 'fostered a reign of terror' culminating in a recent increase in burglaries.

A Board of Trade public inquiry was held by Major-General Carey, R.E., the following month. The Council expressed full confidence in Arthur's scheme; he 'had been associated with a large number of electric lighting schemes'. At a cost of $1\frac{1}{2}$d. in the pound to rates, street lighting would be far more than doubled. Preece testified that he had examined his son's scheme and approved of it: electric lighting was cheaper all round than gas. The Ratepayers' Association opposed the scheme, which included batteries on floating charge to take part of the peak load. They, somewhat illogically, called in Silvanus P. Thompson on their behalf, but his opinion that large-scale electricity supply was not a matter for municipalities was well known. (He gave evidence, subsequently, on behalf of private companies promoting Bills for county and regional supply systems.) He claimed that the scheme was crude and expensive and preferred 'the continuous [supply] system of Kingswood and Keynsham' (of which he had been the consulting electrician). On examination he admitted that no municipality had installed the 'continuous' system (in which a battery of secondary cells is not an integral part).

The Ratepayers had even engaged a Queen's Counsel who pronounced in the fullness of his wisdom that Preece was naturally prejudiced in favour of his son. When it transpired that the Mitcham Gas Company was financing the Ratepayers' opposition, considerable indignation was generated.

Nearly two years later, in August 1897, a Provisional Order

enabling the Council to undertake electricity supply was confirmed by Act of Parliament, and Arthur's scheme approved. The editor of the *Wimbledon News* commented: 'we are satisfied that only those benevolent ratepayers the Mitcham Gas Company, together with persons interested in the concern . . . are now of opinion that the electric light should not be adopted', and later, 'the last chance of the Mitcham Gas Company to grab a little more money from the district, which has suffered so much from their extortion, is gone. We prophesy that as soon as the electric light is in full swing down goes the price of gas.' When the Local Government Board authorized the necessary borrowing of capital the editor observed, 'the warm approval of Mr. Preece's electric lighting scheme expressed at a meeting of the Incorporated Association of Municipal and City Engineers . . . removes any lingering doubts of the advantages to Wimbledon. Revenue will probably increase to three times Mr. Preece's modest estimate of £1,750 . . . for the first year we should not be surprised at an extra 2d. on rates . . . it is in the *near* not the *immediate* future we look for a triumph of the Council's scheme.'

In August the Local Government Board held another inquiry on the Council's application for £5000 to build a dust destructor whereby collected household rubbish could be used as fuel for steam boilers to drive electricity generators. To put waste to use particularly appealed to Preece. His son Llewellyn attended in the place of Arthur who was then in South Africa. The Preeces were particularly pleased that Arthur repeated his father's achievement of thirty-eight years before by winning an Institution of Civil Engineers' Telford gold medal (for a paper on electricity supply).

The editor referred two months later to a phenomenon of which the like is occasionally seen today, electric cables being laid under a path soon after it had been tarred and sanded. He thought it 'seems to argue a lack of foresight on the part of someone but perhaps this may be their notion of economy'. The contractors laying those cables had no easy task for they had been debarred from running them near the gas mains but the gas company often did not know the exact route of its mains, and on at least one occasion, after being given an all clear, the contractors dug a trench to discover that it was directly above a gas main.

* * *

U

The advertising income of the *Wimbledon News* (as did that of other newspapers) benefited that May from a full-page advertisement for Eiffel Tower Lemondade. At its centre was a sketch of the Channel coastlines with the Eiffel Tower in the foreground and a representation of London in the distance: a slogan ribboned between the two, EIFFEL TOWER IS THE BEST DRINK, with a caption below, 'Wireless Telegraphy! The first message from Paris to London.' As Preece had said, the advent of Marconi had stimulated the public's imagination.

Preece had been an early subscriber to the National Telephone Company: in its Metropolitan Directory for 1895 his number is 350. The telephone can have been of no great use to him for very few of the other numbers were of persons with whom he had dealings. There were signs of widening interest in the Wimbledon area for in June 1897 the Commons Conservators refused the National Telephone Company permission to run an overhead telephone line across the Common but agreed that the Company might lay a 'tube' across Putney Heath provided they first removed two 'unsightly' poles on the property of the Chelsea Water Company there.

The London County Council took over most of London's horse-drawn tramways at the beginning of 1899 to reorganize, electrify, and extend them. Tramcars through Wimbledon to the edge of the Common appeared in its plans, to the disapproval of many who lived on the periphery of the Common. We can be sure that Preece, on the contrary, welcomed such an electrically energized social benefit to Londoners.

30

OLIVER LODGE

PREECE wrote on the subject of lightning conductors to *The Times* in August 1872, commenting that thunderstorms had been unduly frequent that summer and – ignoring the result of a suggestion put forward in Glasgow in 1859 that lightning rods should be erected on all buildings, when Glasgow manufacturers were unanimous in their reponse that it was 'cheaper to insure' – recommended each house-holder to clear soot from his chimneys and to fit an external lightning conductor (the lightning rod which Benjamin Franklin had invented in 1742). His optimistic hope for the human future led him to intro-duce a harsh note:

with improved education and the spread of knowledge we may expect that human beings will be able to exercise sufficient judgment so as to avoid dangerous positions in such perilous times (sheltering under trees) but while their intellects are not far in advance of the beasts they herd, we must expect them to suffer in the same way.

Among those stirred to add to the correspondence was his brother-in-law Latimer Clark, who seemed more tolerant of human frailty; he assured nervous readers that a metal bedstead provided complete protection, and ended,

It may further console some to know that after seeing the flash the danger is past, the crash of the thunder, however terrific it may appear, being perfectly harmless.

Replying to criticism a week later, Preece wrote of twenty years' experience in a profession which, according to a correspondent, 'lives by lightning': what he had said was not 'mere scholism'; he did not pretend to be an authority on atmospheric electricity but had learnt from 'the best of all teachers – experience'. He pointed out that sharp angles in a lightning conductor should be avoided. He claimed that all telegraph apparatus was protected (an exaggeration):

I have known one or two clerks knocked down, but principally by fright. If there were any truth in the popular notion that metal attracts lightning, telegraphists would lead a very sorry life during thunderstorms.

One should not infer from this that Preece was casual about protecting telegraphs. Far from it. His first paper to the Society of Telegraph Engineers was on that subject and he had sent instructions to Cape Colony in 1877 emphasizing that,

special care should be taken to see that lightning protectors are fixed at every point of junction of open and covered wires . . . apparatus should in every case be protected against the possible effect of lightning.

Preece admitted, in a paper at the British Association's meeting in Sheffield, two years later, that much telegraph apparatus had not been protected ('the remedy being worse than the disease') but the Post Office had tried a number of devices, of which he gave details, claiming that a high-voltage by-pass then being brought into general service – formed of two metal plates, one leading to earth, separated by 0·002 of an inch of paraffin wax – exemplified 'the survival of the fittest'. Next year protection from lightning was discussed by leading physicists and electricians at a specially convened 'Lightning Rod Conference': the recommendations in its report to the British Association in 1881 were regarded as the last word on the subject, although the signatories acknowledged that little was known of the causes of electric storms.

Such storms in their most violent form were prevalent in South Africa where Doctor Adams had taken a great interest in that phenomena: as a memorial to him funds were allocated for research on lightning and Oliver Lodge, professor of physics, University College, Liverpool, selected to undertake it. When it became known that Lodge would present a paper on his research at the British Association meeting in Bath, 1888, which would challenge the recommendations of the Lightning Rod Conference's signatories, they deputed Preece to open on their behalf the discussion which would follow Lodge's paper to the combined Physics and Engineering Sections. Lodge described the laboratory experiments he had been making with high-voltage electro-static discharges and his astonishment when he calculated that lightning flashes oscillated at more than one million times a second, from which he had to conclude that protection was not simply a matter of providing an easy path to earth, the self-induction as well as the resistance of a conductor had to be taken into account. He later recalled that Preece led a good-humoured attack on his doctrine and 'exercising his well known rhetorical and oratorical powers' succeeded in impressing most of their audience with a belief that he had the best of it. Lord Rayleigh thought Lodge's laboratory experiments might be important as suggestions but that no one would wish to change any system of lightning protection without actual experiment upon a large scale. The Secretary of the Lightning Rod Conference claimed there had been no accidents where its rules had been followed and M. de Fonvielle supported him by stating that Paris was practically free from calamities produced by lightning because they had 'a sufficient number of lightning rods erected according to the principles so admirably indicated by Mr Preece'. William Douglass pointed out that lighthouse towers had fitted copper rods and earth-plates as advised by Faraday fifty years earlier and in each instance of lightning damage they had discovered defects in the conductor: there had been only one accident to surrounding dwellings and that because of a defect in the tower's conductor. Professor F. G. FitzGerald of Dublin University, President of the Mathematical and Physical Science Section that year, said all had heard the discussion with great pleasure: Preece had called attention to the fact that lightning discharge was much more like a discharge between the plates of a condenser than the breaking down of a Leyden jar. FitzGerald held there could be no doubt that lightning rods had protected buildings; perhaps improvements were possible but it was their experience that lightning conductors had been a great protection to mankind.

After the meeting Preece went out of his way to offer Lodge another audience, a meeting of the Institution of Electrical Engineers, at which Lodge gave a paper. In the discussion which followed Preece disclaimed that he had been Lodge's principal critic; he had defended men described by Lodge as 'the older electricians' who could balance many years of practical experience against a few weeks of laboratory experiments. He agreed he had said of lightning conductors in 1872 that quarter-inch galvanized iron wire – a standard fitting on over half a million telegraph poles – was as good as copper and admitted copper wire might be cheaper in the long run. He could not agree that because the discharge from a Leyden jar was oscillatory that it must be so for lightning, or how would it have marked signals on Bain's and Wheatstone's telegraph tapes? Fitz-Gerald thought that would happen when an oscillatory discharge preponderated in one direction. Lodge had said there was no definite area of protection near a rod but, claimed Preece,

I would not hesitate ... to hold a well-earthed one-inch diameter copper rod within range of a thunderstorm.

FitzGerald interposed:

I value Preece too much to see him perform the experiment.

Preece went on to reiterate that lightning rods had been successful in practice; he would not retaliate on Lodge for his denunciation,

It is time the prophets of that old superstition were slaughtered by the brook Kishon,

but quoted Cowper,

O for a Lodge in some vast wilderness ... where rumours of oppression and deceit ... might never reach me more,

and wished Lodge could find himself in some such desert with lightning flashes overhead and his apparatus around him, when he was sure Lodge would speedily conclude that it was better to 'join the old school'. Lodge had said that the Lightning Rod signatories were little less than criminals:

Well like some Irish patriots I am criminal and every signatory to that Conference is criminal; and why? Because he believes in himself and not in Professor Oliver Lodge.

Summing up after further discussion on another evening – Lodge had been unable to attend – Sir William Thomson (Kelvin) the President said the Lightning Rod report still held the field despite flaws pointed out by Lodge; he went on to draw the meeting's attention to the brilliant mathematical work on electro-static induction by Oliver Heaviside.

From Preece's comments elsewhere we can infer that he was not too happy with his criticism of Lodge – lightning flashes could well be oscillatory even if far less than the high frequency of a million reversals a second Lodge had postulated nor did he think Lodge's calculations could be proven – he had since amended an earlier statement and might do so with others – but as most speakers at Bath seemed to support Preece he felt his criticisms justifiable. He admired Lodge's brilliant experiments but thought his speculations therefrom rather fanciful and not to be sustained in the light of experience. Lodge was not particularly helpful when, in 1892, he published *Lightning Conductors and Lightning Guards*, a volume of over 500 pages comprised of his collected papers with no elimination of repetitive material, editing, or summarizing of conclusions.

Lodge had given the Institution of Electrical Engineers a second paper within twelve months but that time he had been circumspect in his phrasing: he had admitted that any protector was better than none and that the best of those in use were 'by no means inefficient'. A submarine cable expert reported that his own protectors had been entirely efficient over twenty years: Lodge's would have to be given a practical test. Preece asked whether Lodge's invention would fill a want, or secure greater economy. The Post Office had 19000 telegraph instruments and 11000 protectors but no protectors were in Ireland where lightning storms were very few – 'very different from political storms', Preece wryly commented. Only the more valuable apparatus was protected and during 1889 none had been damaged. Those protectors cost from 2s. 9d. to 3s. 6d. whereas Lodge's would cost £1:

if there is anything to be gained by having a thorough, sound, practical test of Dr Lodge's protectors, we shall be happy to give them a fair trial.

Preece in his Presidential address to the Institution of Civil Engineers in November 1898 noted that the Lightning Rod Conference report

remains an admirable and useful standard of reference. The principle advocated by Franklin was prevention rather than protection. If a building or a ship be fitted and maintained with good continuous copper conductors, making a firm electrical contact with the earth or the sea, and be surmounted well up in the air with one or a cluster of fine points, all the conditions that determine a charge of atmospheric electricity and a flash of lightning are dissipated silently away and no terrible discharge is possible. . . . Every exposed building should be fitted, but a well-protected dwelling-house is the exception, not the rule. Even when protectors are fixed apathy leads to their imperfect maintenance. The failure to act is always traceable to the neglect of some simple rule. Carelessness is the direst disease we suffer from.

★   ★   ★

Preece had ever been ready to speak in defence of colleagues under criticism from academic sources but Professor G. F. FitzGerald, for one, had no illusions about where Preece stood.

[Preece] emphatically states that 'the engineer must be a scientific man'. . . . Of course no 'laboratory research or professional teaching' can teach all that an engineer should know . . . things that can only be learnt by experience outside schools and universities. . . .
A few failures now and then, a few cases of being taken in by fraudulent or over zealous inventors and our wavering faith in science collapses . . . how many are taken in by specious company promoters! And yet the capitalist has faith in . . . limited liability companies. . . .
Preece expects laboratories to carry on all the researches engineers may require. That is quite as it should be, but such laboratories must be highly endowed.

FitzGerald had also written:

It is much to be regretted that scientific experts are . . . so highly paid to advance causes and so very seldom paid to advance practice.

★   ★   ★

Lodge began, in 1909, what proved to be a sustained correspondence with a fellow spiritualist during which he confessed that anyone who studies much and allows due weight for everything is apt to get overloaded. He would have none of Einstein's special and general theories of relativity (which abolished the conception of absolute space to dispense with that mathematically 'convenient fiction the ether'), affirming that mind was not just a property of the brain but was real and that in the ether of space a bridge might be found between Mind and Matter. He referred to wireless telegraphy, informing his non-technical correspondent that its true originators were Maxwell and Hertz.

Upon them everyone has built . . . a lot of my work which ultimately led to Wireless Telegraphy was done in '88 and '89. It was then I came across the coherer principle. What is called the 'wireless' lecture was given in '94, first at the R.I. in the spring. Next at the Oxford British Association meeting in the autumn even more fully, and exciting considerable attention, but in the optical more than the telegraphic direction; though it was at the first of these lectures that my friend Alexander Muirhead conceived the telegraphic applications which ultimately led to the foundation of the Lodge-Muirhead Syndicate. . . .

It was that R.I. lecture which was published in the *Electrician* and illustrated by the editor because I had no time, being very busy then – illustrated not very well indeed – and that year brought a book called *The work of Hertz and his successors*, for Hertz had recently died and I wished to raise a memorial to his memory.

Two years later (in '96) Marconi came over with the same thing in a secret box, with aristocratic introductions to Preece of the Government Telegraphs, and was taken up and assisted by him – who was more ignorant than he ought to have been of what had already been done.

Marconi had given Preece a list of published references to Hertzian waves, including a report of Lodge's lecture in the *Electrician* and an article by M. Edouard Branly of Paris, before the Toynbee Hall lecture. From Preece's reference in the Royal Institution lecture he was well aware of an estimate of Lodge's that the free oscillations he had produced could not be detected beyond a distance of half a mile.

Lodge decided to enter the commercial wireless lists against Marconi and made the obvious opening move, on 4 March 1898, of writing to Preece:

I hear from Muirhead that you are back in England again & I hope the better for your rest and change.

I have been working for six months & more on a method of magnetic telegraphy, using an oscillating condenser-discharge indeed, but with no propagation of waves worth noticing. Being magnetic it is unaffected by obstacles & it is susceptible of very exact tuning. With very primitive arrangements I can signal from the college to my house [2 Grove Park,

4 March 1898

Liverpool] i.e. nearly two miles; & I have all the calculations ready to plan a circuit for any distance (literally for *any* distance).

It has developed into something not unlike your old plan, with stretched wires along the Sound of Mull &c., hence you may be interested in it. Naturally I should like the Govt. to take it up, as I believe it is the most powerful & by far the simplest plan possible.

A week later – for Preece did not delay a reply in which he suggested that Lodge's 'coherer' system might be more promising – Lodge wrote:

Letter 2 11 March '98 22

the 'coherer' plan . . . may have scope in its proper place & I keep that going alongside the other. However, I believe the magnetic plan is best for ships and lighthouses & for long distances & I should be glad to know what sort of demonstration would satisfy you as to the utility of my improvements in the method – improvements which seem to me indeed to put it on a new basis & constitute practically a new plan.

He wrote again in August:

Letter 3 5 Aug '98

I wish to say that the idea of using induction for Telegraphy occurred to me after reading the account of your experiments & partial successes with it. Also that my present plan, although an outcome of some of my Leyden jar experiments, is practically a development & improvement of your plan.

1898

Preece replied that when Lodge was at the British Association's meeting in Bristol in September to give a paper on wireless he should take a half-day off to inspect the Lavernock–Flat Holm installation. Lodge took his advice and wrote (18th September):

Mr. Partridge [a local P.O. engineer] was most cordial and gave up the whole afternoon to taking me to Lavernock and showing me everything. I was particularly struck with the fact that the system was in regular work. I had not previously known of Evershed's 'cell' [a sensitive tunable relay which, on being operated by an incoming signal, completed a local circuit] or I should have mentioned it at Bristol.

I believe that earth conduction is the chief mode of communication and that it is not true induction – I don't see that this matters practically, but clearly a return wire along the sea beach – without earth plates – would greatly enfeeble the whole thing. I daresay it is best not to disorganise an actual service like that with any experiments. It is clearly the pioneer of all future developments, and it has got into the practical stage.

The work of 'calling' is however very severe and I fully expect that my magnifier will give results that will dispense with any putting of telephone to ear, and will act either for calling or for signalling. A single pair of the series ought to suffice, as the signals are already very audible in the telephone.

At the Institution of Electrical Engineers (8th December) Lodge reviewed three wireless systems. The earliest, first used by Morse, is operated by earth current or leakage whereby strong currents conveyed to earth or sea by two well-separated electrodes cause a slight difference in potential between two other well-separated electrodes at a distance and thereby produces a weak current through a wire joining them. Next, magnetic induction between two insulated wires stretched parallel to one another along opposite coasts, known as 'Preece's system'. For the third system, Hertzian waves, the public owed its knowledge and interest likewise to Preece for if he had not taken up the subject in 1896 very few persons would have heard of Hertzian waves.

Owing to Mr. Preece's great influence and power of lecturing this third and most recent method . . . has become the best known of all.

Lodge gave details of additions and refinements to Preece's system, of which tuning the sending and receiving circuits with each other was an essential part, which Alexander Muirhead and he had devised, and by which he communicated in Morse code between his house and college. His signals must have been a nuisance for

the National Telephone Company's subscribers close to the college unfortunately became rampant.

The essential difference between Preece's and the third system, both open-circuit wireless, Lodge did not really make clear. From Preece's 'two-earths' transmitter electric lines of force move at right angles to the direction of transmission, therefore their intensity diminishes as the cube of the distance whereas at the 'single-earth' transmitter lines of force move in the direction of transmission to decrease in simple proportion to the distance. Affecting the minds of all members present was the glamour of Hertz's demonstration of the truth of Clerk Maxwell's deduction in 1864 of electro-magnetic waves, longer than light waves, their field pervading an absolute

space: in assuming for his mathematical theory the existence of an
ether Clerk Maxwell followed the sixteenth-century Dutch philosopher Huygens who originated the wave theory of light and postulated an imponderable medium, the ether, through which those
waves were vibrated.

Preece opened the discussion of Lodge's paper by thanking him

for bringing such a charming subject before us in such an elegant way. . . .
It is the first time I had listened to anyone else holding forth on the subject
of wireless telegraphy. It is sixteen years since I first brought it before the
British Association.

Lodge commented that in his experience only engineering societies laid themselves out for discussion: in fact no discussion then
followed for the hour was late and even a paper by S. Evershed on
the same subject had to be postponed till the next, fortnightly,
meeting.

Evershed, too, had been experimenting with a variation of Preece's
system and had tried it between Dumpton Gap and North Sand
light-vessel, only to find that seawater, or the ship's hull, almost
completely absorbed his signals. Preece had tested Evershed's method
at Lavernock with Gavey that spring for 'three or four happy days'
and had fitted Evershed's calling device into the existing installation.
C. A. Stevenson had described another variation of the system (19
March 1894) at the Royal Society of Edinburgh. On Preece's instruction P.O. engineers had tested it at Murrayfield, near Edinburgh,
without success, though Stevenson was not convinced of that: said
Preece, 'You can't convince a man against his will.'

Preece followed Evershed's paper with one on 'aetheric telegraphy' in which he recalled his yearly reports to the British Association on a long and continuous research: some had not been
printed. He reviewed experiments from the autumn of 1884 on
Porthcawl sands, 1893 on Conway estuary, 1894 Frodsham on the
Dee estuary and Wimbledon. The telegraph cable between Oban
and the Isle of Mull broke down in March 1895 but, by using his
system, communication was maintained for the seven days before
the cable was repaired. On a Sunday night six months before, he had
utilized a trunk line from Carlisle to Haverfordwest and another
from Belfast to Wexford in an attempt to signal across the Irish Sea,

but it was impossible to distinguish a signal through the wonderful, incessant, and strange sounds that filled the telephone and overpowered everything else . . . The hum of two or three electric light installations working on the alternating current system was evident, but there was a weird, strange babel of noises that were mysterious and disappointing. I am strongly of opinion that these sounds were due to disturbances excited by primary electric effects outside our globe. It can have no practical value, but I had arranged in the event of its success to communicate between England and Europe, and then between Europe and America.

Members were brought up to date by the discussion which followed these papers through several meetings, particularly on communication with light-vessels and off-shore lighthouses. Ayrton reported that he was in correspondence on wireless theory with Oliver Heaviside. Lodge was grateful for Preece's offer to facilitate further experiments with his method but, though optimistic of their outcome, concluded that a cable should be laid wherever it was practicable. A year later he was writing to Preece giving references to earlier work than Marconi's on electro-static signalling and asking for similar information. By now Preece was in private practice and Lodge was complaining that 'the G.P.O. are terribly slow' with regard to licensing the Lodge–Muirhead system. He wrote:

I sincerely hope that you have really recovered from your illness – bronchitis is a horrid thing to have at the beginning of winter. I fancied that you were monopolising Taylor and working away at something on the quiet – instead of being ill!

[margin note:] J. E. Taylor P O Engineer see p. 268

Taylor had, in fact, been working on Preece's system, but entirely on his own, and reported officially three years later that it could not be developed any further for practical purposes.

On 11 November 1899 Lodge wrote to *The Times* to give details of how Preece's system could be improvised by army telegraphists to maintain contact with beleaguered Ladysmith. (The system was later used in the 1914–18 war – in France – to listen-in to telephone messages in the parallel German trenches.)

* * *

The development of wireless telegraphy proceeded slowly for a number of reasons but Preece's participation was largely in an advisory capacity to the Post Office (till 1904) and to the Crown Agents for the Colonies. Muirhead and Lodge developed a system possessing tuning facilities in advance of any other.

Lodge wrote a personal letter to Preece at Penrhos in the summer of 1911 to report that the Marconi Company was illegally using his tuning system and that he had been backed to

an amount of over £10,000 . . . a fighting fund . . . to bring the Marconi company to book and make them apply for a licence. We are bound . . . to give a licence to anyone who applies for it on terms to be either mutually agreed upon or to be settled by an Arbitrator appointed by the Board of Trade. The Helsby Co. and Siemens have applied for a licence; the Marconi Co. have not moved, and I do not suppose that they will move until compelled to.

It is no earthly use my getting an extension of Patent and then sitting down and letting them go on as before. They are clearly infringing, and we have a moral right to royalty. Accordingly I am actively bestirring myself to that end. We have not however as yet made any hostile move: we were bound to wait till the new Patent was issued; and we must then I suppose give them polite intimation either of a public or a private kind. I have no belief in the efficacy of any private negotiations with that Company. Hunter Gray, who is Counsel for them did I believe sound them on the subject. But they are probably advised by Fleming [Professor J. A. Fleming, the Marconi Company's scientific adviser] that they need not do anything. I rather expect that Fleming is the difficulty. . . .

The Lodge–Muirhead Syndicate have felt rather sore about the Post Office refusing licence and otherwise hampering them, but I hope that condition of things will not continue. I never quite understood it, for we have been always friendly with the Post Office and assisted them before the Parliamentary Committee in respect of the International Convention. . . .

I have also seen the First Lord of the Admiralty. It is quite clear to me that the Admiralty must be infringing and I assume that they will act fairly if the fact can be brought home to them. They may in the first instance shelter themselves under the Marconi Co. perhaps.

Naturally I have no love for legal proceedings if they can be avoided, but I do not intend to shirk them. On the contrary when they become necessary they shall be pursued with vigour.

Preece replied without delay:

I agree with every word you say and I am sure you are taking the proper attitude but I am anxious that you should not commence a costly and dilatory campaign. I can see from the present position of affairs that the first attack or opening move should come from the Marconi people and I feel sure that I can force them to do it but I do not want to appear as belonging to either side for I am in a delicate consultative position with the coming customer the Colonial side. It is a question of policy and finance not of Law; you are cock of the walk. As soon as the Coronation is over something must be done. We must meet.

In the meantime Llewellyn Preece had been making discreet inquiries to learn that Godfrey C. Isaacs, Managing Director of the Company, was sure Lodge could not win an action against the Marconi Company but was prepared to meet him on a friendly basis. Writing from Queen Anne's Gate on 21st June to his father at Penrhos, he added:

Very glad to hear that you are feeling so fit. I hope that will continue.

Llewellyn's action had been instigated by his father who considered it worth while to go to considerable trouble if thereby legal proceedings could be avoided, and he wrote again to Lodge suggesting that they both meet Isaacs personally. Lodge felt, with regret, that he could not accept Preece's kind offer:

it seems to me that they should either apply for a licence or make some clear proposition, and that I should not go to them except through lawyers till they have done so. Indeed considering how far things have now gone I do not see that I can possibly go to them, even under your friendly auspices. The time has gone by for making advances. Gray tried negotiations immediately after the Judgement extending my Patent [a further seven years] – tried it as a sort of expert friend on both sides – tried it on his own motion, not on mine; but nothing came of it, and we have heard nothing from them of any kind.

Preece replied by return:

I am very sorry indeed that you cannot come to our Dinner on Monday. [A complimentary dinner in London to Alexander Siemens.] It would have given me the opportunity I want to tell what transpired at my interview with the Marconi people. I was telegraphed for to meet some South African delegates and I being in London telephoned to make an appointment with Isaacs. He fixed 11 a.m. on Thursday morning. I had never met him before and had never entered the offices of the Marconi

Co. I was encouraged to do this by your letter. We had a very long and very interesting meeting. I put the position very plainly and clearly to him and he was equally frank with me. We discussed the pros and cons and I found him extremely well up in all points. I think he will say that I put your case well. He is prepared to recognise your claim and to give you your full recognition of your work. This clearly means payment for your patent rights. It also means engagement as their expert and your full share of profit and credit in the future. I could not have done more except to introduce you personally to him which I hoped to have done on Tuesday. I did not suggest or question any figures nor did he suggest anything. He fully realised that I was a neutral body and could commit nobody. He certainly did not commit himself.

It is for you to follow up this line or drop it. I cannot conceive a position more favourable for you. 'Wireless' is on the move upwards and you will be the principal mover in it. To waste money in legal action with such a prospect before you would be Quixotic.

I should here say that I suggested that the Muirheads should have their work. He said he could fill their shops. This is very satisfactory for them for they (Muirheads) have lost much money.

In my very long experience I have never known a position so advantageous and promising. I will not do anything more until I see you. Remember I did not pose as your advocate but simply as the representative of the Consulting Department.

Lodge replied as promptly:

I cordially recognise your friendly offices, and were I a free individual might try to follow your advice. But the time for the Marconi Co to open negotiations was immediately after my extension grant; and I was then told by Gray, their and my counsel, that they would do nothing. So now everything is in order for a fight, and it is difficult to see how to stop it. All that can be managed is delay – even if that.

If they want to approach us on a Royalty basis why do they not say so? We are ready to quote terms, and they have an appeal to the Board of Trade.

I don't suppose anyone wants litigation for its own sake, but some important people are now in touch with my extended patent, and it is the nucleus of a big scheme. Without their consent I am not in a position to make arrangements, and if I went to see Isaacs it would convey a totally wrong impression. That, you see, is my difficulty. If he wants to open negotiations, by all means let him do so, and then we can discuss matters at a board meeting in a business manner; but for me to attempt private interviews after things have gone so far, does not seem fair or wise. They stand to lose a good deal if a law action is brought off. I don't see that we stand to do anything but win. With kinds regards and best thanks.

In these circumstances Preece used a socially polite fiction in writing to Isaacs to say that Lodge was not well enough just then to travel to London. Two months later Lodge wrote from Gullane, Scotland:

You may remember that Judgment compelled us to grant Royalties to those who applied, on terms approved by an Arbitrator appointed by the Board of Trade. The Helsby Wireless Co. has so applied, and the Board of Trade will soon appoint an Arbitrator.

I expect we shall be called upon to give evidence as to royalties or terms already paid for similar inventions e.g. Hughes &c. No one knows this sort of thing better than you do, and I want to ask whether (always supposing that you are not the Arbitrator) whether you would be willing kindly to give evidence on such a point – evidence which would clearly carry good weight and be a good guide to him.

I am golfing here for a bit and taking a rather much needed holiday.

Alexander Muirhead wrote a few days later:

Do you remember how much Sir Charles Wheatstone got from the Electric and International tel. Co. for his extended patents? If I remember rightly it was about £60,000. Perhaps one could find out by reference to the Ronalds Library. I remember seeing full particulars of the transaction in one of the pamphlets in Latimer Clark's library but I cannot remember what pamphlet it was. P.S. I suppose you know that Oliver Lodge has taken my place in the Lodge-Muirhead Wireless Syndicate. I hope he will be more successful than I have been!

Muirhead wrote again three days later:

I was glad to get your reply this morning for which many thanks – but I am sorry to hear that you are so poorly. Let us hope this fine sunny weather will help you to get better and that you will be spared to us for a good many years yet.

Did not Sir Charles Wheatstone long after 1852 get the patents for the Wheatstone Automatic system extended – for the rights under which the old E.T.C. paid him another big sum? I'm asked to get evidence to put before an arbitrator of the value of electrical or telegraphic inventions.

x

I'm sorry you did not succeed in bringing Lodge and the Marconi Co. together. I think the combination would please the Government departments. All along I have been hoping that a compromise between Lodge and Marconi could be brought about. Not once have the Marconi Co. approached Lodge directly or indirectly – not since 1898 or 1899.

You have a nice fellow in your son Llewellyn to represent you in the Wireless part of your work. Could he and I try to effect a compromise between L.M. Syndicate and the Marconi Co.?!

The following month Lodge wrote to Preece to say that he had taken Preece's advice and come to terms with the Marconi Company:

the settlement is not good as a bargain, but it seemed on the whole better than the worry of litigation, and I am glad to be on friendly terms with the people who have been so enterprising and spirited and successful in world wide practical development.

31

PREECE AND CARDEW

PREECE'S success with his Indian Telegraph trainees, his predisposition to look for simple uncomplicated solutions to practical problems, his manifest awareness of the value of testing and standardizing materials and apparatus, and his readiness to avoid unnecessary expense, particularly appealed to officials with the responsibility of providing British overseas administrations with electrical equipment. His ability to select good men to install and operate that equipment was also called upon, for although a recognized source from which to provide outlets for younger sons of the ruling families had long existed in administrative posts, such men could scarcely be considered for technical posts where a man must be judged on his immediate ability as an engineer to 'make the wheels go round'.

That Preece's response to such requests was invariably prompt, comprehensive, and in terms which could be clearly understood, was appreciated. He had already supplied the Cape of Good Hope Government with a thorough review of methods of insulating telegraph lines when he was invited to visit and report on the telegraph system of that Colony. His regret at not being able to accept had been more than balanced by pleasurable anticipations of a visit to the United States. Sivewright, his Southampton assistant, and collaborator in a textbook on telegraphy, was fortunately available to take Preece's place and, indeed, did so to such good effect that he was prevailed upon to remain in South Africa: he was undoubtedly aided in his task, and the Administration much impressed, by the comprehensiveness of a schedule of instructions that Preece sent,

which it is suggested should be given by the Cape Government to Mr. Sivewright the gentleman selected to inspect and report upon the Telegraph System of the Colony.

Thus it was Preece whom the Crown Agents for the Colonies consulted on all telegraph and other electrical equipment and installations under their purview and who from time to time asked him to select an officer from candidates for advertised posts connected therewith. Mostly he was required to make recommendations, supply specifications for manufacturers, inspect materials and apparatus during manufacture and prior to trans-shipment. For example, he recommended the type of submarine cable to be laid between Hong Kong and Luzon in 1879, at four days' notice he dispatched a considerable quantity of telegraph stores to the Gold Coast with two telegraphists from the Royal Engineers company of telegraphists (which worked for the Southern Division of the Post Office) two years later, and he selected John Hesketh from seventy-five applicants in 1896 for the post of electrical engineer to the Queensland Government. Next year the New Zealand Government thanked him for superintending the building of the cable ship *Tutane Kai* and for his courtesy to Captain Fairchild who came to England to learn about her 'exceptionally complete' cable machinery and to take command of her.

Inevitably, with calls such as those being made upon him and with no falling off in the number of requests for advice and assistance nearer home, he considered setting up as a full-time consulting engineer as the time for his retirement from the Post Office approached. His two elder sons had similar interests and would be members of the firm he planned. A senior partner would strengthen such an organization and he had to look no further for such a man than to his friend Major Philip Cardew, R.E., an Inspector of the Board of Trade and the first director of its laboratory for testing electrical measuring instruments (the forerunner of the National Physical Laboratory), who was likely to be retiring about the same time and had been considering how he might make best use of the experience he had acquired. He had joined the Institution of Electrical Engineers when a lieutenant, being elected to its Council in 1880; four years later he was promoted captain at Chatham with responsibility for the Army's telegraph equipment: he was promoted to major in 1893. In 1884 Preece had lent him a photometer for some experiments he was making following a trial of combined telegraph and telephone apparatus he had designed, on a circuit arranged by Preece between

New Cross and Chatham. When he wrote to Preece from Chatham in November 1884 although his letter was formal in its superscription he had, from a reference he made, clearly been a visitor to Gothic Lodge. Two months later, on a more personal note, he sent a detailed account of tests and subsequent improvements to the combination instrument he had invented and, mindful of Preece's assistance, concluded: 'I thought it right to give you an account of this system, which is being kept dark at present as much as possible.'

Preece's third son, Frank, was reported as working as an electrical engineer but he had left the Home Counties and had not thought it worth while to join the Institution of Electrical Engineers: he was present at Carnarvon with his two elder brothers at his father's inauguration as a freeman, having travelled down from Liverpool. Percy, the youngest son, had followed his maternal grandfather's profession as a solicitor. He was not at Carnarvon on that occasion for he, a keen advocate of voluntary national service, had joined the Army and was on the eve of embarking for Cape Town.

The firm of Messrs Preece and Cardew leased offices in 1899 at No. 8 in Queen Anne's Gate, an eighteenth-century terrace of considerable architectural merit overlooking St James's Park. The house was about two minutes' walk from the Institution of Civil Engineers in Great George Street. That year Preece had been elected a member of the Athenaeum Club under a rule whereby a limited number of persons distinguished in science or public service could be specially elected. The Club's premises were on the far perimeter of the park; he frequently lunched and dined there. The pleasant walk across the park, with its many trees, trim lawns and well-cared-for flower beds, over the lake by footbridge, where he could pause to watch the waterfowl below, added to his enjoyment.

A novel refinement in electric lighting was introduced by the partners in their large main office on the first floor with its sizeable bow window giving a view over the park. They fitted a central pendant carrying half a dozen ordinary electric lamps and placed a mercury-vapour lamp in the window area. The pervading light from the electrolier was slightly yellowish but the mercury-vapour lamp produced red and blue tints, the combination thereby giving a bright daylight effect. Preece claimed that he could walk into his lighted office from outside daylight without noticing the difference.

The partners, in addition to continuing with Preece's Crown Agency commitments, acted as consultants for many electricity supply undertakings, and Preece joined the board of the London Electricity Supply Corporation. He became an enthusiastic chairman of the British Coalite Company: its process of producing smokeless fuel from coal, and at the same time extracting valuable tar and chemicals which would otherwise have fouled the atmosphere as smoke and fumes, particularly appealed to him, for he detested avoidable waste and pollution. He had concluded an address, in 1892, on the available but neglected energy in solar heat, tides, wind and riverfall (and the waste energy in transporting coal from the pit mouth) with,

while our wants are so readily and cheaply supplied by our coalfields there is little chance of much attention being directed at present to other sources of energy: but with the diminution of our output, and the cranks of our labour communities, the attention of our manufacturers and the custodians of our health, safety and comfort, must be directed to those neglected energies which are now 'wasting their sweetness on the desert air'.

The day of reckoning was postponed by utilizing a vast source which Preece had not foreseen – oil – but eighty years later was brought home to us the force of Preece's warning.

*   *   *

The Sanitary Institute was established in 1876 to promote the advance of sanitation: its members arranged annual congresses and exhibitions at different centres at which they awarded medals to manufacturers of hygienically produced foods and equipment calculated to improve personal and public health. Preece had taken an interest in the Institute, had given a paper, in 1890, on the sanitary aspects of electric lighting, and in the year of his retirement felt he could safely accept an invitation to be its President. Thus in August he found himself once again in the Hartley Institute inaugurating the Congress, for that year's venue was Southampton, which he described as a beautiful town where he had spent 'fifteen of the busiest and happiest years' of his life. Naturally, too, he referred to the hall in which he was speaking, where he had in the past demonstrated many 'novelties'.

That day he began with a reference to the human body:

a little world in itself, inhabited by different nations and different races, born, living and dying as we do on this earth, perhaps in peace, generally in war and fortunately for us, not yet free from the abuses of cannibalism. There are many million living micro-organisms flourishing in everybody in this hall. As long as we are in health they live in peace, and we remain unconscious of their existence, but let some external enemy, some mute, inglorious, invisible bacterium force the ramparts and enter the fort, then there is war and either the invader is destroyed by our friends or we ourselves succumb.

From that lively analogy he went to the main theme of his talk which was a eulogy of Moses as a sanitary engineer. He described the Book of Leviticus as a treatise on hygiene and affirmed that the Jew was the healthiest and longest lived type of humanity. The Mahometan continued to practise some of the health tenets of Moses but the Christian had thrown them to the winds:

we have left undone the things which we ought to have done and the world in general thinks that life would be very miserable if we only did what we ought to do. Hence we are no better than David was,

which was to survive three score years and ten, whereas Preece opined that, by hygienic living,

there is now no reason why we should not make our years five score.

Warming to his subject Preece thought it well to express a hope that he would

tread on the fewest possible corns . . . wherever work is done on the earth it is at the expense of energy drawn from somewhere else. The sun is the centre and spring of all energy on this earth. The function of the engineer is to apply this principle of energy to the comfort, health and happiness of man . . . the principle of life is beyond our comprehension . . . if we cannot divine the reason for its existence it is because we are able to read the book of God only through a glass, darkly.

He summed up Moses' doctrine as the ensuring of pure air, water, and food and clean soil, dwellings, and bodies. From that early emphasis on ventilation and refuse-burning he drew attention to modern refuse destructors producing heat for electricity generating stations. He compared the air space of railway carriages, factories and private houses with lunatic asylums, hospitals and workhouses. The minimum cubic footage per person in a hospital was scheduled as a thousand but in a factory a quarter of that amount. He had recently been in a private dining-room with four gas burners alight (each equivalent to five persons), the air soon became stagnant and his head 'an aching mass'. In a third-class railway carriage the cubic footage per person was only forty-seven when it was full. Nor did he seem to think an exaggeration his claim that if electricity – which did not vitiate air – was properly utilized in our homes our span of life would be lengthened.

On water his comments apply equally urgently today: rivers were being polluted by manufacturing refuse as well as by human excreta: the Rivers Pollution Act of 1876 was ineffective and pollution had yet to be made a penal offence. He compared, in passing, a daily use per person of 25 gallons in English cities with 60 in New York City and 90 in Philadelphia. He suggested that the L.C.C. could double its supply of water for domestic use if they had a supply of non-potable water for public purposes (for which Bournemouth and Great Yarmouth were using seawater). On the search for supplies further afield he warned the L.C.C. that

it is better for them to go to the sea, which is near to them, than to go as far as to gallant little Wales that does not intend, in spite of its gallantry, to let London rob it of its water.

On food he commented that pork in the East was uneatable. He recommended householders to sterilize milk by boiling, for it was not under the control of sanitary authorities, and he praised the food inspectors of Surrey ('I live there') and hoped their colleagues else-where were equally energetic but didn't seem optimistic about what might be happening in

little towns . . . too often the arena of personal squabbles, party spirit, melancholy ignorance and self-interest. Tennyson said, 'If God made the country and man the town, the Devil made the little country town.'

On soil he called attention to Moses' injunction to cover excreta with earth and reviewed modern mechanical, chemical, and bio-logical disposal methods, praising the systems in Portsmouth, Torquay, Brighton and Margate; adding that it was

not economy or wisdom to make too much use of the sea.

Since the introduction of the treated sludge system improvement in the River Thames had been very marked. Wimbledon had recently added biological filtration to the sewage farm process.

Unfortunately sewage farms as a rule do not pay . . . we have seen during the last session of Parliament how the Camp Sewage Farm at Aldershot has been violently attacked.

Brewery waste was difficult to treat but lately the Anglo-Bavarian Brewery Company at Shepton Mallett had at their own expense, and in a fine public-spirited manner, successfully treated their own waste. He approved the new biological treatment with septic tanks, introduced in Exeter in 1895.

The water supply of Carnarvon, where I have a summer residence, is drawn from a lake called Cwellyn, into which the drainage of the village Rhydd du indiscriminately enters without any treatment whatever . . . this had alarmed the Council of Carnarvon, who have very properly agreed to share the expense of treating the sewage.

On dwellings he held that slum-clearance legislation had been hindered by vested interests. Edinburgh had spent over half a million pounds on rehousing the City's poor and by so doing had brought the death rate down from twenty-eight to seventeen per thousand. The rate for Surrey was fourteen, for North Wales twenty:

3000 souls per annum ought not to die in North Wales if sanitary matters were duly looked after!

Electric light ('essentially the poor man's light'), tramway travel and suburbs would improve conditions. He spoke of Moses and the treatment of lepers and regretted that hygiene was not taught generally in schools nor preached from pulpits. Cleanliness promoted cheerfulness, 'the greatest doctor we have'.

He felt that the Institute's Congresses removed apathy and excited enthusiasm. His peroration was an affirmation of his belief that

Nature is only another term for God . . . the stars in their courses and the bacteria in their operations follow one fixed and settled design:

'One God, one law, one element,
And one far off divine event,
To which the whole creation moves.'

A sequel to his address that day was a letter of great appreciation from the Chief Rabbi in London and expressions of thanks from Jews 'in all countries'.

* * *

In 1898–9 Preece had served as President of the Institution of Civil Engineers, and as its immediate Past President he attended a number of meetings and annual dinners of provincial branches of that Institution. Early in February 1900 he addressed its Association of Students in Glasgow and during his talk, in which he reviewed the advance of science and technology from civilization's earliest days on the banks of the Euphrates and the Nile to the current work of the Institution's members, he specified his ideas on the education of an engineer.

I am still in school, and rarely fail to acquire some new fact each day of my life. The first foundation is clearly a broad, solid, general education, not specialized in any way until the pupil has reached the stage when he can work and think for himself. But from the very earliest years – in fact, from infancy – I advocate the cultivation of the powers of observation, a systematic training of the memory, and an encouragement of the exercise of thought. This is, in reality, the scientific method. Many people advocate the early teaching of science, but I do not. I advocate the collection and naming of plants, the love of animals and knowledge of their habits, the observation and explanation of the daily occurrences in the house, the air and the ground. The fire, a candle, the teapot, cooking, blacking boots, the dewdrop, clouds, rain, wind and storm, the ebb and flow of the tide, the performance of tops and bicycles, familiarly explained, excite a love of Nature and of Science, and train the mind to observe, to think and to remember. Cramming the young mind with ill-digested text-book science, illustrated by experiments that generally fail, excites ridicule – the common accompaniment of ignorance.

. . . it is clear that an engineer would waste his time in acquiring abstruse sciences that would be of no subsequent use to him. He must confine himself to those branches of Science which will be of service to him in his future career, so as to enable him to apply them to living, industry, and commerce. Mathematics, the shorthand of thought and the purest form of logic, experiment, the handmaiden of observation, measurement, the instigator of accuracy and precision, and reasoning, the organ of commonsense, are the tools that shape his store of knowledge which memory brings to his help when he has to practise what he has learnt. The boy who has passed well through the ordinary curriculum of school, and proceeds thence to a University, from which he emerges as a young man not only well imbued with the refining influence of literature and art, but with a well-earned degree of science, is fully prepared to commence his engineering training and to enter the workshop or the drawing-office where alone he can acquire that combination of knowledge and skill, and that training of the brain and the hand for mutual aid which is called Technical Education.

★　　★　　★

The Paris Universal International Exhibition of 1900 provided an opportunity for the American Institute of Electrical Engineers to hold joint meetings in that city with their British colleagues. Members of both Institutions foregathered in London, and chartered a special steamer to take them to France. At their Extraordinary General Meeting on 16th August, in the United States National Pavilion, they listened to papers on the relative merits of alternating and direct current electricity systems. Preece – who in October 1884 had been elected the first honorary member of the American Institute – referred obliquely to that distinction during discussions by telling the meeting that he felt like 'the blank page between the Old and the New Testaments' (a blank page was generally thus inserted in bibles). He told the members he had used either system as requirements had dictated but he readily agreed that for transmission of current over a distance an alternating supply was pre-eminent. He urged the advisability of standardizing its frequency, pointing out that in England it was generally 50 cycles a second but in the City of London that frequency was doubled, while in America it ranged from 25 at Niagara to as high as 130.

Participants in such congresses usually agree that the most valuable return from them is as a result of taking opportunities thus afforded to make and cement friendships and to share experiences on an informal plane. Thus we learn that one evening W. E. Ayrton and his wife, Preece, Silvanus Thompson and his wife, with a number of American and British colleagues (including A. E. Kennelly and Carl Hering, President of the A.I.E.E.) entertained Harry Ward Leonard (the American responsible for remarkable improvements in electric-motor controls) and his wife to an informal dinner in a Paris restaurant.

An account of telegraphs and telephones at the exhibition was given later in the year at an Institution of Electrical Engineers' meeting by John Gavey. Preece, who opened the discussion, selected as the greatest novelty shown in that field a microphonograph (a magnetic speech recorder invented by Valdemar Poulsen of Copenhagen) by which a conversation could be recorded permanently on a steel wire.

*   *   *

The new century began with no great promise: the Boer War still dragged on and, to the grief of most subjects at home and many overseas, Queen Victoria died in January 1901. After such a long reign she had become almost a religious figure to her peoples. Later that year Preece, who had earlier served on British Association committees, was elected chairman of its committee for co-operation in magnetic observations, with Falmouth observatory as its home base (the committee was dissolved in 1912). He was also elected, after more than twenty years of service as a council member, to the Chair of the Society of Arts. In his address, in November, he looked back over the Queen's reign. Reviewing the development of telephony he urged that the only solution to present discontents was State purchase but, in the meantime, he remembered his early persuasion:

Everyone who uses an exchange should visit it to appreciate the work done in his service and he should regard himself as part of the machine.

And on telegraphs he reminded members that

the magic wire connects Printing House Square [*The Times*] with its own correspondents in every capital in Europe and 160 000 miles of submarine cable keeps London in touch with every quarter of the globe.

He drew attention to the need for better warning of approach to land from sea, better communication between ship and ship, and between ship and shore. The twentieth century, he foresaw, would produce great improvements in telephones and in safety at sea. He was enthusiastic about worldwide action planned for 1902:

all the nations are going to unite to conquer the mystery of the disturbance of the mariner's compass. Will religion and politics do what science has done? Gather together in one fold all the nations of the earth to follow one fixed purpose on one mature plan. . . .

He spoke of expanding towns and traffic congestion: slums should be replaced with planned suburbs served by electric tramways. A network of improved roads should be built, and in town centres separate routes – above or below the traffic – for pedestrians.

All roads should be made wide enough for two tram tracks, room for up and down light and heavy vehicles, room on each side for stopping vehicles, and ample footways.

He also referred to a projected high-speed mono-rail electric train which had fired his imagination. Earlier that year F. B. Behr, who as managing director of the Lartigue Railway Construction Company had been responsible for a mono-rail train which ran at over 80 miles an hour on a three-mile elliptical track at the 1897 Brussels Exhibition, had given a paper to the Society on a similar railway between Liverpool and Manchester for which a Bill had been promoted in 1900. Preece publicized it at the Bradford meeting of the British Association when he described a coach, seating 64 passengers, straddling an overhead mono-rail, to run the 34½ miles between those two cities non-stop in 20 minutes, at 10-minute intervals, to work at 650 volts on power supplied by Warrington electricity station. Proposed fares were rather less than for the conventional railway.

In 1886 the Lartigue Company had shown a working model of a steam-driven mono-rail train on the site of the Roman Catholic cathedral in Westminster, and in March two years later had opened such a railway between Ballybunion, at the mouth of the Shannon, and Listowel, nine and a half miles distant. Preece, who was in the chair at Behr's lecture, referred to his inspection of that railway, which had never had an accident. He was impressed by it but a friend with him, a 'distinguished engineer', had said:

there's nothing in it. . . . I never saw such a clumsy thing in my life.

(Rising operational costs following the 1914–18 war, and the development of motor-cars, led to the closure of that railway in October 1924.)

Preece was elected Chairman of the Society of Arts for a second term, which he opened with a review of existing financial and commercial problems. He spoke of improvements to the Limited Liability Act of 1862 by the Companies Act of 1900 which he was sure would minimize professional company promoters' dubious operations.

He felt that Parliament was legislating for the railways with no regard to ordinary commercial prudence: before long railway traffic would be reduced by automobile and electric-tram competition.

The enforcement of cheap fares and workmen's trains at the expense of shareholders is pandering to a sentiment and savours of a bribe to catch votes.

Local authorities were

insatiable in their unscrupulous assessment for local taxation. The taxation of railways has increased 75 per cent, in the last ten years while that of the whole community only 39.

Electric traction would increase speed of running so as to carry more traffic on the saturated local lines of large cities, but there was little sign at that time of running main lines economically by such means.

He felt that trade unions had generated serious labour troubles. Shorter hours and more pay were desirable, but managers could not have union officials take over their functions without resulting chaos and bankruptcy. (He had expressed concern elsewhere that union officials as their organizations increased in importance might become tyrannical and ultimately eliminate interest in work from the minds of their members.)

The State purchase of telegraphs in 1870 had proved a good bargain: telephones would have to be similarly purchased. (They were taken over by the State in 1911.) To scrap obsolescent plant was sound economy, even though it might offend British prejudices. A commercial intelligence system was needed, such as that of the Germans and Americans. His firm Preece and Cardew, often had information on foreshadowed electrical work in Crown Colonies from those sources, but never from a British source.

There seems to be something radically wrong with some giant combines. It is startling to learn that each White Star £1000 bond holder will receive £14 625 for it from the new Atlantic Shipping Combine. . . . Whence are the new profits to come?

The University of Birmingham had recently created a Faculty of Commerce, a move which should be copied by every other seat of learning. Only that day he had taken part in a function to beg support for King's College. Technical Institutes languished for want of financial support. A value added tax of five per cent on foreign manufactured goods imported would place all technical and scientific education in the British Isles on a sound basis.

The average man who is not wedded to party politics feels strongly that there is something wrong with the doctrine of Free Trade. Nations which have not adopted it have flourished more than the solitary nation which has. Our working man does not earn as much money as the American working man, nor does he live so well, nor bear so high a character. We have spent £300 million in making South Africa an integral part of the British Empire and at once it is made an open market to our competitors who have paid nothing towards the formation of the market, but have reviled us in ways which will not easily be forgotten.

*   *   *

Preece supplied the Crown Agents, in May 1899, with a report on the current level of wireless telegraph development. He prefaced it with an historical survey, in the light of which he concluded that the Wireless Telegraph Company (Marconi) would not be able to obtain the monopoly for which it was striving and, clearly, from the arguments he adduced and figures he quoted, submarine cables despite their high capital costs were under no threat from Marconi, whose company had yet to earn a dividend although each £1 share was being quoted at £9. That company's prohibitive charge of £500 a year for the use of a station's equipment prevented him recommending its system to anyone.

He brought his review up to date in February 1902 when he reported with regret on a proposal to link by wireless telegraph Lagos (Nigeria) with Forcados (also on the coast, a hundred miles to the south-east) that a reliable system of doing so had not been evolved.

We are now required to believe on somewhat doubtful evidence that the
Atlantic has been bridged. Mr. Marconi is such an accomplished experimenter that he ought not to be deceived. But there is no one so easily
deceived as a sanguine experimenter. I myself when lecturing at the
Royal Institution in 1878 on the 'Telephone' implicitly believed that I
heard certain bugle calls from Southampton which I expected and which
to my surprise Lord Tennyson could not hear. But there had been none
to hear for none were sent. My Assistant had mistaken the night. . . . It
will be time enough to believe that the Atlantic has been bridged when
actual words and messages have been passed. It is not impossible but it
has not yet been effectively done.

He reported again in 1905, when he noted that

Much has been done to fit up ships of war . . . and the war between
Russia and Japan has brought it [wireless] into great prominence. Not only
has it been in use on all ships of war of all nations in the Far East, but it
has maintained communication between Port Arthur and Chifu during
the greater part of the siege. *The Times* also with great enterprise and
spirit chartered a steam-ship the *Hai-mun*, fitted her up with 'wireless'
plant of the De Forest type, established a well equipped shore station near
Wei-hai-wei, and transmitted much news to Printing House Square
by Eastern Telegraph Cable: 2,000 uncensored words were one day sent
across 180 miles of sea at a mean speed of 30 words a minute, and thence
14,010 miles to London, where they were printed in *The Times* the next
morning with marvellous accuracy. The experiment was too successful
for it showed a power of anticipating movements that might prove
seriously detrimental to the success of strategic operations. The Japanese
Government as well as the Russian took prompt measures to stop the
practice.

A panic selling of shares in cable companies had followed the first
report of a message being transmitted across the Atlantic, but
nothing practical had yet been attained. The cable companies, however, decided to use wireless on their repair ships and to supplement
their services with wireless extensions. The Admiralty, thanks to
Captain Jackson, was in the van of navies using wireless telegraphy,
and the Marconi Company had fitted many liners with apparatus.
Lloyd's was using the Marconi system at a number of signal stations.
Slaby had made great advances with the Telefunken system in
Germany, as had Fessenden and De Forest in the United States with

their systems. When within three days of reaching the British Isles the captains of trans-Atlantic liners were transmitting weather reports to the *Daily Telegraph*, an arrangement the Meteorological Office proposed to adopt.

The Crown Agents had from the date of Preece's first report been alive to the possibility of wireless communication in a number of Colonies. In 1906 Preece was describing five 'fairly reliable systems' which might be used in the Orange River Colony but did not recommend one of them – the Marconi system – because of charges being too much.

Preece's report was passed to the Secretary of State for the Colonies, and the Colonial Office wrote to the Crown Agents that Mr Secretary Lyttelton wished them to convey an expression of his appreciation of 'the valuable report' Preece had made: a copy of that letter was duly sent to Messrs Preece and Cardew.

Preece had been retained in 1905 by the London County Council to give evidence in favour of its electric power scheme then before a Parliamentary Committee. By now he was devoting less time to the affairs of his firm, which in 1909 took on an additional partner. Llewellyn specialized in wireless. Arthur continued with electricity undertakings which were to be throughout the British Empire, China and South America: he was knighted, in 1932, for his services to the Crown Agents. That was in the future, but in 1903, his father, as so often before, was nominated a British Commissioner to an international exhibition. That it was at St Louis, Missouri, especially pleased him but when he was due to travel to St Louis next year he was, to his intense disappointment, too ill to do so. In recompense came an unexpected call to cross the Atlantic when in 1907 the University of Pennsylvania, Philadelphia, proposed as part of its Founders' Day celebrations on 13th April, to award honorary degrees to twelve Englishmen and to Marconi. Preece and Marconi were among those to receive a Doctorate of Laws whilst Sir Edward Elgar received a Doctorate of Music. From accounts of what Preece had learnt during that visit, which he gave at meetings of the Institution of Electrical Engineers and the Society of Arts he was, though seventy-three, manifestly as alert and observant as ever. Indeed he planned to return in the autumn of 1913, in April of which

A²

year he had been elected an honorary member of the New York Electrical Society.

It remained for the University of Wales to honour one whose achievements had brought unalloyed credit to the Principality and on 11 November 1911 an honorary degree of Doctor of Science was conferred on him at Bangor, ten miles from his birthplace.

32

SOUTH AFRICA

FOR the third time Preece kept a diary of a journey – posted home at intervals as before – when, in 1911, he travelled on his own to South Africa combining a convalescent cruise with work on behalf of his firm.

His first trip to South Africa had been in 1905 when he travelled in company with other members of the British Association. On that occasion the Welsh members of the party, five men and a woman, were given a special welcome by the Cape Cambrian Society whose members rose to their feet and sang, 'For he's a jolly good fellow' when Preece was called upon to speak. Surprisingly that of the 380 travellers to South Africa, on three steamers, to assemble in Cape Town they numbered only six. The South Africans were most generous hosts to the visiting Association members and gave them free hospitality when they visited, as a body, Durban, Maritzburg, Johannesburg, Pretoria, Bloemfontein, Kimberley, Bulawayo, and the Victoria Falls. Nearly two thousand South Africans joined in the Association's deliberations.

On his return Preece talked about his experiences of visiting 'five colonies and two protectorates'. He compared the lot of the black population unfavourably with that in Jamaica which he had visited 'shortly before going to South Africa'. He approved the early inculcation in its white youth of habits of physical training, discipline and military ways, including marksmanship – which Lord Roberts had 'inaugurated at home'. He compared prices, noting that a house that could be rented for £20 a year in London would fetch £85 in Johannesburg. He paid a tribute to the 'devoted work' of the Guild of Loyal Women in South Africa in tending war cemeteries.

The British Commissioner of Railways in Natal, then on a visit to

England, complimented Preece on carrying away after so short a visit such an accurate impression of what was going on in South Africa. Preece replied that during the whole of his life he had never troubled with politics and believed that he had a clearer judgement of what was happening in the world than 'people who mixed themselves up with different parties to which, in many cases, they had sold their consciences'.

*   *   *

Off Oporto, on 14 January 1911, aboard the Union Castle steamer *Saxon*, he wrote of a pleasant send-off from Waterloo Station.

I am not disturbed by any worry . . . all presages a speedy recovery on the sea and a glorious trip to South Africa. But I must 'touch wood' for its too early to boast . . . the train ran without hitch or stop right into the Docks. What a change in Southampton! I would scarcely know it if I were dropped there from an aeroship. Many old friends – including the Mayor and Sheriff – came to see me off.

I have a splendid cabin to myself. I was introduced to the Captain and am placed at his right hand at table. The cabins are very nicely warmed by steam . . . the *Saxon* on our upper deck is a very silent ship.

Jan 15th at 7 a.m. I thought the ship was on fire. My cabin was lighted up rapidly with flashes of fire from outside. I jumped out of bed and I found we were just off Ushant & the light flashes were from the most brilliant lighthouse in the world. The French lead the world in lighthouse illumination.

He noted meteorological details and the vessel's rate of progress.

Jan 17th. We are off the coast of Morocco. We met the *Norman* [sister ship] on her right course. She started from Cape Town and we . . . met exactly on the right spot. It shows the perfection of Kelvin's compass. Sailors owe a deep debt of gratitude to Kelvin & I am told they would cheerfully subscribe to any memorial to him.

Jan 18th. . . . 3 p.m. arrived at Las Palmas. Too rough to land . . . the Residents were allowed on board to sell their products – lace embroidery, toys, tobacco, and sticks. I bought a stick of coconut wood for my collection.

Jan 19th. . . . Sports Committee formed today. I took no part in it for I am too seedy to act. . . . Resting in my deck chair under the bridge, sheltered from the sun and the wind, under a cloudless sky and on a comparatively calm sea, in a ship as steady as a rock though propelled forward at 16 knots I am experiencing delightful repose . . . heavenly for those who want to read or write quietly. . . . In spite of rheumatism and internal troubles I am quite blissful and feel that 2 or 3 more such days will put me straight. . . . The stars are very bright and beautiful especially *Canopus* but we have not yet seen the Southern Cross.

Jan 20th. . . . I am much better which is a great relief. Indeed rheumatics have quite disappeared. . . . The sky was cloudless and flying fish abounded. Met a steamer dipping to the waves merrily while we steamed steadily and soberly on. . . . I have been invited to lecture and have agreed to give an hour on 'What has electricity done?'

Jan 21st. . . . It is not to be wondered that we see so few ships for we see from the deck of the ship a zone of only 15 miles. . . . Birds (a kind of black gull) are appearing. There was a dance in the evening but it was a very poor show. There are not enough ladies.

Jan 22nd. Sunday. . . . All officers & Crew appeared in white uniforms. We had service at 10.30 read by the Captain very well indeed. Singing and music by the Band excellent. There are 6 performers; piano, 2 violins, double bass, cornet, clarionet. (We have music every morning on deck.) The Psalm 107 about those 'who go down in ships to the sea and occupy their business in great waters; these men have seen the works of the Lord and his wonders in the deep'. . . . Service on board ship is much more impressive than on shore especially when well read by the Captain. You cannot help thinking there is but a plank between you and eternity.

I inspected the ship with the Captain. She is really splendid. Electric power is much used especially for ventilating and there is telephone communication. . . .

Jan 23rd. . . . It came on to rain so thickly that the Captain had to treat it as a fog. At noon our Latitude was 1° 8′ 10″ N Longitude 10° 39′ W Run 365 miles. Temperature was 79° falling to 75° after the storm. The temperature of the sea was 80°!

Jan 24th. . . . We had a very excellent amateur concert last night. The Band formed the orchestra and singers and piano players were from the first and second class. There is little difference between the two classes. The accommodation and grub are the same. They join us in sports and do very well. . . .

The Captain & officers of the ship are not allowed to take part in our entertainments. When Kipling & his wife were going to South Africa one winter 4 or 5 years ago Mrs. Kipling saw, as she thought, *all* the officers present. She asked one of them 'who was working the ship?'. He replied in joke 'The Cook!' She took it earnestly and told Rudyard & begged him to go to the bridge to see. He went to the wrong bridge saw nobody and confirmed her opinion. He wrote to the Company and they at once issued a circular which is a source of great dissatisfaction. ... There was another small dance in the evening on deck but only 3 couples turned up!

Jan 25th. Wednesday 11th day. . . . We had crossed the equator early on Tuesday morning. . . . We had the first day of general sports which commenced 2.30 p.m. and were very well sustained.

A printed programme showed events for the first day as: ladies event, potato race; ladies and gentlemen, cigarette and tie race, and threading the needle; gentlemen's events, sack race, 'are you there?', potato race, cock fighting, and standing long jump. Events for the second afternoon were: children, flat race; ladies, egg and spoon race; ladies and gentlemen, chalking the pig's eye, whistling race, and driving competition; gentlemen, bolster bar, turtle pull, and tug-of-war (1st v. 2nd).

Jan 26th. I lectured last night . . . it went off very well indeed for I brought in every story I could remember and left Science severely alone. . . . Lord & Lady Calthorpe attended the lecture and I tea'd with them today. . . . There was a fancy dress ball in the evening. Many strange gets-up . . . the barber always keeps a stock of costumes which he lets out. It was quite successful. Prizes are given for the best dresses. . . .

Jan 27th. . . . Ship gave first indication of movement but no one affected. I have not seen sickness on board. All my rheumatics have disappeared and I am wonderfully better but not sufficiently active yet. It is the absence of exercise that is keeping me back. I think I shall reach the Cape quite well. . . . We have seen no ship for five days but today smoke was seen on the horizon from two ships each of which was fitted with wireless. The Captain spoke with them. Although we saw no ships we were never out of wireless communication. This is an immense security. If fire or accident occurred help is always within reach. The Capt'n says his burden is much lightened. It is a great misfortune that this business [wireless] has been so grossly mismanaged.

Jan 28th. . . . The ship is quite steady and walking is quite comfortable . . . we are slowing down a bit so as to reach Cape Town early on Tuesday morning. I went over the engine room . . . [he then gives details of the engines and their performance]. I went through the tunnel to the stern and the screws. . . . A capital concert – amateur – in the evening.

Jan 29th. Sunday. . . . Wind stronger – ship rolling to waves coming from the S.W. The Capt'n says it is always so as we approach the Cape. It has cleared the decks very much but service was conducted at 10.30 a.m. by the Captain and was well attended.

It has been remarkable how much politics has been the subject of discussion on board and how universal is the antipathy to the present party in power. The difference between the black and white races and the action of the Cape and Australian Governments in dealing with Indians & Japs is seriously taken and thought to be approaching a dangerous crisis. There is much dissatisfaction about and this is quite independent of Whig and Tory – Radical and Conservative. It is looked upon as a Great British question affecting our National prestige. We have hitherto been the champions of the enslaved and oppressed but we have now ceased to occupy such a position. We do not even protect our own children. Those born on our own soil are being deported to India and elsewhere. Our colonists are getting sick of their Mother Country. When will it end? It may lead to a rupture of the British Empire and this is freely discussed. . . .

Jan 30th. Monday. Sun rose at 5 a.m. . . . it is 'packing up day'. . . . Noon . . . to Cape Town 208 miles. We get there 5 a.m. tomorrow and shall breakfast in dock. We shall have steamed 6,027 miles. I am sorry the journey has come to an end. It had done me immense good. I am practically well but I do not feel quite out of the wood yet. . . .

Jan 31st. Rough night – ship rolling. . . . Alongside dock quay at 6 a.m. breakfast 7 a.m. Edwards turned up. Went to GPO and saw Harrison . . . Went to Mount Nelson Hotel . . . visited E.T. Co. & sent message home. . . . Very hot on shore.

★ ★ ★

The remainder of his diary covers the three months he then spent in South Africa. He has many fewer sketches than in his earlier diaries but a number of quarter-plate photographs of passengers on deck are included, one of which shows him white-haired and stooping, and wearing winter suit, muffler and cloth cap. Women passengers, in other photographs, are most noticeable for their long full-sleeved dresses, the skirts of which almost brush the deck, and their huge wide-brimmed hats.

Feb 2nd. The Mount Nelson Hotel is an extremely comfortable well situated place . . . it possesses practically everything one wishes. . . . It was delightful to be able to sleep with a wide open window and to feel the warm breeze playing on you. I had a magnificent night's rest and awoke feeling quite well. It is very difficult to get over the points of the compass. The sun rises E on your right hand. It passes the Meridian at noon due N and sets at your left hand W – it is topsy-turveydom. . . . I had to give up the idea of returning by the Red Sea route. The heat is said to be terrible, the ships small, the accommodation limited and no possibility of a cabin to myself. Also all berths are engaged in the *Balmoral Castle* leaving March 22nd and the next ship leaving March 29th. People are going home for the Coronation. Dr. Merriman is staying here and I have had some long and interesting talks with him.

Feb 3rd. Lunched with Merriman at the Parliament House and met 5 other members . . . too hot to venture into the House to hear a Debate. I spent the afternoon with Harrison (Eng. in Chief) and discussed many points of business.

Feb 4th. . . . Left for Somerset West . . . where a Cape cart met me & took me to Lorenzford. It was a slow, hot, uninteresting train journey through a scrubby bare sandy country with many squatters about and all black people. The natives are 5 to 1 in Cape Colony. We passed an ostrich farm.

It took us 25 minutes to drive to Lorenzford which looks as beautiful as ever. The Oleander and hybiscus [tree] are in full bloom and grand *bright blue* hydrangeas are abundant. The iron in the soil is said to give them this brilliant blue. The same plant . . . turned out pink . . . at Penrhos. We see the Southern Cross every night.

Lorenzford like all Dutch Houses is of only one storey and covers much ground. This saves labour but it decreases security for natives may enter and even snakes! The cobra and puff adder are found here but I have not seen either. Sitting under a shady oak I was showered by acorns large & plump. The oak has been imported from Great Britain & flourishes well. The largest trees are apparently the Camphor. There are 8,000 acres about the place, all under cultivation and very many orchards. Indeed this year they have sent 8,000 tons of fruit to market! There are very few birds and none that sing, beautiful butterflies very shy . . . plenty of flies & Mosquitoes which have left their marks on my bare skin.

I measured the trunk of one camphor tree . . . its circumference 50 feet!

They [Miss Page and Miss Biden] have very little trouble with their fruit for it is sold as it is on the trees and it is gathered & sent to market by the fruit merchant.

Feb 5th was a very quiet Sunday where I worshipped under the trees – the rippling river singing hymns and all Nature humming to the Glory of God.

Feb 6th. . . . returned to Cape Town by a slow & tedious train in the heat of the day and it *was* hot! The reports of the doings of the Gladstones are quite sickening. A more incompetent Governor General could not have been sent out. Lady G. is even worse than Lord G. Everyone of every nationality and every party unites in condemnation. They are trying to play the parts of King and Queen without any training or knowledge and are acting a pantomime exciting ridicule and irritating everyone. . . .

Feb 7th. I had a long and interesting interview with Sir David Graaf this morning at 9.30. I start my journey North tomorrow and I have promised to inspect telephones and wireless everywhere and on my return . . . to discuss all questions with him. I think I have established quite pleasant relations with all and am in great hopes that I shall return home with satisfactory arrangements agreed to. I start tomorrow for Johannesburg at 11.30 a.m. and reach there on Friday morning at 9.30 a.m. after a journey embracing 2 nights and 46 hours! Shall I be alive?

Feb 8th . . . a beautiful morning with the Table Cloth laid on the mountain and a pleasant S.E. wind blowing. I had a compartment to myself. . . . The Eucalyptus is planted very much along the railways and indeed everywhere it flourishes and gives a grateful shade. The gauge of the Railway is only 3 feet 6 inches and this involves narrow coaches and slow travelling . . . a mean rate of 20 miles an hour. The rise in elevation is very gradual . . . to 6,000 feet. . . . Most of the land we passed through was the Karoo desert bleak and brown with the grey karoo bush which gives its name to the desert and food to the sheep. Nearly the whole way the horizon is lined with brown sandstone hills. . . . There is a slight mirage about but nothing compared with Egypt. I never saw a single wild animal and very few birds. My night's rests were very poor . . . from noise and shaking. The days were very hot and I travelled in my shirt sleeves. There was an excellent dining car and we were well fed. The Cape white wines are very nice and they bucked me up a bit. Flies (musca) are very abundant and annoying.

Feb 10th. I was glad to reach JOH at 9 a.m. punctually . . . to end a hot tedious but by no means unpleasant journey . . . it was however a great treat to sit down at a solid & quiet table to have a steady meal at Mrs. Diamond's. A day's rest put me quite right. . . .

Feb 12th. Spent very quietly at Parktown. . . .

Feb 13th. The value of gold extracted on the Rand up to date is 65,358,764 oz. . . . the average price had been £4.25 . . . per oz.

The Native question is becoming a very serious one. The race is growing more rapidly than the white one. This is the result of peace. There is no internecine fighting. Disease has been checked . . . the result of civilization but the native is not being educated to appreciate the improvement in his position. Sammy Marks . . . thinks that he should be treated as a child and educated up to his work in true educational and technical style. . . . The native is now an uneducated animal with the passions restrained by careful watching by his masters but ever ready to break out & does so only too frequently. He is quite competent & willing to be trained into an educated workman. This is done in Diamond's house where 3 kaffirs make excellent domestic servants doing cooking, housemaid and parlour-maid work. I am valetted by one of them. There are also 2 kaffir gardeners.

The native at present wants nothing. He does not appreciate comfort. . . . His sole ambition is to have a wife and to produce children. Sammy Marks thinks he should be trained to appreciate luxuries so that trade might be benefited and be brought up as a carpenter, builder, & tradesman. He is experimenting himself in this direction and growing cotton.

I find that Vasco da Gama came across the Bushmen when he landed in Mossel Bay and that they had as their TOTEM the Scarab and many Egyptian traditions. They drew pictures of extant animals on their cave walls – for they were cave dwellers – and their tombs were of Egyptian origin. I saw several of those stone pictures on Saturday in the Museum in Pretoria.

I am surprised to find how early the Portuguese were exploring the Cape. England was in the agonies of the War of the Roses . . .

Feb 14th. Hill [P.O. Engineer] drove me in his car about the suburbs and along several telegraph routes. The work is excellent.

I visited . . . the Municipal Electrical Engineer and inspected his Power Station where a magnificent building is disfigured by the disused gas plant which remains rusting . . . a sad and distressing sight – the mistake of our British Engineers. . . . The introduction of Gas Plant, however perfect, on a coal field where excellent steam coal is obtained at 2s. per ton was an outrageous blunder. The coal required for gas costs 24s. per ton!

Here Preece gives details of the new electrical plant and comments that Johannesburg is 'undoubtedly now the great centre of electrical enterprise in the British Empire'.

Diamond gave my birthday dinner this evening. We had a very pleasant party.

Feb 15th. . . . I spent the morning with a very interesting Canadian [Nissen] . . . he has a new and promising stamp machine for crushing and breaking up ore into 'pulp'. . . .
   Lunched at Diamond's and Nissen motored me over to a gold mine near Jermistown where I was shewn the whole process of . . . extracting gold.

Preece then describes the process in detail, and remarks of a number of ink blots on the page as 'due to the vagaries of a mosquito'.

Feb 17th. . . . The Association of Engineers gave me a luncheon at the Rand Club. . . .

Feb 18th. Saturday . . . to Pretoria in the GPO car with Hill. We saw the sights . . . on our way back we were caught by terrible dust storms as dark and impenetrable as a thick London fog but 10,000 times worse for the sand was red, turning my hair to that colour & filling my nose and throat with solid sand! This was followed by intense thunder and the most brilliant lightning all around & about us. We were on the Veldt without shelter and the rain came down in tropical torrents, converting the road into a river crossed by great rushes of water which tore the road up into small valleys. These ruts tried our car most severely . . . after 20 miles (and more than an hour) broken clouds and blue sky appeared . . . an experience that I appreciated very much for the dust, thunder and lightning exceeded all previous examples. We dined with comfort and I fulfilled an engagement at the Institution of Chemical, Metallurgical & Mining Society of South Africa where at 9.30 p.m. I gave an address. . . .

Feb 20th. I visited the Fereira Mine . . . very up to date mine and one of the most profitable on the Rand . . . nearly played out and has only 2 years to last. I find the most terrible confusion here in ordinary terms. Each mine has its own patois . . . terms used are remnants of bygone days: Dutch, Yankee, German, Australian & British. Everything is quite changed since I was here last and almost every process is new. But fortunately there is a strong Mines Committee who keep all the mines up to date. There are no secret processes . . . standard working characterizes every mine. I am striving to induce them to form a Standardizing Committee to unify and define terms and processes and I think they will do it. I find I am known to the Diamond's Kaffirs or 'Boys' as the 'Inkos' or Chief, which I take to be a very high compliment.

Feb 21st. Raining & chilly. I decided to postpone my departure home for I could not possibly catch the *Norman* on March 15th. so I secured my old cabin on the *Kildonan Castle* which leaves Cape Town on April 5th. . . .

Feb 22nd . . . I visited the City Deep Mine with Rider . . . it is the newest mine . . . they have introduced reinforced concrete to a very large extent and it is very doubtful whether it will stand the shocks and vibrations of stamping and milling . . . everything in this mine is worked by electric power supplied by the Victoria Falls Power Co., at 0.55d per unit. . . . Rider is preparing drawings showing all the operations of a mine from beginning to end and I am writing the text . . . I shall have sufficient notes to keep me well employed on my journey home. . . .

Feb 23rd. . . . I caught a nasty cold on our motor ride to Pretoria and it has got into my throat so I am careful but I had to go and lunch with the Schumackers. Rider called for me and Mrs. Diamond. We picked up Mrs. and Miss Rider and motored to the most beautiful situation I have ever seen in S.A. We could see Pretoria 30 miles away and while admiring the scenery we saw a terrific explosion about 15 miles away. The smoke took the form of a great cloud tree. We heard a roar like a short thunder clap and the wall of the verandah against which I was leaning vibrated as though it were an earthquake. . . . It was the Dynamite Works of the Eckstein Group and naturally Schumacker and Boyd, two directors of the Co., were much concerned. The telephone had broken down & we could get no information. . . .

The *Johannesburg Leader*, 24th February, reported that at one-thirty the previous afternoon two white men and three natives working at the Modderfontein Dynamite Factory had been killed in an explosion which completely destroyed two large buildings. A theory had been advanced that the building in which they had been working had been struck by lightning from a summer storm overhead: the concussion set off an explosion of nitroglycerine in a nearby building but those working in it had time enough to run out into the open to escape serious injuries.

Feb 24th. . . . Rider, Price [Eng. in Chief of the Victoria Falls Co.] and I motored to Rosherville to see the new Power House put up by the

A.E.G. . . . . their coal costs them 7s. per ton. There are 5 × 10,000 K.W. Turbines and Alternators sending out three phase A.C. at 40,000 and 20,000 volts with a frequency of 50. Only one set is at work. Their plant was shipwrecked near East London and has delayed them. They fix substations at the Mines they serve, and distribute from them at 10,000 volts. There are only 2 substations at present each taking 3,000 K.W. They compress air and distribute it at 100 lbs. per inch in 24″ pipes to the mines where it is used underground for drilling. This cannot be economical. It would be cheaper in energy to compress at the mine. The loss of energy in compressing air is very great. They are anticipating at the end of 1911 to be supplying 300,000,000 units.

All the work is excellent and creditable to A.E.G. . . . . I am very doubtful whether they will replace many existing plants but all new mines will certainly become their customers for they will save half the capital required to start a mine. . . .

Feb 25th. Saturday. . . . I was very tired & seedy from my cold for Wednesday, Thursday & Friday had been very busy days involving much exertion. . . . I am resting indoors today. . . . I have thoroughly inspected Telegraphs & Telephones here. . . .

Feb 27th. . . . A quiet day. I took a party of ladies over the Telephone Exchange which nobody ever goes to see and showed them how their ignorance of telephone working was the cause of 9 tenths of the troubles of working. The usual impression is that the same girl always attends to them, listens to all they say and is the cause of all their troubles. I showed them that the subscribers alone were in possession of the line and that rapid & correct working depends on them. This was an eye opener and the knowledge of it will fly around JOH where the switch is quite up to date. Subscribers are always leaving their instruments off the hook – so much so that Hill has ordered 'howlers' – and some take it off to avoid interference & leave it off – thus running down the battery. The howler will stop this practice.

Feb 28th. Hill drove me to Roodeport along the Main Reef Road, to see his new Trunk line of 300 lb. copper wires. All the work around and about JOH is excellent. You can look down many miles of iron poles without seeing the slightest departure from the vertical. . . .

Mar 1st. St. David's Day . . . I dined with the S.A. Cambrian Society and had to make a speech . . . at the Carlton Hotel – 160 sat down. . . . The speeches were limited to 10 minutes to which I adhered but the shortest of the others was ½ an hour. We did not finish up until 12 p.m.

in consequence. I found poor Diamond who goes to bed before 10 p.m. 'cussing and swearing like anything' at being kept up to let me in!

Mar 2nd. . . . I caught the 8 p.m. train for Maritzburg & had a good send off.

Mar 3rd. . . . the road is execrable and though I had a sleeping compartment to myself I could not sleep from the jolting, noise & tossing. We reached the war country & saw Majuba at daylight. The train was an hour late at Newcastle owing to our slow running – about 17 miles an hour! It is a single line . . . badly graded . . . a terrible block to the prosperity of S.A. Politics & racial fads seem to monopolise the thoughts of papers & people and the preparation for a commercial uprising is entirely neglected. Natal is a magnificent country. It has a glorious climate. Nearly everything of value grows here . . . it is curious to see as we approach Durban how tropical characteristics increase. The great stride is in the cultivation of the 'wattle'. It is an Acacia . . . bark produces *tannin* and the stem very fine timber. It reaches maturity in 7 years. There are many more birds in Natal than in Cape Colony or the Transvaal but they have no song. . . . Maritzburg at 4.30 p.m. & Hibberd [Postmaster-General of Natal] met me. I *did* enjoy a cup of tea . . . to bed before 10 p.m. and a thorough good night's rest.

Mar 4th. Hibberd without consulting me had arranged for a photographer and a reporter to interview me. I was vexed but the reporter was a very nice young Welshman from Carmarthen & softened me. You will see [from the press cutting] that Hibberd had an eye to himself. . . .
  I went all over Maritzburg – saw the P.O. & Telegraph men – all old friends. . . . We visited the Government Laboratory at Atterton and were shewn over by Mr. Herbert Watkins-Pitchford a very well known veterinary & poison authority. He constructed the Lab. for Government & has been in charge for 14 years. He has traced out the causes of several horse and animal diseases & discovered remedies for them. The presence of the 'tick' is the principal cause of the conveyance of these diseases especially of the East Coast Fever which has been terribly destructive to cattle & horses. He has introduced several new antidotes and dips. Several farmers have introduced a regular system of periodic dipping. Pitchford is a great authority on snakes and their poison. The principal venomous snakes in S.A. are the Black Mamba, the Puff Adder and the Cobra. He manufactures antidotes made from the original venom which is squeezed out of the snake's mouth by human force & which has proved quite successful. He is quite a remarkable man very modest and retiring –

hates writing paper but he ought to be an F.R.S. We were motored over to Atterton by Mr. Alexander – a very nice Scotchman – and full of stories. A Scotch boy was asked 'Who represented his family?' 'I and my brother,' said he. 'But where is your brother?' 'Oh, he is in the Museum. He has Twa heeds.'

Mar 5th. Sunday. The altitude of Maritzburg above sea level is 2,218 feet. We motored after lunch to 'Nel's Rust' 13 miles away the home of Mr. Thos. Baynes a great friend of Hibberd's and a very enterprising farmer. He cultivates 2,400 acres. The car was a Benz 14–16 h.p. driven by its owner Mr. Bartholdi a German and a friend of Hibberd's. We had a very rough ride over very rough roads and encountered much difficulty in crossing a *drift* (which is Dutch for a ford) owing to recent rain. We had tea with Mrs. Baynes and then were shewn all over the place by Mr. B. He goes in for milk, wattle, mealies, cattle, pigs, horses &c. Nel's Rust is a model Dairy Farm & quite up to date. His capability may be judged from the fact that on one occasion he turned out $5\frac{1}{2}$ tons of butter in one day. There is a colony there of 150 B.I. coolies. They are well housed, well cared for and seem perfectly happy.

He used water power (turbine + dynamo) for every operation in the processes especially of freezing & sterilizing. Baynes is perfect master of every detail of his business and is a very remarkable man.

We had a bad puncture on our way home. There was no spare tyre! Bartholdi had ordered one but it had not come. He removed the inner tube and stuffed *the cover with maize grass*! We were able to go ahead again but presently it suddenly became dark. There is no twilight in these parts. Our lamps had no oil!! However we were not very far from Maritzburg and at the first house we reached we got some oil & reached home safe at 8.15 p.m. where we enjoyed an excellent supper, laughed over our misfortunes and went to bed early & very tired.

Mar 6th. Weightman, retired Chief Engineer of Natal, came to see me & drove me to the station. He and Hibberd saw me off by the 9.5 train. I had a capital compartment reserved for myself. It was a lovely day but very hot & the scenery was magnificent all the way. The character of the scenery is more that of the Downs than mountains. But great maize fields with Kaffir kraals scattered all about singly & in groups gave freshness to the scene. They are hemispherical with a very small entrance through which they creep for rest.

The stations along the line are admirable – quite handsome buildings each with its garden splendidly cultivated. The Station Masters vie with each other and with the tropical nature of the plants becoming more tropical as we approach Durban they produce effects that are really beautiful. Natal is the garden of S.A. Harrison [Engineer-in-Chief] Hopkins [Surveyor & Div. Engineer] and Dayson [Harrison's secretary] met me on arrival and we went to the Royal Hotel to cool and refresh. The temperature was only 85° but being so very near the sea & humidity being about it was as bad as and as perspiring as 110°!

Mar 7th . . . Visited the Wireless Station on the 'Bluff'. . . . The receiver is Marconi's Electromagnetic Detector – a very great improvement on the Coherer. The signals are read on a telephone . . . I read signals from a ship about 100 miles away which were excellent. . . . The Bluff was a steep & stiff ascent (about 250 feet) but I did it without turning a hair! . . . I have written separately to Bo about the pole sparking pieces which are giving trouble. . . .

   After lunch . . . I was introduced to the Mayor . . . who was attending his Council . . . in a very brief speech I expressed my admiration of their beautiful building which besides containing all the Municipal Offices possesses a magnificent Concert Room, a Museum, and an Art Gallery. . . .

Mar 8th . . . I inspected the Telephone Exchange. It is Municipal . . . 1,783 subscribers . . . was being erected when I was there in 1905. . . . I also inspected the GPO's Central Telegraph Office and saw much old plant and many old friends. . . . Quad was working well to JOH and also *superimposed telegraph ccts* on [telephone] Trunks.

Mar 9th. . . . went for a drive in a carriage and pair all over Durban and the Berea – the elevated fashionable suburb . . . great beauty in gardens. . . . The roads are avenues lined with tropical trees. The Hybiscus is in full bloom and a Mauritius tree – called the Flamboyant – in deep red bloom.

Mar 10th. . . . Coleman [Postmaster] gave me a very nice stick of red ivory-wood (Kaffir name *Unzimbee*) . . . uncommon heavy & much prized . . . heat has brought out a very unpleasant rash, itching being like 10,000 fleas scampering over me. . . . I thoroughly inspected the Borough Power House & Rly Co's workshops where all the power is electrical. . . . The Borough & Rly Engineers lunched me at the club and afterwards . . . the port Captain took me around the Harbour in his steam launch. . . . I left Durban with regret by the 5.50 p.m. train and reached JOH (482 miles) on the evening of the 11th.

Mar 13th. I am extremely glad to get back to JOH. It is like Home. I have never met a more charming woman than Mrs. D and D himself is a very cheerful happy host. . . . I find there is quite a demand for my books here. They are included in the syllabus of the College and Technical Institute.

Mar 14th was spent in reading & writing up my address to be given on Thursday on 'Some aspects of modern theory'. I took a long walk after to drive away the cobwebs. Writing was a bore but the S.A. climate has changed that & I have written & spoken with ease & comfort.

Mar 15th . . . a drive on the Veldt . . . to Rooseport . . . Krugersdorp and examined the Paer de Kraal Monument . . . also visited the great Central Mill of the . . . Randfontein gold mine. . . . We found a pretty woody oasis on the green Veldt where we rested and picnic'd . . . the Veldt like the sea for . . . the road disappeared in the grass but we steered for the Smoke of the Rand which was some 10 miles away and came across a well marked road which took us to Doornkop where the Jameson Raid was brought to an end by the capture of the whole crowd and eventually led to the War.

Mar 16th was spent in writing the address which I delivered in the evening to the local Institution of Electrical Engineers . . .

Mar 17th. . . . very wet. I lunched with the Mayor . . . a very enjoyable meal.

Mar 18th. . . . Visited City Deep Mine with their metallurgist. . . . He took me through every process and discussed their merits and demerits.

Mar 20th. . . . quite a wet Welsh day, cold & cheerless and it rained all day long.

Mar 21st. Fine again – sun bright & cheerful . . . I visited the Jupiter Gold Mine but I did not go down it. . . .

Mar 22nd. *Wednesday*. I visited Bedford Farm with Mrs. Diamond. It is the seat of Sir George Farrer. The housekeeper, Governess & friend is Miss Bury an old friend of the Bidders who I used to meet frequently at Mitcham. It is a very fine house in the Dutch style outside but old English style inside. It is 7 years old. The gardens are beautiful. The farm buildings are admirable and there is a very fine show of prize cattle. There are 3 charming girls under 12 who are very observant and clever. They ride their ponies astride in fine style. It was quite a pretty sight to see them mount & start away with their groom for their afternoon ride. They are all coming to London for the Coronation.

Mar 25th. . . . My departure [for Cape Town] from Parktown was dramatic I wanted to give the 3 Kaffirs who attended me 10s. each in gold but Mrs.

B²

D. thought it too much. However as I thought they would appreciate gold however small more than silver I persisted and Mrs. D. who speaks Kaffir wished them goodbye for me and said I had a present for each of them. The cook came first and held out his two hands touching each other as though I was going to give them a drink but when I dropt in the half sovereign the 3 of them shouted with joy, fell on their knees, raised their hands over their heads and shouted '*Umkulu Inkos. Bayete Bayete*'. This they did 3 times as I gave each his half sov. I never saw such joy expressed. They smiled and laughed and would have danced if the kitchen had been big enough. 'Bayete' is the Royal Salute which they give to their Supreme Chiefs. When I drove away an hour or two after they formed a line of 3 in the garden and looked very picturesque in their white suits. They gave me a final salute without kneeling and when I took my hat off and said 'Goodbye, goodbye' they again raised their right arms and cried 'Bayete Bayete'.

★   ★   ★

Preece was in the habit of carrying a small book in his pocket in which to jot down notes, usually in pencil. Only one has survived: 3 by 4½ inches, 140 pages, leatherbound, it carries his Wimbledon address and date '1910'. He numbers each page and has rubbed out *aides memoire* on its first 20 pages as he dealt with matters noted. He has jotted down information on the Mohammedan dating system, on Hans Holbein, and Samuel Johnson. Finding in the ship's captain a man who appreciated Lord Kelvin's outstanding contributions to navigation he notes a promise to send him a copy of Silvanus P. Thompson's biography, which had been published, in two volumes, the year before. He had then written to Thompson to tell him of his admiration for Thompson's handling of 'so many intricate questions', and of the infinite pleasure with which he had read the biography. He wrote in that letter, 'I am now nearly played out', adding that he was in his 'seventy-seventh year'. He translates verses 23 and 24 of Psalm 107 into Welsh.

He attends the inaugural meeting on board of a Sports Committee but feels that he is not well enough to accept an invitation to be its chairman. Alan Lloyd, elected secretary, he described as 'a great American, active, energetic, tactful, useful and a great favourite'. On 29th January he is attempting to analyse the form and movement of breaking waves. Next morning he walks six times around the deck before breakfast.

He jots down quotations: Brewer's *Phrase and Fable*, Matthew Prior, the Bible, Shakespeare, and has pasted in his pocketbook a press cutting of the *Tempest* epilogue, 'Our revels are now ended . . .' Here and there he records a formula, for example, friction on road of iron, solid rubber, and pneumatic tyres, or mnenomic, 'the Ram, the Bull, the Heavenly Twins . . .' He notes amusing anecdotes and jokes, such as, 'Are you Appius Claudius?' 'No, I'm as miserable as hell.'

Most of the remaining pages are given over to a very brief daily record (which closes 7 March 1911 with 'to new book') on which he based his dairy, interspersed with miscellaneous comments such as on the educability of native Africans when he outlines his scheme, to include English speaking, thinking, use of tools, and personal hygiene, adding that natives should be trained as teachers. He observes that 'within Latitude 34° the Southern Cross is always visible'. He notes the physicists' discovery of electrons and the new view of physics it occasions but makes no reference to his own Royal Society paper twenty-six years earlier 'on the peculiar behaviour of glow lamps when raised to incandescence', an electronic effect pressed into service in the two-electrode 'thermionic emission' valve patented in 1904 by Professor J. A. Fleming, scientific adviser to the Marconi Company.

33

TURNS AGAIN HOME

The safety bicycle, once it had been fitted – in 1889 – with pneumatic tyres, had a wide appeal. By the mid-nineties such bicycles were being manufactured in sufficient numbers to be generally available, and Preece was to be counted among those who cycled around Wimbledon Common, in Richmond Park, and further afield each fine Sunday. The Post Office had been experimenting with cycles for telegram deliveries since 1883 but that was not a matter with which Preece was concerned, nor was he involved in the test of a Daimler motor van to carry mail between the G.P.O. and Victoria Street in 1896, nor in a petrol-fired steam van tried that year for relieving the Brighton horse-drawn parcel coach over the G.P.O.–Redhill stretch of its route. He was, however, called upon when the London Electric Cab Company offered the Post Office a van for trial early in 1897. Powered by accumulators, it worked quite successfully for the month's duration of its test on four miles of the most congested routes in London, between St Martin's-le-Grand and Paddington via the West End.

That led to Preece being asked to inaugurate the London Electric Cab Company's taxi-cab service upon Scotland Yard granting it a licence to ply for hire. This he did from its depot in Juxton Street, Lambeth Walk, on 27th August. He spoke of the new service with enthusiasm and compared its potential safety with the perils occasioned by runaway cab-horses.

★　　★　　★

On his retirement two years later he began to spend more time in Carnarvon but neither Preece-powered bicycle nor electrically powered car were at their best on the road gradients of North

Wales and he had decided, moreover, to postpone buying an electric motor car till a battery had been invented capable of driving the car for a hundred miles without recharging. 'What a blessing it would be' he said, 'if an electric omnibus were plying between Carnarvon and Waenfawr instead of miserable old horses staggering along on Saturday nights with a dozen persons after them.' He recognized that, in 1901, automobiles were 'the rage of the day': perhaps not in North Wales for five years later when Sir Richard Bulkeley invited members of that region's Automobile Club to his house at Beaumaris the local paper proudly recorded that 'more than 20 cars turned up'. Preece thought that ultimately an electrically driven car would be favourite 'when a *real* battery appears in the twentieth century' for such cars were silent and odourless.

Meanwhile the automobile was capable of a fairly reliable performance so he bought one, confessing that he found the experience of riding in such a car very exhilarating. He had joined the Automobile Club (later R.A.C.) in 1897 within a few months of its formation. Among his earliest actions when furnishing Penrhos had been to install an electric lighting plant with a battery of secondary cells. One of the duties of his chauffeur was to carry on the tradition established at Gothic Lodge by *le jardinier de M. Preece*.

★   ★   ★

Penrhos is a larger version of Bryn Helen. Its main entrance is protected by a pillared porch: Preece fitted a wind-direction indicator dial (operated by a weathervane high above the house's three storeys) on the wall at the side of the doorway so that a visitor, after pressing the electric bell-push, can contemplate on wind direction whilst waiting for the door to be opened. The house, with several acres of garden, orchard, and paddocks, is surrounded by wild moorland. Extensive outbuildings include a square stone-built castellated tower fifty yards to the rear of the house with an external iron staircase rising twenty feet to its flat roof. Caeathraw village to the south does nothing to interrupt a panorama of Snowdonia. To the north Carnarvon, 200 feet below, is hidden by hillside slopes, while the western side of Anglesey filled most of the horizon (a view obstructed today by a conifer plantation).

On the surrounding moors Preece would occasionally pot a rabbit, more from the pleasure of handling his well-balanced hammerless shotgun than anything else. He further indulged his fancy by purchasing a steam yacht – its cost in those days amounting to a few hundred pounds. Already in the Straits were Williams-Bulkeley's S.Y. *Monsoon* (he was Commodore of the Royal Anglesey Yacht Club) and Lloyd W. G. Hughes's S.Y. *Sunbeam*. Preece's yacht, the *Coey*, reached the Straits from Barnstaple on 29 June 1901. Early that year the Harbour Trust had decided to buy a steamer, the *Seiont*, which was given its trial run at the end of the year. Within a few years Preece disposed of his yacht but he continued to accompany his fellow Trustees when they inspected all the buoys for which they were responsible, on a summer's day each year aboard the *Seiont*.

Preece's sister continued with the *ménage* at Wimbledon but his two unmarried daughters, Mary ('Prissie') and Amy preferred Penrhos where they were joined within a few years by their widowed sister Agnes (Mrs David Moseley) who had notable skill in artistic needlework.

Preece was appointed Commissioner of the Peace for Carnarvon in 1900, became chairman of the local branches of the British and Foreign Bible Society, and National Service League, and in August 1906 presided at a meeting which inaugurated the Welsh Folk Song Society, to continue as its President with Amy as its Secretary.

From time to time he carried out wireless experiments across the Seiont estuary and in the Straits. In February 1901 he talked on wireless telegraphy at Shiloh Chapel, Llandudno, which was crowded: he recalled his first visit to Llandudno when, in 1842, his father had driven him to the only house there at that time. His talk is memorable for a demonstration he gave of an invention of Richard Kerr's. Kerr had travelled from London to participate. Impulses controlled by a telegraph key actuated at minute intervals the hands of a clock which was hung from the chapel gallery 60 feet from Preece, who reported that Kerr had operated such a mechanism from distances of up to six miles and hoped to adapt it for the remote control of torpedoes.

Three years later Preece allowed a company of Royal Engineers to use Penrhos as a station when they tested wireless telegraph transmission from Llanrwst in the Conway valley eighteen miles to the east, and hidden by mountains of over 3000 feet. The soldiers found that those mountains completely masked signals to Penrhos and moved their transmitter ten miles further inland from Llanrwst when a pass through the mountains allowed signals to reach Penrhos.

At a meeting of the Harbour Trust in April 1910 Preece described Carnarvon as the centre of the richest history field in the Principality and proposed that the Trust should adapt one of its buildings, the Battery, as a museum – 'every tripper would pay tuppence' – and reported that he had picked up several 'evidently neolithic' items around Penrhos which could be included among exhibits. The site of Segontium was especially rich in Roman relics. Clearly from the discussion he stimulated there were others of his mind but such a project was outside the scope of the Trust and the mayor, who was present at the meeting, promised to raise it at a Town Council meeting. Although Preece gave his idea fairly wide publicity eleven years had passed when Mortimer Wheeler took charge of the excavation of the Roman fort of Segontium. The site was enclosed and an excellent museum associated with it; all of which came under the care of the National Trust in 1937.

*   *   *

The Carnarvon Town Council had not let Preece's comments on lighting in 1899 go unheeded for they appointed an Electricity Committee (24 May 1901) with Robert Parry as Chairman: 'before making any recommendation it was thought desirable to ask Sir William H. Preece who had kindly expressed his willingness to help the Council in this matter whether he will attend a meeting of the Committee'. Preece was at their next meeting a week later when he advised that the Council should apply for an Electric Lighting Order and leave till later to decide whether they or a company under their authority should carry out the work. He promised 'as a freeman of the Borough' to assist them without charge. Early in August the committee was expecting Preece's return to Carnarvon and by mid-September agreed the schedule for the Order. Two months and four meetings later the committee thanked Preece for his help during preliminary planning and asked at what charge he would prepare plans, specifications, estimates and the like.

He recommended that the generating station should operate in conjunction with a refuse destructor using household refuse as a fuel for steam boilers as had been done by the Vestry of St Pancras ten years before. (The St Pancras Undertaking had appointed Professor Henry Robinson as consulting engineer but had also obtained the opinions of John Hopkinson and Preece.) Preece attended a committee meeting in December when provisional sums were agreed of £15000 for the Electricity Works and £3000 for the associated refuse destructor. The committee reported in June 1902 that the Board of Trade had granted an Order. Six months later, no further progress having been made, the National Electric Wiring Company offered to take over the supply of electricity to the town. The Company's manager attended a meeting of the committee and Preece's advice was sought on the resulting draft agreement. The manager was present at a meeting in March 1903 when he suggested he could reduce his estimate if his option was extended from seven to ten years. Preece advised acceptance, at which stage seventeen meetings of the committee had been held and Preece had been present at four of them. Two meetings later the Harbour Trustees were to be asked to sell a site, near the gas works, for the station building, which the Council bought, after some haggling, for £700, less than 2s. 6d. a square yard: twelve months later plans of the site were sent to Preece.

The North Wales Power Company then offered to take over the scheme (September 1903) but Preece recommended adherence to the agreement with the first company, whereby users were to be charged $4\frac{1}{2}$d. a quarter for each 25 c.p. lamp and could purchase the installation at any time for 16s. 6d. Representatives of both companies were invited to the next committee meeting when it decided to remit the matter to a public inquiry by the Local Government Board. Preece was asked to continue as adviser. He proposed at a meeting on 23 October 1903 that the National Electricity Company (it had changed its title by that thirty-fifth committee meeting) should bring temporary plant into operation until the North Wales Power Company could supply in bulk from a projected hydro-electric scheme at Llyb Llydaw. The National Company declined such terms whereupon the North Wales Company offered to put in temporary plant at Carnarvon. In Preece's absence the committee contemplated seeking 'outside expert opinion' on the relative merits of the two companies' proposals.

In the event the Council acted on Preece's advice that the National Company should be allowed to go ahead (with the Council holding options to take over the Company after ten, fifteen, or twenty-five years). With due ceremony, in February 1905, the Carnarvon Electric Light Works were opened. After-dinner speeches that evening were not brightened by Preece for he was wintering in Egypt. As a result of five weeks of canvassing, forty applicants had asked for a total of 630 lamps, and the company had little doubt their example would be followed by many more townsmen.

*   *   *

A Pan-Celtic Congress was held in Dublin in the summer of 1901 to stimulate interest among Celtic peoples in 'everything that touches the Gael, except matters of current politics and religion'; Preece was one of the Carnarvon delegates who attended and proposed that the next Congress be held in Carnarvon. That invitation was accepted so in 1904 Carnarvon Town Council laid on a programme of trips and junketings, with papers being presented each afternoon. The congress was divided into several sections, Preece chairing one on 'customs, costumes, and folklore'. With no trace of political undertone the Congress was rated a great success. Preece himself contributed a short paper for discussion. His opening statement was, 'a recent enforced visit of long duration in Egypt has supplied me with sufficient of the wisdom of the Egyptians to enable me, I hope, to excite some new considerations'. It would seem that his winter holiday in Egypt had to be prolonged because of the persistence of bronchitis which had sent him there. He referred to British Museum papryi of Ptah-hetep and Ani, 'Egyptian magnates of about five thousand years ago'. Those documents, he held, would show that ethics in Egypt 'on the threshold of civilization', were of the highest order. The Egyptian 'knew and practised his duty to his God and to his neighbour'; the Supreme Being was symbolized by the sun and later the powers of nature were personified and apotheosized'. He mentioned a few similarities between Egyptian and modern Welsh syntax, and explained the persistence of older languages, 'the ruling race changes but the workers remain. . . . The fighting men are killed off, but the mothers and children flourish and with them their language.'

He suggested Egyptian priests' affinities with Druids and echoed William Stukeley's obsession when he claimed that the Druids knew and used 'mechanical powers as testified in Stonehenge, Avebury, Cromlechs, Menhirs, and Logan stones [!]'. But he soon had comments of his own to make:

'Like money by the Druids borrowed
In t'other world to be restored'

This practice I believe had not yet left us.

Externally and on Sundays we are a very religious nation. Our internal practice of Christian ethics would be very much improved if we could impress upon ourselves the maxims of Ptah-hetep and Ani.

When he went on to ascribe similar virtues and religious beliefs to the Druids it would appear he had accepted statements in *The Mythology and Rites of the British Druids*, an imaginative work of a century earlier which well fitted the 'noble savage' political philosophy of the eighteenth century and evaded the conclusion to be drawn from available evidence that the Druids were a survival from a far less civilized past.

The first issue of the quarterly *Celtic Review* that October published a selection of papers and correspondence criticizing them. Professor H. H. Johnson of Rennes University was the only one to refer to Preece who

The other day wished to connect Welsh and Coptic. The Hamatic tongue is old enough in all conscience, but Hamatic is not Aryan.

and sagely observed 'surely we have as good Welshmen little cause to connect ourselves with Gibbon's "race of illiterate beggars" ', but soon reached the main purport of his letter, the criticism of a philological paper, to which Professor J. Morris Jones of Bangor University replied that a Celtic speaking population inhabited Western Europe before the arrival of the Aryans, 'who are thus, vide W. H. Huxley, "secondary Celts" '.

*   *   *

That autumn saw, too, an anonymous letter in *The Times* referring to the temples of Philae Island, a mile upstream of the Aswan dam, on which construction started two years before and to an earlier 'understanding' to avoid flooding the island which was 'to be torn up'. 'No one impugns the excellent intentions of zealous engineers. The intentions of Torquemada were excellent . . .' Preece would have none of this and dispatched a letter by hand from his office in Queen Anne's Gate to Printing House Square. It was published the next day.

Does it occur to 'FRS' (why will correspondents use such letters of distinction to disguise their identity when expressing timid and often foolish opinions) that the Philae temples are quite modern compared with those in Egypt. Visitors ascending the Nile become surfeited with Ptolemaic and Roman parodies of pure Egyptian culture and irritated with the political morality which throws over the beauties of Greek arts to foster an effete and decaying civilization. What is more ludicrous than a Roman emperor posing as a Egyptian god? There is much that is beautiful in Philae, but mostly that is epoch marking. The Kiosk or Pharaoh's Bed would be far more attractive if erected on the south end of Elephantine Island. The other temples can remain where they are. They will be seen at Low Nile. They will not be damaged by the full reservoir, but they will beautify a charming lake and a delightful boating resort. The outcry against the heightening of the dam is sentimental 'rot'.

The island was, in the event, almost totally submerged each year from December till midsummer with no damage to the monuments even with a raising of the dam level. (The recent scheme to build a High Dam four miles upstream of the island, which will result in a daily 'tide' of six metres, does constitute a threat to the monuments: a plan has therefore been made to re-erect them on another island safe from flooding, and all profits from the Tutankhamen Exhibition at the British Museum in 1972 went towards the cost of that undertaking.)

Preece had lectured to the R.S.A. on Egypt five years before. He surveyed the Navigation of the Nile, when he showed that his voyages on that river had not for the most part been spent half asleep in the sunshine. He calculated that a fifth of the water impounded by the Aswan dam was lost by evaporation, a proportion which would decrease as the height of the dam was raised. 'Every square meter of exposed water evaporates $2\frac{1}{2}$ tons a year.' He recommended dredging the river bed to make the channel navigable at Low Nile and indicated the obstructive banks and shoals which would have to be removed to that end. He estimated that each year fifty million tons of valuable mud was washed down to the Delta where three-fifths of it was swept out to sea. Most of that lost mud, valuable soil, could be dredged from the river and deposited along its banks to increase the holdings of the riparian cultivators and the quantity of the food they grew.

The present writer lately talked with Kenrick Evans of Carnarvon who recalled a lecture he attended in the town under the auspices of the Carnarvon Literary Union (a short-lived organization whose first meeting in October 1901 was chaired by Preece) probably in 1908. Preece had recently returned from Egypt with photographs he had taken using the earliest colour transparencies, which the Lumière Brothers had put on the market the year before. Preece made these into lantern slides to illustrate his lecture. An impressive view of the Great Pyramid was projected on a screen as Preece spoke of its endurance through the centuries but the heat from the lantern's acetylene flame was too intense for the dyed potato-starch grains of the photograph and in shocked delight the audience silently watched the pyramid's slow collapse to an amorphous heap. Preece, no stranger to demonstrations going adrift at his lectures, good-humouredly shared the joke with his audience.

Preece had told of his first public lecture on several occasions: he gave it in Southampton, one evening two years before the Electric Telegraph Company had laid an armoured cable between Orfordness and The Hague, in 1858, to replace lighter cables during five years and less on the sea bed which had often been broken by trawls and anchors. With the ready co-operation of Head Office he arranged to communicate via a cable with continental cities at an appropriate point in his talk:

we first of all spoke to Amsterdam, and asked how the weather was, and the answer came saying 'It is very wet'. We were placed in communication with Berlin and the same question was asked, and then we went in communication with Vienna.

In the early part of the lecture I had described the effect of the difference in time due to the difference of longitude – how it was that messages received in London were timed an hour later than Vienna; and when we were put in communication with Vienna an inquisitive editor amongst my audience said, 'Now let us test what Mr. Preece has told us about time. What is the time in Vienna?' Of course I had the question put to Vienna.

the time being nine o'clock in Southampton, and the answer came back that it was 'eight o'clock'. The editor said, 'That's a lie! the time in Vienna is nearer half-past ten',

and denouncing Preece as an impostor, he left the hall. Later Preece learnt that lines beyond Amsterdam had been disconnected and, rather than disappoint Preece, his friend in London had impersonated the distant operators: knowing that the time difference in Vienna was about an hour he had mistakenly subtracted it: Preece had been as much a victim as his audience.

★   ★   ★

Silvanus P. Thompson and Preece were at the last Royal Institution lecture of Tyndall's, in January 1886, when he maundered on well over his usual hour, repeating himself again and again: Preece said to Thompson as they were leaving:

When you and I come to that stage I hope some friend will be kind enough to prevent us making an exhibition of ourselves.

Tyndall had been appointed the Institution's Professor of Natural Philosophy thirty-three years before, when Preece had heard his first lecture there; he died four years later from accidental poisoning with choral at the age of seventy-three.

Preece gave his last formal lectures (apart from two in South Africa in 1911) in 1908, but he was asked by Lady Kelvin to present a marble bust of her husband (by McFadden Shannan) on her behalf to the Institution of Electrical Engineers in February 1912. Kelvin (William Thomson) had died in December 1907 and Preece was the oldest friend of his in the profession. Having recently recovered from a severe bout of ill-health, Preece spoke for only a few minutes, during which he said:

Kelvin's mind will ever be with us, for his works are classic and his conclusions immortal.

He praised Silvanus Thompson's biography of Kelvin ('he deserves to rank second to Boswell') and promised to present the Institution with a bust of Faraday to match that of Kelvin. (He gave the commission for that portrait bust next summer to D. G. MacDougald, and his son Llewellyn presented it to the Institution in October 1914.)

The winter months which followed he passed in the congenial and familiar setting of Egypt. In mid-July 1913 he sent a donation to *The Times* fund for purchasing for the public the Sydenham Parkland on which the Crystal Palace had been re-erected. Its editor quoted from Preece's covering letter in which he had recalled seeing that building in course of erection, being present on 1 May 1851 at the opening ceremony, and hearing at Evan's music hall a song celebrating that opening. By the beginning of August Preece was confined to his bedroom in Penrhos, and in mid-August *The Times* reported that he was too ill to be moved to 'a warmer climate': no longer could he summon sufficient reserves to recover and, on 6th November, he died there whilst five miles to the east of Penrhos a great trans-Atlantic wireless telegraph station was in the course of construction on Cefndu, a lesser peak of Snowdonia.

The national, provincial, and technical press published nearly 200 obituaries, many including an anecdote of his and instancing his benevolence and kindliness. A correspondent summed up their general tenor with, 'the world has lost a good friend'. He wrote of walking into Preece's

room one day and telling him that machinery could be made to think, and I remember his genial and at the same time caustic reply, as he offered me a cigar and told me to 'sit down and tell me about it'.

He concluded:

Society owes a great deal to Preece, more perhaps than it may ever realise.

At a meeting of the Board of Directors
of the
American Institute of Electrical Engineers
held November 14, 1913, the following
resolutions were unanimously adopted:

Whereas, the entire electrical engineering
profession has sustained a great loss through
the death, on November 6th, 1913, of

Sir William Henry Preece,

one of its most distinguished votaries, whose
professional career covered a period of
fifty years of successful endeavor; and

Whereas, Sir William Henry Preece, in
September, 1884, attended in Philadelphia,
as guest of the Institute, the first convention held by it, and on October the 21st, 1884,
was elected the first Honorary Member of
the Institute, remaining for many years
its only Honorary Member; be it

Resolved, That the Board of Directors of the
American Institute of Electrical Engineers
hereby places on record its appreciation of
his personality, career and attainments, and
its sense of the great loss sustained; and be it
further

Resolved, That the sympathy and conde-
lence of the Board of Directors of the Institute
be extended to the bereaved family, and to
the Institution of Electrical Engineers,
which honored him twice by electing him
President; and be it further

Resolved, That suitably engrossed copies
of these resolutions be transmitted to the family,
and to the Institution of Electrical Engineers,
and that a copy be preserved in the archives
of the Institute.

C. O. Mailloux.
President

F. L. Hutchinson
Secretary

Appendix 1
PRINCIPAL LECTURES AND
PUBLICATIONS

There is no more useful mode of imparting knowledge than of lecturing . . . the lecturer often learns more than his audience.

W.H.P., Soc., Telegraph Eng. 1880.

1860 On the maintenance and durability of submarine cables in
       shallow waters. *Inst. Civil Eng. Proc.* vol. XX

1862 Electro-polarization. *Electrician* vol. I pp. 197–9, 209–11
       Testing cables. *Electrician* vol. II pp. 100–02
       On railway telegraphs. *Electrician* vol. II pp. 172–4, 195–7, 209–11

1863 On railway telegraphs and the application of electricity to
       signalling and working of trains. *I.C.E. Proc.* vol. XXII

1864 *The application of electricity to domestic purposes.* 24pp illus. Truscott
       & Simmons, London. pub. Southampton
       A new ships' steering electric telegraph (with Arthur Gilmore).
       Pub. London
       On railway electric signalling (explanation of the block system).
       39pp. illus. pub. London

1866 On the best means of communicating between passengers,
       guards, and drivers of trains in motion. *I.C.E. Proc.* vol. XXV

1867 On the Brit. Assoc. unit for electricity measurements. *Phil.
       Mag.* vol. XXXIII

1869 On the parallelogram of forces. *Phil. Mag.* vol. XXXVIII

1870 *Telegraphy* (with James Sivewright). Longmans Green, London.
       11th ed. revised by T. M. Goodeve 1895; rewritten by
       Llewellyn Preece 1914

C²

1872 On lightning and lightning conductors. *Jour. Soc. Tgh. Eng.* vol. I
Duplex telegraphy. *Tghic Jour.* vol. I pp. 197–9, 214–17, 145–7, 277–9, 309–10
Telegraphy in relation to railway work. Royal Cornwall Poly. Soc. Falmouth (Aug 27)
On a new telegraph wire gauge (with Capt. H. Mallock)
On the advantages of a scientific education (communicated)
Telegraph poles in Norway; sulphate of copper plugs (communicated). *Jour. Soc. Tgh. Eng.* vol. I

1873 On the block system of working on railways (with Capt. H. Mallock)
On the percentage of averages. *Jour. Soc. Tgh. Eng.* vol. II
On the application of electricity to the protection of life on railways. *Royal Inst. Proc.*

1876 *Lectures delivered at the School of Military Engineering, Chatham;* Autumn session. Printed for private circulation: Gale and Polden, Old Brompton, Kent
Railway travelling and electricity. *Popular Science Review* vol. 15

1877 On shunts and their application to electrometric and telegraphic purposes
On the measurement of currents. *Jour. Soc. Tgh. Eng.* vol. VI
On the telephone. *Brit. Assoc. Rep.* (Plymouth). *Nature* vol. XVI pp. 403–4
The telephone and its application to naval and military purposes. *Jour. Military Science.* London

1878 The American telegraph system
On the phonograph
On the connection between sound and electricity. *Jour. Soc. Tgh. Eng.* vol. VII
On some physical points connected with the telephone. *Phil. Mag.* Series 5 vol. 5 pp. 281–92
The telephone. *Notices of Proc. of the R. Inst.* vol. VIII
Electric light. Soc. Tgh. Eng. Exhibition R. Albert Hall (May)
The electric light. *Phil. Mag.* Series 5 vol. 7 pp. 29–34
On the phonograph. *Jour. Soc. of Arts.* vol. XXVI
Lightning protectors for telegraph apparatus
Recent progress in telegraphy. *British Assoc. Rep.* (Sheffield)
Edison's phonograph or speaking machine described. London and Chilworth

1879 Studies in acoustics (with A. Stroh). *Royal Soc. Proc.*
    Recent advances in telegraphy (Cantor lectures (5) Apr.–May).
       Jour. Soc. of Arts vol. XXVII
    Birmingham Wire Gauge. Rep. of S.T.E. cttee. London 70 pp.
       (signatory)
    Multiplex telegraphy. *Notices of the Proc. of the R. Inst.* vol. VIII
    The electric light. *Phil. Mag.* vol. VII
    Les progrès récents de la télégraphie. *Jour. Télégraphie* vol. IV

1880 Recent wonders of sound (Juvenile lectures)
    Recent wonders of light (Jan.). *Jour. Soc. of Arts* vol. XXVIII
    Presidential address: the nature of electricity
    On the durability of some iron wire
    The behaviour and decay of insulating compounds used for
       dielectric purposes
    The photophone and the conversion of radiant energy into heat.
       Jour. Soc. Tgh. Eng. vol. IX
    The electric light. *United Services Inst. Jour.* vol. XXIII
    The telegraphic achievements of Wheatstone. *Notices of the Proc.*
       of the R. Inst.
    On some thermal effects of electric currents. *R. Soc. Proc.* vol. XXX
    On the peculiar behaviour of copper
    On the proper form of lightning conductors. *Brit. Assoc. Rep.*
       (Swansea)
    On the space protected by a lightning conductor. *Phil. Mag.* vol. X

1881 The electric storm of Jan 31st. 1881. *Nature* Feb. 10
    Radiophony. *Jour. Soc. Tgh. Eng.* vol. X
    On the conversion of radiant energy into sonorous
       vibrations. *R. S. Proc.* vol. XXXI
    Recent advances in electric lighting. *Jour. Soc. of Arts* vol. XXVIII
    On the practical measurements of electrical magnitudes. *Tghic.*
       Jour. vol. IX pp. 465–7, 481–3, 505–7
    Recent wonder of electricity (Juvenile lectures)

1882 Recent wonders of electricity (Dec.–Jan.) *Jour. Soc. of Arts* vol. XXX
    Interim rep. of cttee on practical electrical standards
    Recent advances in telephony
    On a new arc lamp *Brit. Assoc. Rep.* (Southampton)
    Multiple telegraphy. *Notices of Proc. of the R. Inst.* vol. IX
    The Munich Electrical Exhibition
    The Leclanché battery (communication). *Jour. Soc. Tgh. Eng.* vol. XI

Sur le mesure pratique des grandeurs électrique. 25pp. Paris

*Report to the Street Committee . . . Commissioners of Sewers of the
City of London relative to Electric Lighting.* 14 pp. (Nov. 2)

Incandescent electric light; Du Moncel, Preece, Howell, and
Siemens. 176 pp. New York

The age of electricity. *Time* (London) vol. 7 pp. 80–9, 192–205

Electrical Exhibitions. *Jour. Soc. of Arts.* vol. XXXI

1883   The effects of temperature on the EMF and resistance of batteries.
        R. Soc. Proc. vol. XXXV

        On a new standard of illumination and the measurement of light.
        R. Soc. Proc. vol. XXXVI

        *Rules & regulations recommended for the prevention of fire risks from
        electric light* STE Cttee (signatory)

        The progress of telegraphy. *I.C.E. Proc.* Van Nostrand's Eng.
        Mag. vol. XXIX

        Telegraphic communication. *Brit. Assoc. Rep.* (Southport)

        On the progress of electric lighting. *Jour. Soc. of Arts* vol. XXXII

        Electrical conductors. *I.C.E. Proc.* vol. LXXV

1884   On the progress of telegraphy. *I.C.E. Proc.*

        On the law regulating the connection between current and
        intensity of incandescence of carbon filaments in glow lamps

        On the watt and horse power

        On the use of secondary batteries in telegraphy

        Rep. (2nd) cttee for gauge manufacturing of small screws in
        tgh. and electric light apparatus (signatory). *Brit. Assoc. Rep.*
        (Montreal)

        On the heating effect of currents. *R. Soc. Proc.* vol. XXXVI

        International conference of Electricians: Philadelphia 1884. Rep. and
        addresses (including Preece's) New York (300 pp.)

        On the progress of electric lighting. *Jour. Soc. of Arts* vol. XXXII

        Electric lighting in America. *Jour. Soc. of Arts* vol. XXXIII

        On the Electrical Congress in Paris

        A visit to Canada and the United States. *Jour. Soc. Tgh. Eng.* vol.
        XIII

        Rep. STE & E cttee on electrical nomenclature and notation

1885   On domestic electric lighting. *Brit. Assoc. Rep.* (Aberdeen)

        On the peculiar behaviour of glow lamps when raised to
        incandescence

        On charging secondary batteries. *R. Soc. Proc.* vol. XXXVIII

On a new scale for tangent galvanometers (with H. R. Kempe)
Electric induction between wire and wires. *Brit. Assoc. Rep.*
(Birmingham)

1886 Domestic electric lighting. *Jour. Soc. of Arts* vol. XXXIV
Long distance telephony
Delany's system of synchronous multiplex telegraphy
(communication). *Jour. Soc. Tgh. Eng.* vol. XIV

1887 On the specific resistance of commercial iron
On the coefficient of self-induction in telegraph wires
On copper wire
On electric induction between wire and wires
On the Brit. Assoc. standard screw gauge
On an improved railway reading lamp (no description published).
Brit. Assoc. Rep. (Manchester)
On the limiting distance of speech by telephone
On the heating effects of electric currents. *R. Soc. Proc.* vol. XLII
Fifty years progress in telegraphy. *Jour. Soc. of Arts* vol. XXXVI

1888 The application of electricity to lighting and working. Two
juvenile lectures (Jan.). *Jour. Soc. of Arts* vol. XXXVI
Safety lamps in collieries. *Notices of the Proc. of the R. Inst.*
Chairman's address, Mechanical Section Brit. Assoc. Practical
applications of electricity
On the C.G.S. and practical units of measurement. *Brit. Assoc.*
Rep. (Bath)
Rep. of Ctte. on Standards of Light (Preece, Rayleigh and others)
On fire risks and Fire Office Rules. *Jour. Soc. Tgh. Eng.* vol. XVI

1889 On secondary batteries. *Jour. Soc. of Arts* vol. XXXVII
On the relative effects of steady and alternate currents of different
conductors. *Brit. Assoc. Rep.* (Newcastle-on-Tyne)
On the disturbances arising from the use of the 'earth' for electric
lighting purposes. *Jour. Inst. Elec. Eng.* vol. XXII
Self induction and retardation. *Electrician* vol. XXII pp. 101–2
The Telephone (with Julius Maier). Whittaker, Specialist series;
London
Das Telephon und dessen praktische Verwendung. Stuttgart 1889
Le Téléphone translated by G. Floren; Paris 1891
A manual of telephony (with A. J. Stubbs). Whittaker, Specialist
series; 1893

1890   Ocean telegraphy. Crewe Scientific Soc. (Jan.)
      On heating effects of electric currents. *R. Soc. Proc.*
      On the character of steel used for permanent magnets
      On the form of submarine cables for long distance telephony.
        Brit. Assoc. Rep. (Leeds)
      The sanitary aspects of electric lighting. *Trans. Sanitary Institute*
        vol. II

1891   *St. Pancras Electrical Exhibition* (Addresses by Messrs Robinson,
      Preece, Slatter, and Sweet. Introduction by T. E. Gibb) Spon;
      London
      On some points connected with mains for electric lighting
      On the specification of electric conductors for electric lighting and
        other purposes. *Jour. I.E.E.* vol. XXI
      On the relative merit and cost of gas and electricity for lighting
        purposes. Assoc. of Municipal and County Eng.
      The London–Paris telephone. *Brit. Assoc. Rep* (Cardiff)

1892   On some points connected with mains for electric lighting.
        Jour. I.E.E. vol. XX
      On the utilization of the waste forces of nature. Welsh National
        Soc. and Liverpool Eng. Soc.
      The art of internal illumination of buildings by electricity. R.
        Inst. Brit. Architects (May 16)
      On the dielectric of condensers
      On secondary batteries in use at the Central Telegraph Office,
        London
      On the earth current storms of 1892
      On the destruction of lightning protection by recent Municipal
        legislation. *Brit. Assoc. Rep.* (Edinburgh)
      Rep. of Cttee. on standards for use in electrical measurements
        (Ayrton, FitzGerald, Fleming, Kelvin, Lodge, Preece, Rayleigh,
        Thompson and others)

1893   Presidential address: review of applied electricity. *Jour. I.E.E.* vol.
        XXXII

1894   Notes on a trip to the United States and Chicago. *Jour. I.E.E.* vol.
        XXIII
      On electric signalling without wires. *Jour. Soc. of Arts* vol. XLIII
      Signalling through space (text of lecture in Chicago). *Electrician*
        vol. XXXIII pp. 460–3

Earth currents. *Nature* vol. XLIX p. 554

Hampstead Central Electric Light Station. Assoc. of Municipal
and Country Eng.

Daily insulation testing of telegraph lines (communication). *Jour.
I.E.E.* vol. XXIV

1895 On an improved portable photometer. *Brit. Assoc. Rep.* (Ipswich)

Telegraphy by induction. London Chamber of Commerce (May)

1896 Screw Gauge (Rep. of a committee)

On the testing of glow lamps

On the disturbances in submarine cables. *Brit. Assoc. Rep.*
(Liverpool)

Address to Yorks. Assoc. I.C.E. Students as Senior V-P I.C.E.
Leeds

Telegraphy without wires. Toynbee Hall (Dec.)

Electricity in connection with building

1897 Watt and the measurement of power: Watt anniversary lecture.
Greenock Phil. Soc. (Feb)

Twenty-five years of telegraphic progress. *Elec. Review* vol. XLI
pp. 678–80

Signalling through space without wires. *Notices of the Proc. of the
R. Inst.* vol. XV

1898 Introduction to *Wireless Telegraphy popularly explained*: by
Richard Kerr. Seeley & Co., London Presidential address:
Forty years progress in electrical science and industry

I.C.E . Proc. Liverpool Eng. Soc. (Feb. 9)

Electricity at the G.P.O.

On the abuse of power houses. Assoc. of Municipal and County
Eng. (June)

Aetheric telegraphy. *Jour. I.E.E.* vol. XXVII

1899 Aetheric telegraphy. *Jour. Soc. of Arts* vol. XLVIII

Inaugural address: Engineering Conference (June). *I.C.E. Proc.*

Presidential address: Sanitary Inst. Congress (Southampton)
Jour. Sanitary Inst. vol. 20 pt. 3

The student's textbook of electricity by H. M. Noad, F.R.S. New
edition with additional chapters by W. H. Preece. Crosby
Lockwood, London

1900 The relations between electricity and engineering (James Forrest
lecture). *I.C.E. Proc.*

On the Liverpool and Manchester Lighting Express Railway. Assoc. of Municipal and County Eng.

The functions of an engineer. Assoc. of I.C.E. Students Glasgow (Feb.)

Manchester and Liverpool Express Railway. *Brit. Assoc. Rep.* (Bradford)

The future of electricity. Crewe Mechanics Institute (Nov.)

Wireless telegraphy (article on). *Encyclopaedia Britannica* 10th ed.

1901   Chairman of Council's address. *Jour. Soc. of Arts* vol. L

Terrestrial magnetism. Royal Cornwall Poly. Soc. (Nov.)

The telautograph. Carnarvon Y.M.C.A. (Dec.)

1902   Wireless telegraphy. *Page's Magazine* (Aug.)

Exhibitions and education: Presidential address. Royal Cornwall Poly. Soc. Falmouth (Aug.)

The utilization of electric energy in Wales. Welsh Nat. Soc. (Nov.)

Chairman of Council's address. *Jour. Soc. of Arts* vol. LI

1903   The science of taxation and business. *Jour. Soc. of Arts* vol. LII

1904   The connection between the ancient Egyptians and the ancient Britons. *The Celtic Review* Edinburgh vol. I

Egypt. Carnavon Literary Union (Oct.)

The culture of ancient Egypt. Carnarvon Literary Union (Dec).

1905   The navigation of the Nile. *Jour. Soc. of Arts* vol. LIII

Wireless telegraphy. *Brit. Assoc. Rep.* (South Africa)

The British Association in South Africa. *Jour. Soc. of Arts* vol. LIV

1906   A trip to South Africa. St. Helen's Inst. Penisa'rwaen (Apr.)

The connection between science and engineering. W. University of Pennsylvania (Pittsburg)

1908   America revisited. *Jour. I.E.E.* vol. XLI

Technical education in America. *Jour. Soc. of Arts* vol. LVI

Prize-giving speech; Technical education in Germany. Wolverhampton Tech. School (Sept.)

This appendix includes a few examples of many talks to local organizations but no official Post Office reports or articles in Post Office staff magazines; nor does it list arbitrations, inquiries and commissions at which Preece gave evidence, or correspondence in technical periodicals and *The Times*.

Appendix 2

PATENTS TAKEN OUT

(with date of application)

I do not think I have made any money from any patent I have taken out ...
finance and commerce settled the profit a patentee would obtain.

W.H.P. 1906

1855 Nov. 19 *No. 2608* Improvements in telegraphs. A new duplex system

1858 June 26 *No. 1449 (jointly with J. Latimer Clark)* A new method of terminating and insulating line wires

1862 Jan. 10 *No. 77* Railway signalling: assimilating outdoor and electrical signals

1864 June 6 *No. 1405* Improved domestic telegraph apparatus
    Dec. 28 *No. 3227* Railway signalling. Communication between passengers and guard.

1865 Aug. 3 *No. 2016* Locking railway signals

1870 May 3 *No. 1268* Improved locking signals by electricity

1873 Jan. 14 *No. 153* Railway signalling: preventing false signals due to lightning

1874 Oct. 13 *No. 3521* Communication between passenger and guard

1878 June 1 *No. 2203* Telephones. Sound amplifier

1882 Jan. 10 *No. 129* Lighting railway trains by electricity

1892 July 30 *No. 13894* Improvements in submarine telegraph cables

GENERAL INDEX

(see also *Index of Persons & Index of Places*)

party politics, 5, 25, 39, 326, 329
Patent laws, 235, 278
pen makers, 14
penny steamboats, 12
percussion caps, 9–10
periodicals
  Bentley's Miscellany, 39
  Boston Recorder, 39
  Bothnia Illustrated Times, 172
  Celtic Review, 348
  Electrical Review, 107
  Electrician, 205, 299
  Frazer's Magazine, 39
  Gentleman's Magazine, 240
  Illustrated London News, 218
  Nature, 288
  Our Magazine, 59
  Philosophical Magazine, 66, 109, 205, 208, 223
  Punch, 15–16, 39
  Scientific American, 196
  Tait's Magazine, 39
  Telegraphic Journal, 106, 109, 122
  Truth, 287
Persian antiquities, 283
photography, 14 350
picture galleries, 120, 125–6, 129–30
plays, 37, 121
polariscope, 147
police, 122, 127–9, 134, 139, 156, 220
politics and the Civil service, 245
porpoises, 149
porters, 119, 123
portrait busts, 351–2
post, uniform penny, 13
Post Office Savings Bank, 88, 103, 230
Post Office to establish telephone system, 173
Post Office Specifications, 197
Post Office Tower, 31
Postal Surveyors, 96, 103
Practical Telegraphy, by R. S. Culley, 109
prize-fighters, 16
Protestant Dissenters, 24
Public Accounts Company, 103, 108
public call offices in shops, 205
public relations, 56–7
Pullman cars, 78, 163, 167

quadruplex telegraphy, 109, 157, 160
Queen's birthday, 163
Queen's Road, Primrose Hill, 116

race meetings, 61, 72
railway accidents, 73, 76
Railway Act of 1844, 194
railway block working, 73
  Preece's system, 74–5, 237

1874-80 MANNERS (q.v.)
PMG 1880-84 FAWCETT (q.v.)
1891-92 FERGUSSON (q.v.)
1892-95 MORLEY (q.v.)
1895-1900 Norfolk (q.v.)

railway companies and lines
  Ballybunion-Listowel mono-rail, 319
  Baltimore and Ohio, 165, 167
  City and South London (Electric), 235
  Erie, New York, 168
  Euston–Camden, 44
  Grand Trunk, 170
  Great Eastern, 78, 229
  Great Northern, 76, 78, 233
  Great Western, 44–5
    Canada, 167
  Hull & Barnsley, 78
  Lancashire & Yorkshire, 78
  Lartique mono-rail, Brussels, 319
  Liverpool and Manchester, 43
  London and Birmingham, 44
  London and Blackwall, 12, 46
  London, Brighton & South Coast, 77, 233
  London, Chatham & Dover, 118, 232
  London and Croydon Atmospheric, 12
  London & North Western, 74
  London & South Western, 68 *et seq.*, 233
  London Underground, 6
  Metropolitan District, 232
  Michigan Central, 167
  Mid-Hants, 70
  Midland, 77
  South Eastern, 49, 233
  Taff Vale, 91
  Waterloo–Wandsworth, 35
railway signalling codes, 74, 76–7
railways, American night expresses, 164–5
Regent Street
  cast iron pillars (270) from Quadrant, sold to railways 1848, 38
Regent's Park, 30
River Pollution Act, 314
road traffic congestion, proposed solution, 319
Royal Academy, 277
Royal Albert Hall, 106
Royal Indian Engineering College, 86
Royal Institute, 13, 17, 43, 182–3, 269, 299, 322, 351
Royal National Lifeboat Inst., 264
Royal Society of Edinburgh, 302
Royal United Services Inst., 240
Royal Commission —— p. 259 et
St Pancras electric lighting, 229
St Paul's cathedral, 5
sanitation, 14, 313, 315
Science Museum, 278
Sewage discharged into sea, 314
Shakespeare, 16, 57, 341
ships
  Abyssinia, Cunard R.M.S., 145 *et seq.*
  Agamemnon, H.M.S., 65
  Argus, 261
  Aurania, S.S., 243

Scilly Isle wreck p.
Stanley 1860-68? P 88
1868/71 Hartington (q.v.)
1871/73 Monsell (q.v.)

Secretary to P.O.   Rowland Hill (q.v.)   1846–54
                      George Murray (q.v)   1899–1903
                      John Tilley   1864–80
                      Hartington   1868–71

INDEX OF PERSONS

GS Kemp — on Marconi's payroll 273

INDEX OF PLACES